D1093991

APHRODISIACS
AND
LOVE STIMULANTS

A GEM FROM THE ROMAN
MUSEUM

Venus with Cupid, heating
a phallus-shaped quiver

Aphrodisiacs
and
Love Stimulants

with other chapters on
THE SECRETS OF VENUS

being the two books by
JOHN DAVENPORT

entitled

'Aphrodisiacs and Anti-
Aphrodisiacs' and
'Curiositates Eroticae Physiologiae,
or Tabooed Subjects Freely Treated'

Now for the first time edited
with Introduction and
Notes by
ALAN HULL WALTON

Illustrated

★

LYLE STUART, INC.
New York
1966

Published in the United States of America
by Lyle Stuart, Inc.
239 Park Avenue South
New York, N. Y. 10003

Printed in U.S.A.

CONTENTS

LIST OF PLATES

INTRODUCTION

I. THE MAN

LITTLE is known of the life of the author of the two works here printed together. Most of what is known is to be found in Pisanus Fraxi's *Index Librorum Prohibitorum*, privately printed in a small edition in London during 1877,[1] and from this work the following recension has been made.

John Davenport was born in London on June 8th, 1789, at 8 Huggin Lane, in the City. His father came from Staffordshire, and had established himself as a silk-warehouseman at the above address. But he eventually went bankrupt, and the family found themselves in difficulties. Mrs Davenport had been a Miss Forbes, the daughter of a Common Councilman of Cripplegate. Their first child was William, who was born in 1781. He became an ensign in His Majesty's 58th Regiment, then known as 'The Devil's Own'.

John was brought up to be a business man, and at the appropriate age entered his father's counting house. Between his fifteenth and sixteenth years, however, his health gave great uneasiness, and it was recommended that he take a holiday and a short sea voyage. So he went to stay with his brother who was stationed in Jersey, and remained there two months or more. On his return to England he travelled in the coach with a young lady and her brother, and in later years described her as follows:

The lady appeared to me between eighteen and twenty years of age, her figure and tournure most attractive, and her face, without being beautiful,

---

[1] The three rare and celebrated bibliographies, *Index Librorum Prohibitorum*, *Centuria Librorum Absconditorum*, and *Catena Librorum Tacendorum*, in 1960 were re-issued in a sumptuous facsimile of the original by Charles Skilton, London, the edition being strictly limited to 395 sets. Pisanus Fraxi was the pseudonym of Henry Spencer Ashbee, a collector whose priceless library finally became the base of the Private Case at the British Museum.

was so interesting as to equal Belinda's (Pope's heroine in his *Rape of the Lock*).[1]

Like many a young man since, young John was smitten with his travelling companion's charms, and shortly after his return to London he had the good fortune to meet her again at a ball, where he was introduced to her, and discovered that she was a Miss Quick, daughter of a celebrated comedian of that time. Admiration ripened into love and affection, and in spite of much opposition from the parents he eventually married her at Islington Parish Church.

Davenport's interests were not all commercial. He studied hard and with much concentration, becoming proficient in a number of Oriental languages, as well as Greek, Latin, and the foremost European languages. He earned his living by writing and compiling books, and by teaching languages—chiefly Oriental.

So far as we know, his career was quiet and without unusual event. It was, in fact, like that of many another scholar. But he was unable to earn enough money to provide for his old age, and after the death of the wife he loved so much he found himself in very straitened circumstances. His eyesight failed him, and he was incapacitated from following his vocation as teacher and literary man.

Eventually he reached a state of complete penury, and died on May 11th, 1877, at 30 Huntley Street (then 15 Alfred Street), London, W.C.1—which runs parallel with Tottenham Court Road, on the Bloomsbury side. During the last months of his life he was supported by donations from the Royal Literary Fund and by the bounty of private individuals.[2]

II. HIS WORKS

1. *Aphrodisiacs and Anti-Aphrodisiacs*, London, privately printed, 1869. (The edition was very small, and was prepared for the press by John Camden Hotten. Although it bears the date 1869, it was not issued until 1873.)

[1] 'If to her share some female errors fall
Look in her face and you'll forget them all.'
[2] See *Centuria Librorum Absconditorum*, London, 1879 (or facsimile edition, London, Charles Skilton, 1960), p. xiv.

This work is erudite, well written in the style of the period, and, once again for the period of its composition, fairly exhaustive regarding the subjects of which it treats. It undoubtedly retains value as a work of reference, and Davenport himself intended it as a kind of supplement to Richard Payne Knight's *A Discourse on the Worship of Priapus*.[1] Hotten announced the book as to appear in an edition of 100 copies, and in his circular described its contents as follows:

> Mr Davenport has made a valuable contribution to literature, which will be acceptable alike to the antiquarian and the general scholar. The Phallic worship, of which the first essay treats, once prevailed throughout the whole world, among a people probably different in race from ourselves, but fully our equals in culture, and our superiors in architectural skill, as well as in purity of thought.[2] They adored the sun as possessing and diffusing the divine potencies of Heat, Light and Actinism: they cherished the Bull as representing the Sun at the Vernal Equinox, when the world is annually resuscitated; and the human organs of sex, to represent Divine Love, and the Perpetuation of Animated Existence.
>
> Mr Davenport shows how the pillar, the cross, the mystic letter Tau, the monumental shaft, and the church spire, were all derived from this archaic symbolism, and mean the virile symbol and the life everlasting. So also the sacred ark or ship, the crescent, the font, the lamp, and the grotto, were types of the organ and principle that denote the Female, and were commemorated by the Bona Dea, the Great Mother, Anna Purna, Sara Ismati, Isis, Juno and Cybele. Abraham's servant placing his hand at his master's thigh, and Jacob setting up and anointing a pillar at Bethel, performed Phallic worship, as Mr Davenport has shown. It pervaded all the ancient faiths, and is to be perceived in modern creeds and superstitions . . .

ii. *Curiositates Eroticae Physiologiae, or Tabooed Subjects Freely Treated*, London, privately printed, 1875. (The edition was limited to 250 copies, of which 200 were sent in sheets to J. W. Bouton, an occult publisher in New York; and the remaining

---

[1] *A Discourse on the Worship of Priapus . . . to which is added an Essay on the Worship of the Generative Powers*, London, privately printed (Hotten), 1865. Facsimile reprint, London, Charles Skilton, 1952 (limited to 675 copies), under the comprehensive title of *Two Essays on the Worship of Priapus*.

[2] See Mulk Raj Anand, *Kama Kala* (Some Notes on the Philosophical Basis of Hindu Erotic Sculpture), Geneva, Nagel, 1957; London, Charles Skilton, 1958 (pp. 5–9).

fifty copies, bound in half-morocco, were sold in London by
George Rivers.)

This volume treats of such subjects as virginity, marriage, castration,
hermaphrodism, etc., with all the contemporary erudition of the
previous volume, and it would be true to say that it would be difficult
to find so much information on these subjects—and from little-known
and even forgotten sources—within the space of a single volume. At
the same time it must be emphasized that much has been learnt since
Davenport's time; and, learned as he was, he remained subject to
certain superstitions and imaginings still prevalent in his day. His
volumes should, therefore, be read with this fact in mind.

Unfortunately, when the above two books were in process of being
set the author's eyesight was extremely poor, and a great many errors
of punctuation and spelling passed unnoticed. More shall be said of
this in the following section of this Introduction.

The remainder of Davenport's published work comprised mostly
dictionaries and educational works and is listed in detail in Pisanus
Fraxi.

What Ashbee (Pisanus Fraxi) claimed to be one of his best works
remained in manuscript, and has presumably been lost. It was entitled:
A Peep at Popes and Popery, and constituted, according to the above-
named bibliographer, a 'succinct . . . history, and a bitter satire of the
Church of Rome'.

III. THE EDITING OF THE PRESENT EDITION

The volume before the reader contains material from Davenport's two
books: *Aphrodisiacs and Anti-Aphrodisiacs*, and *Curiositates Eroticae
Physiologiae* (omitting two essays only: see below).

The essays have been numbered consecutively throughout, com-
mencing from the first volume, so that the first essay of the second
volume appears herein as *Essay IV*, whereas in the original edition of
the *Curiositates* it appeared as *Essay I*. The order of the essays from
the first volume has however been altered, so that the one on phallic
worship is no longer the initial chapter in this edition.

It has already been pointed out that Davenport's eyesight was failing when the books were printed, and, as he absolutely insisted on correcting the proofs himself, many errors of typography, spelling, punctuation, etc., crept into the volumes. The number was, in fact, almost unbelievable.

The editor has corrected gross errors in punctuation, spelling, and a large number of literals for which the original compositors were responsible. At the same time he has retained what seemed to be Davenport's original intention, style, etc., and has neither abridged nor expurgated the text in any manner, apart from deleting some small material in Italian, Latin and old French difficult for the general reader to follow.

All Davenport's notes have been included, but in many the titles of books quoted have necessarily been italicized; and the editor has expanded some of the author's notes, as well as adding a large number of his own.

It is in his annotation that Davenport is exasperating, as he rarely, if ever, gives sufficiently detailed bibliographical information. We are generally given only the title and date; frequently *only* the title. And where different editions might exist (and certainly exist now), it is impossible to tell which edition might have been used from those existing at that time. This, unfortunately, is a fault which is still common amongst modern authors. To revise, correct, and expand in this way all of Davenport's notes would be an unusually extensive labour; and as many of the volumes or texts he lists are now extremely rare the difficulties would be great. Therefore, apart from obvious corrections in the case of better-known works, his notes have been left as they originally appeared—excepting gross errors in punctuation due to his sight. A considerable number of additional notes have been made by the editor, generally bibliographical, or as comment; and occasionally he has extended one of Davenport's short notes with further pertinent information. All Davenport's notes are indicated by a 'D' in brackets at the end of each note thus: [D]. The present editor is responsible for all other notes and comments.

The final essay in the *Curiositates* has been omitted. It was entitled: 'On Death', and extended from page 191 of the original to page 216. It is not easy to understand why the author included it in his work, as it has no connection with the previous essays, all of which are connected with various aspects of sex. Also omitted is the essay 'On Generation' which is very out-of-date and much less interesting than the rest of the book.

It might be added that the author's original spelling has been retained for English as well as foreign words, even though a standardization may now have been agreed as to many of them. About three of the original notes have been eliminated, as they contained references and very brief quotations, extremely corrupt, and impossible to verify. Undoubtedly a few errors remain, and the editor begs the indulgence of the reader for these, for, as has already been hinted, access to rare or original sources has often been impossible.

One word might be said about aphrodisiacs. The use of such ought to be approached with care. The most potent so-called aphrodisiac is cantharides (Spanish Fly), which is an extremely dangerous and frequently fatal drug. The ignorance of the general public on these matters is still astonishing, even amongst educated people. Attention was drawn to this by a sensational case which appeared in the Press during 1954. The manager of a firm of wholesale chemists had, in his office, administered to two young girls a concoction of cantharides and coconut ice, the cantharides being obtained from supplies existing on the premises. The girls were taken violently ill, and died almost immediately.[1] The manager admitted that he did not realize the danger inherent in the drug and was sentenced to a long term of imprisonment for manslaughter. Again it must be emphasized that such an ignorance of these dangers is not uncommon.

ALAN HULL WALTON

---

[1] See Alan Hull Walton, *Love Recipes Old and New*, London, Torchstream Books, 1956 (reprinted in the U.S.A. as *Aphrodisiacs: From Legend to Prescription*, Associated Booksellers, Westport, Connecticut, 1958), pp. 106–7. See also: Furneaux, *Famous Criminal Cases*, 2, London, Wingate, 1955, pp. 171–6 ('The Love Potion that went Wrong').

PART ONE

＊

ESSAY 1

Aphrodisiacs, or, Erotic Stimuli, and their Opposites, as known to, and used by, the Ancients and Moderns

WHEN it is considered how strongly sexual desire is implanted in man, and how much his self-love is interested in preserving or in recovering the power of gratifying it, his endeavours to infuse fresh vigour into his organs when they are temporarily exhausted by over-indulgence, or debilitated by age, cannot appear surprising.

The remark particularly applies to natives of southern and eastern climes, in whom erotic ardour makes itself more intensely felt; since it is there that the man's imagination, as burning as the sky beneath which he first drew breath, reawakens desires his organs may have long lost the power of satisfying, and consequently it is there more especially that, notwithstanding the continual disappointment of his hopes, he still pertinaciously persists in searching for means whereby to stimulate his appetite for sexual delights. Accordingly it will be found that in the remotest ages even the vegetable, animal, and mineral kingdoms have been ransacked for the purpose of discovering remedies capable of strengthening the genital apparatus and exciting it to action.

But however eager men might be in the above enquiry, their help-mates were equally desirous of finding a means whereby they might escape the reproach of barrenness—a reproach than which none was more dreaded by Eastern women. Such means were at last discovered, or supposed to be so, in the mandrake,[1] a plant which thenceforth became, as the following quotation proves, of inestimable value in female eyes.

[1] From μανδρα relating to cattle, and αγαρος, baneful, injurious. [D]

17

And Reuben went, in the days of wheat harvest, and found mandrakes in the field, and brought them unto his mother, Leah. Then Rachel said to Leah, Give me, I pray thee, of thy son's mandrakes.

And she said unto her, Is it a small matter that thou hast taken my husband? and wouldest thou take away my son's mandrakes also? And Rachel said, Therefore he shall lie with thee to-night for thy son's mandrakes.

And Jacob came out of the field in the evening, and Leah went out to meet him, and said, Thou must come in unto me, for surely I have hired thee with my son's mandrakes. And he lay with her that night.

And God hearkened unto Leah, and she conceived, and bare Jacob the fifth son.[1]

There is only one other passage in the Bible in which this plant is alluded to, and that is in *Solomon's Song*:

The mandrakes give a smell, and at our gates are all manner of pleasant fruits, new and old, which I have laid up for thee, O my beloved.[2]

All that can be gathered from the former of the above quotations is that these plants were found in the fields during the wheat harvest, and that, either for their rarity, flavour, or, more probably, for their supposed quality of removing barrenness in women, as well as for the stimulating powers attributed to them, were greatly valued by the female sex. In the quotation from *Solomon's Song* the Hebrew word Dudaïm expresses some fruit or flowers, exhaling a sweet and agreeable odour, and which were in great request among the male sex.[3]

According to Calmet, the word *Dudaïm* may be properly deduced from *Dudim* (pleasure of love); and the translators of the Septuagint and the Vulgate render it by words equivalent to the English one—mandrake. The word *Dudaïm* is rendered in our authorized version by the word mandrake—a translation sanctioned by the Septuagint, which, in this place, translates *Dudaïm* by μῆλα μανοραγορῶν mandrake —apples, and in *Solomon's Song* by οἱ μανδραὁραὶ (*mandrakes*). With

---

[1] *Genesis*, XXX., v. 14, 15, 16, 17. The last verse must be considered as decisive of the efficacy of the mandrake. [D]

[2] *Solomon's Song*, VII, v. 13. [D]

[3] See the word *Dudaïm*, in Dr Kitto's *Cyclopaedia of Biblical Literature*. The learned doctor has given a sketch of the plant Mandragora. [D]

this, Onkelos[1] and the Syrian version agree; and this concurrence of authorities, with the fact that the mandrake (*atropa mandragora*) combines in itself all the circumstances and traditions required for the Dudaïm, has given to the current interpretation its present prevalence.

Pythagoras was the first (followed by Plutarch) who gave to this plant the name of ἀνθρωπο μο ρφος (man-likeness), an appellation which became very generally used; but why he gave it is not precisely known: Calmet, however, suggests as a reason the partial resemblance it bears to the human form, from the circumstance of its root being parted from the middle downwards.

The opinion respecting the peculiar property of the mandrake was not confined to the Jews, but was also entertained by the Greeks and Romans, the former of whom called its fruit—love-apples, and bestowed the name of *Mandragoritis* upon Venus. Dioscorides knew it by that of ανδροορας, and remarks that the root is supposed to be used in philters or love-potions;[2] and another writer lauds it as exciting the amorous propensity, remedying female sterility, facilitating conception and prolificness, adding the singular fact that female elephants, after eating its leaves, are seized with so irresistible a desire for copulation as to run eagerly, in every direction, in quest of the male.[3]

Speaking of the plant Eryngium, the elder Pliny says: 'The whole variety of the Eryngium known in our [the Latin] language as the *centum capita* has some marvellous facts recorded of it. It is said to bear a striking likeness to the organs of generation of either sex; it is rarely met with, but if a root resembling the male organ of the human species be found by a man, it will ensure him woman's love; hence it is that Phaon, the Lesbian, was so passionately beloved of Sappho.[4] If it be true, as is asserted by medical writers, that the above root contains an essential oil of peculiarly stimulating qualities, the fact would account not only for Sappho's passion for Phaon but also for the high value set upon it by the rival wives of Jacob.

[1] Onkelos was a celebrated rabbin contemporary with St Paul, and to whom the Targum, that is, a translation or paraphrase of the Holy Scriptures, is attributed. [D]

[2] Lib. IV, cap. 76. [D]

[3] Quoted by Oct. Celsius in his *Hierobotanicon*, Part I, par. 5, art. *Dudaïm*, from Epiphan: *Physilog.*, c. 4. [D]

[4] Pliny's *Natural History*, Vol. IV, p. 397 (Bohn's Classical Library). [D]

For the same reason as that suggested by Calmet, Columella[1] calls the mandrake *semihomo*:

> Let it not vex thee if thy teeming field
> The half-man Mandrake's madd'ning seed should yield:

and qualifies its seed by the epithet *vesanus*, because in his time (the first century after Christ) it was still supposed to form one of the ingredients of philters or love-potions. The superstitious ideas attached to the mandrake were indeed so current throughout Europe during the middle ages that one of the accusations brought against the Knights Templars was that of adoring, in Palestine, an idol to which was given the name of Mandragora.[2] Even, comparatively, not very long ago, there might be seen in many of the continental towns quacks and mountebanks exhibiting little rudely carved figures, which they declared to be genuine mandrakes, assuring their gaping auditors, at the same time, that they were produced from the urine[3] of a gibbeted thief, and seriously warning those who might have to pull any out of the ground to stop their ears first, for otherwise the piercing shrieks of these plants would infallibly strike them with deafness. Wier thus describes the manufacture of these interesting little gentlemen:

Impostors carve upon these plants while yet green the male and female forms, inserting millet or barley seeds in such parts as they desire the likeness of human hair to grow on; then digging a hole in the ground they place the said plants therein, covering them with sand till such time as the little seeds have stricken root, which, it is said, would be perfectly effected within twenty days at furthest. After this, disinterring the plants, these impostors, with a sharp cutting knife, so dexterously carve, pare, and slip

[1] Columella, *De hortorum Cultu.*, v. 19, 20. [D]

[2] See a manuscript Interrogatory still preserved in the Bibliothèque Nationale. Fonds de Baluze, Rouleau 5. [D]

[3] The more usual explanation is that the mandrake springs from the earth beneath a gallows and which has been moistened by human semen. As Havelock Ellis and others have pointed out, strangulation frequently produces erection and ejaculation, and a hanged man was supposed to ejaculate as he was hung. The Marquis de Sade devotes not inconsiderable space to the erotics of hanging in his *Justine.* Bloch also discusses the matter in his *Geschlechtsleben in England* (*History of Sexual Morals in England*), of which the best translation is that by Forstern, originally published in London by Aldor, and more recently by the Encyclopaedic Press.

the little filaments of the seeds as to make them resemble the hair which grows upon the various parts of the human body.[1]

'I have seen', says the Abbé Rosier, 'mandrakes tolerably well representing the male and female parts of generation, a resemblance which they owe, almost entirely, to manual dexterity. For the intended object, a mandrake is chosen having a strong root, which at the end of a few inches, bifurcates into two branches. As the root is soft, it easily takes the desired form, which it preserves on becoming dry.'[2] The author then describes the process of producing the resemblance of human hair, and which is similar to that given above.

In the year 1429 a Cordelier, by name Brother Richard, fulminated from the pulpit a vigorous sermon against the amulette then much in vogue and called 'Mandragora'. He convinced his auditors, both male and female, of its impiety and inutility, and caused hundreds of those pretended charms which, upon that occasion, were voluntarily delivered up to him, to be publicly burnt. It is no doubt, to these mandragoras that an old chronicler alludes in the following strophe:

> J'ai puis vu soudre en France
> Par grant dérision,
> La racine et la branche
> De toute abusion.
> Chef de l'orgueil du monde
> Et de lubricité;
> Femme où tel mal habonde
> Rend povre utilité.[3]

In the fifteenth century the mandrake enjoyed in Italy so great a reputation as an erotic stimulant that the celebrated Machiavelli wrote a much admired comedy upon it called *La Mandragora*. The subject of this piece, according to Voltaire, who asserts

qu'il vaut peut-être mieux que toutes les pièces d'Aristophane, est un jeune homme adroit qui veut coucher avec la femme de son voisin. Il engage, avec de l'argent, un moine, un *Fa tutto* ou un *Fa molto*, à séduire sa maitresse

---

[1] See *De l'imposture des Diables*, par Jacques Grévin, Tom. IV, p. 359. [D]

[2] From Wier *De Mag: demonia.* Cours complet d'agriculture par l'Abbé Rosier, Tom. VI, p. 401. [D]

[3] *Recollections des choses merveilleuses advenues en notre temps*, par Georges Chastelain, Edition de Coustelier, p. 150. [D]

et à faire tomber son mari dans un piège ridicule. On se moque tout le long de la pièce de la religion que toute l'Europe professe, dont Rome est le centre et dont le siège papal est le trône.[1]

Callimaco, one of the dramatis personae of this comedy, thus eulogizes[2] the plant in question,

You must know that nothing is so sure to make women conceive as a draught composed of Mandragora. That is a fact which I have verified upon four occasions and had it not been for the virtues of this plant, the Queen of France, as well as many noble ladies of that kingdom, would have proved barren.

By the Venetian law the administering of love-potions was accounted highly criminal. Thus the law *De maleficii et herbarie.* Cap. XVI of the code, entitled 'Della Commissione del maleficio', says: 'Statuimo etiam dio che se alcun homo o femina harra fatto maleficii, iguali so domandono volgarmente *amatorie,* o veramente alcuni altri maleficii, che alcun homo o femina se havesson in odio, sia frusta et bollade, et che hara consigliato, patisca simile pena.'[3]

The notion of the efficacy of love-powders was also so prevalent in the fifteenth century in our own country that in the Parliament summoned by King Richard III, on his usurping the throne, it was publicly urged as a charge against Lady Grey that she had bewitched King Edward IV by strange potions and amorous charms:

And here also we considered how that the said pretended marriage betwixt the above named King Edward and Elizabeth Grey, was made of great presumption, without the knowing and assent of the Lords of this land, and also by sorcery and witchcraft committed by the said Elizabeth and her mother Jaquet Duchesse of Bedford, as the common opinion of the people and public voice and fame is through all this land. (From the *Address of Parliament to the high and mightie Prince Richard, Duke of Gloucester.*)[4]

[1] *Lettres d'Amabed,* Vol. XXXIV, p. 261. Edition Beucheot, Paris. [D]

[2] *Mandragora,* Atto II, scena vi. See also La Fontaine's tale of 'La Mandragore', founded upon the above comedy. [D]

[3] See Warburton on Shakespeare's *Othello.* Act I, sc. iii, '*By spells and medicines bought of mountebanks*'. [D]

[4] See Speed's *Historie of Gt. Britaine,* 'Richard III', Book II, p. 913, folio edition, 1632. [D]

Modern writers, as might be expected, have taken a very wide range in their inquiries as to what kind of plant the Dudaïm really was, some regarding it as lilies, roses, violets, snowdrops and jasmine; others as melons, plaintain fruits, whirtleberries, dwarf brambles, the berries of the physalis or winter cherry, grapes of some peculiar kind, or even underground fungi, as truffles, etc. Many have supposed the word to mean the ingredients, whatever they might have been, of a charm or love-potion, and hence have recurred to the mandrake, celebrated, as already said, throughout antiquity, for its supposed virtues, and whose history has been tricked out with all the traditional nonsense that might be imagined to confirm that report of such qualities.

Liebentantz[1] in 1660; the younger Rudbeck,[2] in 1733, and Celsius,[3] in 1745, have displayed much erudition and research in their inquiries; but the first of these writers arrived at the conclusion that nothing certain could be come to on the subject; while the second proposed raspberries as the Dudaïm; and the third maintained that they were the fruit of the Zizyphus, the Spina Christi of the disciples of Linnaeus.

Maundrell, who travelled in the East in the seventeenth century, informs us that, having asked the chief priest of Aleppo what sort of a plant or fruit the Dudaïm, or (as we translate it) the *mandrakes*, were which Leah gave to Rachel for the purchase of her husband's embraces, the holy man replied 'that they were plants of a large leaf bearing a certain sort of fruit, in shape resembling an apple, growing ripe in harvest, but of an ill savour, and not wholesome. But the virtue of them was to *help conception*, being laid under the genial bed. That the women were wont to apply it at this day, out of an opinion of its prolific virtue.'[4]

Some writers have supposed the Dudaïm to be neither more nor less than the truffle. Virey asserts it to be a species of Orchis; and, indeed, considering the remarkable conformation of the root of this plant,[5] the slightly spermatic odour of its farinaceous substance, as well as that of

---

[1] *Exercitatio de Rachelis Deliciis*, 4to, 1678. [D]
[2] *Atlantica illustrata*, 1733. [D]
[3] *Hierobotanicon*, 1745. [D]
[4] *Journey from Aleppo to Jerusalem at Easter, A.D. 1697*. [D]
[5] *Orchis* is a Greek word signifying *testicle*, a name given by the ancients to this plant on account of the supposed resemblance of its root to that organ. [D]

the flowers of another one belonging to the same family, an odour so similar to the emanation of an animal proverbial for its salaciousness, and to which its bearded spikes or ears give additional resemblance, the almost unbounded confidence which the ancients reposed in its aphrodisiacal virtues cannot appear surprising.

One of the most extraordinary aphrodisiacs upon record is that reported to have been employed by the Amazons. The 'Amazons', says Eustathius,[1] 'broke either a leg or an arm of the captives they took in battle, and this they did, not only to prevent their attempts at escape, or their plotting, but also, and this more especially, to render them more vigorous in the venereal conflict; for, as they themselves burnt away the right breast of their female children in order that the right arm might become stronger from receiving additional nutriment, so they imagined that, similarly, the genital member would be strengthened by the deprivation of one of the extremities, whether a leg or an arm. Hence, when reproached by the Scythians with the limping gait of her slaves, Queen Antianara replied: 'ἀριότα Χωλὸς οιφεῖ," "The lame best perform the act of love." '

Among the ancient Romans, it was impossible that philters, or love-potions, should not be introduced amid the general depravity so common in every class; and hence we meet with frequent allusions to them in their writers.[2] Thus, the emperor Julian, surnamed the Apostate, writing to his friend Callixines[3] comments,

> But you, Callixines, observe that Penelope's love to her husband was always thus manifested. To this I answer, who but he *that has habitually drunk Mandragora* can prefer in a woman conjugal affection to piety?

The over-excitement caused in the nervous system by such potions

---

[1] *Eustathii Commentarii ad Homerum*, Vol. I, pp. 325, 403–9. Editio Lipsiae, 1827. [D]

[2] Much detail is given in Dufour (i.e. Paul Lacroix): *Histoire de la Prostitution chez tous les peuples du monde* . . . (Vol. 2, chap. 21), Paris, Séré, 1851–3 (in six volumes). There is an English translation in three volumes, by Samuel Putnam, published by Covici of Chicago in 1926, and later reprinted in a revised edition of two volumes at New York, 1932. Indication as to the beginning and ending of each of the original French (six) volumes is given in this translation, which increases its utility for the researcher.

[3] *Juliani Callixenae Epistola*. [D]

frequently proved fatal. Such, according to Eusebius, was the fate of the poet Lucretius, who, having been driven to madness by an amatory potion, and having, during the intervals of his insanity, composed several books, which were afterwards corrected by Cicero, died by his own hand in the forty-fourth year of his age.[1] It should, however, be remembered that this account has been questioned by the poet's translator and annotator, Mason Good, in these words:

By whom the potion was administered is conjectured only from a passage in St Jerome,[2] who says that a certain Lucilia killed her husband or her lover by giving him a philtre, which was intended to secure his love, but the effect of which was to make him insane. This Lucilia is supposed to have been the wife or the mistress of Lucretius, but by whom the supposition was first made, I am not able to discover.[3] Suetonius relates the same thing of Caius Caligula, who although, when he arrived at manhood, endured fatigue tolerably well, was still occasionally liable to faintness, owing to which he remained incapable of any effort. He was not insensible to this disorder of his mind, and sometimes had thoughts of retiring.[4] It is thought, he continues, that his wife Caesonia administered to him a love-potion, which threw him into a phrensy.[5] It is in allusion to this that Juvenal writes:[6]

> Some nimbler juice would make him foam and rave,
> Like that Caesonia to her Caius gave,
> Who, plucking from the forehead of the foal
> The mother's love, infused it in the bowl:
> The boiling blood ran hissing through his veins,
> Till the mad vapour mounted to his brains.

These concoctions were publicly sold at Rome, their ingredients consisting of herbs of various kinds, in the culling and testing of which

---

[1] 'Amatorio poculo furorem versus, quum aliquot libros per intervalla conscripserat.' [D]

[2] *Epist. dissuas:* ad Rufinum C. 22. Tom. XII, p. 245, ad. Varon. [D]

[3] *Remarks on the life and poems of Lucretius,* p. vi. (Bohn's Classical Library). [D]

[4] Probably to Anticyra, a Greek town situated at the mouth of the river Sperchius, and reputed to produce the genuine hellebore, recommended by the ancient physicians as a cure for insanity, whence the well-known adage, 'Naviget Anticyram'. [D]

[5] Sueton. *Calig.,* 50. [D]

[6] Juvenal. *Sat.* VI, v. 614. [D].

the shepherds were often employed. The remora, or sucking-fish, certain bones of the frog, the astroit, or star-fish, and the hippomanes were also used. Horace[1] informs us that dried human marrow and liver were also had recourse to:

> That his parch'd marrow might compose,
> Together with his liver dried, an amorous dose.

Del Rio[2] and Wallick[3] assert that to the above were likewise added nail-parings, sundry metals, reptiles and the intestines of particular birds and fishes, and even *semen virile* and *sanguis menstruus*. During the concoction of these filthy, disgusting, and abominable compounds the Infernal Deities were earnestly invoked.

Of all the above ingredients the most famous was the hippomanes, which, according to Wier, was a piece of flesh upon the forehead of a young colt, of a black or brown colour, in size and shape like a fig, which the mare is said to bite off as soon as she has foaled, the mare forsaking her offspring when prevented from so doing; hence the hippomanes, which was in reality nothing more than a caul or part of the omentum attached to the head of the foal, as it is also sometimes to that of infants, was thought to be particularly effective in conciliating love, especially when calcined or reduced to powder and swallowed in some of the blood of the person beloved. This superstition is, however, in some degree excusable if it be considered that even in the present day many persons in our own country firmly believe the human caul to have the power of saving its possessor from drowning; and that in the good old times it was regarded as a visible indication that Providence had designed the infant so furnished for the service of religion, such children, whether male or female, being destined, in consequence, for the cloister.

Virgil thus mentions it as one of the ingredients of the philter that Dido caused to be made for her previously to her committing suicide:[4]

---

[1] Hor. *Epod.* V, *Lib.* Epod., v, 37. See also the admirable notes of Dacier and Sanadon upon the above ode. [D]

[2] *Disquisitionum Magicorum*, Lib. III, quaestio III. De Amatorio Maleficio, p. 7. [D]

[3] *Cinq livres de l'imposture et tromperie des diables*, Lib. II, p. 216, 1569. [D]

[4] *Aenid*, Lib. IV, v. 513, 514, 515 and 516. [D]

Herbs are brought, by moonlight mow'd
With brazen scythes, big, swol'n with milky juice
Of curious poison, *and the fleshy knot*
Torn from the forehead of a new foal'd colt
To rob the mother's love.

The following curious account of the wonderful effects of the hippomanes, and which fully justifies the etymology of that word, is given by Pausanias:

Among these [offerings] you may behold those of Phormis Menalius. . . . His gifts in Olympia are two horses and two charioteers, one of which horses the Aelians assert to have been made by a magician, of brass, into which metal he had previously infused the *hippomanes*, and which, in consequence, possessed the power of exciting in horses a mad desire for coition. The horse so made by the magician, was, both in size and shape inferior to many horses which are dedicated within Altis, and was rendered still more deformed by having no tail. Horses desire connection with this image not only in spring, but every day throughout the year, for, breaking their bridles or running away from their drivers, they rush into Altis and attack the horse in a manner much more furious than if it was the most beautiful mare, and one they were acquainted with. Their hoofs, indeed, slip from the side of the image, but nevertheless they never cease neighing vehemently and leaping furiously on the figure till they are driven off by the whip or by some other violent means, for till such methods are applied, it is impossible to disengage them from the brass.[1]

Many formulae for love-potions may be found in the work of Albertus Magnus, who, among other things, particularly recommends 'the brains of a partridge calcined into powder and swallowed in red wine', a remedy which is also much insisted upon by Platina,[2] who in praising the flesh of the partridge, says, 'The flesh of the partridge, which is of good and easy digestion, is highly nutritious; it strengthens the brain, facilitates conception and arouses the half-extinct desire for venereal pleasures.' Mery[3] confidently prescribes, for the same purpose, the *partes genitales* of a cock prepared and administered in like manner.

The following compositions enjoyed a vast reputation during the seventeenth century:

[1] Pausanias, *Graeciae Descriptio*, Lib. V, c. 27. [D]
[2] In his work, *De valetudine tuenda*. [D]
[3] *Traité universel des drogues simples.* [D]

FORTUNA VENERIS.—Take of pismires or ants (the biggest, having a sourish smell, are the best) two handfuls, spirits of wine one gallon; digeste them in a glasse vessel, close shut, for the space of a month, in which time they will be dissolved into a liquor; then distil them in balneo till all be dry. Then put the same quantity of ants as before; do this three times, then aromatize the spirit with cinnamon. Note, that upon the spirit will float an oil which must be separated. This spirit [continues the inventor] is of excellent use to stir up the animal spirits insomuch that John Casimire, Palsgrave of the Rhine, and Seyfrie of Collen, general against the Turks, did always drink thereof when they went to fight, to increase magnanimity and courage, which it did even to admiration.

This spirit doth also *wonderfully irritate them that are slothful to venery*.[1]

AQUA MAGNANIMITATIS.—Take of ants or pismires, a handful of their eggs two hundred, of millepedes (wood-lice) two hundred, of bees two hundred and fifty; digeste them together, the space of a month, then pour off the clear spirit, and keep it safe. This water or spirit is of the same value as the former.

But, quitting these 'fond conceits', as honest old Burton[2] calls them, and investigating the subject upon acknowledged and recognized principles, it will be found that, as the ancient philosophers and naturalists regarded the semen as the purest and most perfect part of our blood, the flower of our blood, and a portion of the brain, so the sole object of all aphrodisiacal preparations should be to promote its copious secretion.

Before, however, proceeding to indicate the means most conducive thereto it may prove interesting to the reader to be informed what were the opinions of some of the most celebrated philosophers of antiquity upon the semen. Says Montaigne:[3]

Let us first know whether, at least, all they [physicians] agree about the matter whereof men produce one another. . . . Archesilaus, the physician, whose favourite and disciple Socrates was, said that men and beasts were formed of a lacteous slime, expressed by the heat of the earth. Pythagoras says that our seed is the foam or cream of our better blood. Plato, that it is the distillation of the marrow of the back-bones; and raises his argument

---

[1] *The Holy Guide*, by John Heyden Gent, a servant of God and a Secretary of Nature, Lib. V., p. 61. [D]

[2] *Anatomy of Melancholy*. [D]. Available in 3 vols. in Everyman's Library.

[3] *Essays*, Vol. II, pp. 262–3. Translated by Cotton, London, 1743. [D]

from this: that that part is first sensible of being weary of the work. Alcmeon, that it is a part of the substance of the brain, and that it is so, says he, is proved by its causing weakness of the eyes in those who are over-immoderately addicted to that exercise. Democritus, that it is a substance extracted from soul and body. Aristotle, an excrement drawn from the aliment of the last blood which is diffused over all our members; others, that it is a blood concocted and digested by the heat of the genitals.

But, to return from this digression. Under whatever point of view the *semen virile* be considered, whether as containing, according to some physicians, all the parts of the foetus, under the name of organic molecules, or as being, in the opinion of others, merely destined to fecundate the female egg, it will be equally true that the semen is a fluid impregnated with a vivifying principle regarded as the most important (*validissimum*) of our humours, by Hippocrates, who, in support of this his opinion, adduces the fact of our becoming debilitated, however small the quantity we may lose of it in the venereal act.[1]

Zeno, the father of the Stoic philosophy, called the loss of semen the loss of part of the animating principle; and that sage's practice was conformable with his principles, for he is recorded to have embraced his wife but once in his life, and that out of mere courtesy.

Epicurus and Democritus were nearly of the same opinion as Zeno; and the Athletae, that their strength might be unimpaired, never married. For the same reason Moses forbade indulgence before battle.

Says a writer in the *Dictionnaire des Sciences Médicales:*[2]

Les êtres qui font le plus abus de leurs facultés intellectuelles et sensitives extérieures sont les moins capables d'un coït fréquent, tandis que les idiots, les crétins, l'exercent bien davantage. De même, l'âne, le cochon se livrent plus stupidement à l'acte de propagation et répandent beaucoup plus de sperme que les espèces intelligentes; enfin les animaux à petit cerveau, tels que les poissons, montrent use d'extrême fécondité.

If now it be asked what will best promote the secretion of the seminal fluid, or, in other words, which is the best aphrodisiac, it may be confidently answered, the use of a substantial nourishment, such as

---

[1] 'Cujus rei istud est argumentum, quod ubi rem veneream exercemus, tantillo emisse, imbecilles evadimus.'—*De Genitura.* [D]

[2] Tome 52, p. 286 et seq. [D]

medical men designate as an analeptic diet.[1] Food of this description, without fatiguing the gastric organs, furnishes an abundant chyle, from which is elaborated a rich blood, and in which the secretory organs find materials of an excellent quality, and in an almost constant proportion with the regular consumption of their products. All food of easy and quick digestion is an analeptic. But the same substance which is an aleptic to one person, may prove indigestible and innutritious for another. The numerous treatises upon digestion render it unnecessary to specify here the different aliments most proper for convalescents, suffice it to say, generally, that those meats in which azezome is found are the most nutritious. This animal principle is that extractive matter of animal fibre which produces the red appearance of uncooked meat; it is also that which forms what is called the *brown* of roasted meats, gives the flavour to broths and soups, the peculiar smell to boiled meat, and constitutes the much admired *goût* of game and venison. It is not found in the flesh of young animals, which is said, with reason, to be, on that very account, less nutritious. It is only when they have attained the adult age that it appears in them; it is abundant in beef, mutton, kid, hare, pigeon, partridge, pheasant, woodcock, quail, duck, goose and generally in all animals having dark coloured flesh. Mushrooms and oysters also contain some, but in a very small proportion.

Food in which this principle exists appears to impress upon the membrane of the stomach an increase of activity; the digestion is easy, and from a small mass of alimentary substance an abundant chyle is obtained. The chyliferous vessels derive a very great proportion of reparative materials; there is found but little excrementitious residue, the blood is enriched and its course accelerated, while the impulsive

---

[1] These matters are also discussed by modern writers:

Iwan Bloch, *A History of English Sexual Morals* (*Geschlechtsleben in England*), trans. William H. Forstern, London, Francis Aldor, 1936 (and reprints). Originally published in German at Berlin, 3 vols., 1901–3, respectively.

Havelock Ellis, *Studies in the Psychology of Sex*, 4 vols., Random House, New York, 1936, or the more recent complete reprint in two volumes, London, Heinemann. Reference should be made to the general index of subjects.

Th. Van de Velde; *Fertility and Sterility in Marriage*, London, Heinemann, 1929 (and reprints); also *Ideal Marriage*, London, Heinemann, 1928, and many reprints (New York edition, Covici, Friede, 1930, etc.).

force of the heart and arteries is strong and more lively. Under the influence of this regimen a greater quantity of heat is developed and, in a given time, there is a greater absorption of oxygen than during a vegetable one; the respiration is performed more freely, the organs increase in size, but it is then a genuine embonpoint; nutrition is, in reality, more active, it is not a deceptive turgidity; the energy of the secretions and exhalations is redoubled, cutaneous perspiration becomes more abundant, and the glandular apparatus fulfil their functions with greater facility. A man who adopts this food becomes consequently very well fitted to make the sacrifices exacted by the calls of love to which he is then more frequently solicited.

The mollusca in general, and testaceous animals in particular, have been considered as endowed with aphrodisiac properties. Juvenal[1] attributes this quality to oysters which, together with mussels, have in this respect become vulgarly proverbial.

> For what cares the drunken dame
> (take head or tail), to her 'tis much the same
> Who at deep midnight on fat oysters sups.

Wallich informs us that the ladies of his time had recourse, on such occasions, to the brains of the mustela piscis. The Sepia octopus was also in great repute, and Plautus, in his play of Cisina, introduces an old man who has just been purchasing some at the market.

Apuleius, the celebrated author of the *Metamorphoseon de Asino aureo* (Metamorphoses of the Golden Ass), and who lived in the second century, under the Antonines, having married a rich widow, was accused by her father Aemilian, before Claudius Maximus, pro-Consul of Asia, of having employed sorcery and charms in order to gain her affections (a parallel case with that of Shakespeare's Othello). The love-potions alleged to have been administered were asserted to be chiefly composed of shell-fish, lobsters, sea hedgehogs, spiced oysters, and cuttle-fish, the last of which was particularly famed for its stimulating qualities. Apuleius fully exonerated himself in his admirable *Apologia ceu oratio de Magica*, so esteemed for the purity of its style as

---

[1] Juvenal, *Sat.* VI, v. 302. 'Ad venerem', says Lubinus in a note on this passage, 'miris modis instigant (i.e. ostreae), inde turpissimae illae bestiae (feminae) ostrea comedebant, *ut ad Venerem promptiores essent*.' [D]

to have been pronounced by Saint Augustine (*De Civitate Dei*, Lib. XVIII, c. 20) as *copiosissima et disertissima oratio*.[1] The reason adduced by Aemilian for believing that Apuleius had chiefly used fish for the purpose was, that they must necessarily have great efficacy in exciting women to venery, inasmuch as Venus herself was born of the sea.

Venette[2] supports this view when he says:

> Nous avons l'expérience en France que ceux qui ne vivent presque que de coquillages et de poissons qui ne sont que de l'eau rassemblée, sont plus ardents à l'amour que les autres, en effet, nous nous y sentons bien plus portés en *Carême qu'en toute autre saison parce-qu'en ce temps-là nous ne nous nourrissons que de poissons et d'herbes qui sont des aliments composés de beaucoup d'eau.*

Should this be true, the Infallible (?) Church must have committed an astounding blunder in thinking to mortify, for six weeks, the sinful lusts and affections of its dupes, by confining them for the above period, to the exclusive use of such articles of food.

There are also some aliments which, although not included in the class of analeptics, are, nevertheless, reported to possess specific aphrodisiacal qualities; such are fish, truffles, and chocolate.

The following anecdote relative to this property in fish is related by Hecquet:[3]

> Sultan Saladin, wishing to ascertain the extent of the continence of the dervishes, took two of them into his palace, and during a certain space of time, had them fed upon the most succulent food. In a short time all traces of their self-inflicted severities were effaced, and their *embonpoint* began to reappear.
>
> In this state he gave them two Odalisques[4] of surpassing beauty, but all whose blandishments and allurements proved ineffectual, for the two holy men came forth from the ordeal as pure as the diamond of Bejapore.[5]

---

[1] A translation into English from Apuleius's *Apologia* is included in *The Works of Apuleius*, under the title of *The Defence of Apuleius: A Discourse on Magic*, London, H. G. Bohn, 1853. The same volume contains *The Golden Ass*, and other works.

[2] *De la génération de l'homme*, p. 272 [D]

[3] *Traité des dispenses et de Carême*, Paris, 1709, en 12mo, réimprimé trois fois. [D]

[4] Names given to the female slaves or concubines in the harem of the Sultan. [D]

[5] A large province of the Deccan, said to have been famous, in ancient times, for its diamond mines. [D]

The Sultan still kept them in his palace, and, to celebrate their triumph, caused them to live upon a diet equally *recherché*, but consisting entirely of fish. A few days afterwards they were again subject to the united powers of youth and beauty, but this time nature was too strong, and the too happy cenobites forgot, in the arms of voluptuousness, their vows of continence and chastity.

This peculiar property in fish has been attributed to the presence of phosphorus, which is known to exist somewhat plentifully in the substance, and has also been discovered in their roes in a simple state of combination. Now, phosphorus is one of the most powerful stimulants: it acts upon the generative organism in a manner to cause the most violent priapisms; but this principle does not act alone, and there must also be taken into account the different seasonings and condiments which form the basis of most culinary preparations to which fish are subjected, and which are all taken from the class of irritants.

The prolific virtues of fish have, no doubt, been greatly exaggerated, and it is certain that too much importance has been given to the observation made (upon rather slight grounds) by travellers as to the abundant population of ichtyophagic nations; nor would it be difficult to adduce facts to prove to the incredulous that the continuous use of fish excites lasciviousness in such persons only as are constitutionally inclined thereto.

The following instances sufficiently establish the aphrodisiacal qualities of phosphorus. A drake belonging to a chemist having drunk water out of a copper vessel which had contained phosphorus, ceased not gallanting his females till he died. An old man to whom a few drops only of phosphoric ether had been administered, experienced repeated and imperious venereal wants which he was compelled to satisfy. Leroy and Battatz, two celebrated French physicians of the last century, tried the effects of phosphorus upon themselves, with similar results.[1]

---

[1] Suggestion is undoubtedly causative during the administration of many so-called aphrodisiac drugs. Discussing androgenic treatment and various physiotherapies, Georgene H. Seward says: 'Since a strong dose of suggestion is administered with every drug or hormone, suggestion rather than hormone may well be the therapeutic agent in successful cases. This interpretation is supported by the fact that no apparent loss results from substitution of a control oil for hormone without the patient's knowledge.' See Seward, *Sex and the Social Order*, Harmondsworth, Pelican Books, 1954, p. 177.

Sensations of the same kind are said to be experienced by persons whose occupation requires the frequent handling of this drug. It may thus be considered as satisfactorily proved that the above substance is essentially an energetic stimulant of the genital organs; but should still further evidence be required, it may be found in the fact that the administration of it, even in small doses, has been productive of the most horrible and fatal results, instances of which are recorded in many medical works both foreign and English, but more particularly in those of Brera, Magendie, and others.

The erotic properties of truffles and mushrooms are considered by most writers as better established than those of fish. The ancient Romans were well acquainted with truffles, and obtained them from Greece and Africa, especially from the province of Libya, the fungi found there being particularly esteemed for their delicacy and flavour. In modern times, also, the truffle is regarded as the *diamond* of the kitchen, being highly valued for its capability of exciting the genesiac sense, it being a positive aphrodisiac which disposes men to be exacting and women complying.[1]

The following instance of its effects is given by Brillat Savarin,[2] to whom the circumstances were communicated, in confidence, by the lady who was the subject of them. She said:

Je soupai un jour chez moi en trio avec mon mari et un de ses amis dont le nom était V . . . C'était un beau garçon et ne manquant pas d'esprit qui venait souvent chez moi, mais il ne m'avait jamais rien dit qui pût le faire regarder comme mon amant, et s'il me faisait la cour, c'était d'une manière si enveloppée qu'il n'y avait qu'une sotte qui eût pu s'en fâcher. Il paraissait, ce jour-là, destiné à me tenir compagnie pendant le reste de la soirée, car mon mari avait un rendez-vous et devait nous quitter bientôt. Notre souper avait pour base une petite volaille truffée. Les truffes étaient délicieuses, et quoique je les aime beaucoup, je me contins, nonobstant; je ne bus aussi qu'un seul verre de Champagne, ayant quelque pressentiment que la soirée ne se passerait pas sans événement. Bientôt mon mari partit et me laissa

---

[1] That Coryphaeus of voluptuaries, George IV, so highly appreciated this quality in truffles that his Ministers at the courts of Turin, Naples, Florence, etc., were specially instructed to forward by a state messenger to the royal kitchen any of those fungi that might be found superior in size, delicacy, or flavour. [D]

[2] *Physiologie du Goût*, par Brillat Savarin, Paris, 1859. [D]

seule avec V. . . . qu'il regardait comme tout à fait sans conséquence. La conversation roula d'abord sur des sujets indifférents, mais elle ne tarda pas à prendre une tournure plus sérieuse et plus intéressante. V . . . fut successivement flatteur, expansif, affectueux, caressant, et voyant que je ne faisais que plaisanter de tant de belles choses, il devint si pressant que je ne pus plus me tromper sur ses prétentions. Alors, je me réveillai comme d'un songe et me défendis avec d'autant plus de franchise que mon cœur ne me disait rien pour lui. Il persistait avec une action qui pouvait devenir tout à fait offensante; . . . et j'avoue, à ma honte, que toute espérance ne lui serait pas interdite. Enfin, il me quitta, j'allai me coucher et dormis tout d'un somme. Mais le lendemain fut le jour du jugement; j'examinai ma conduite de la veille, et je la trouvai répréhensible. J'aurais dû arrêter V . . . dès les premières phrases, et ne pas me prêter à une conversation qui ne présageait rien de bon. Ma fierté aurait dû sonner, crier, me fâcher, faire, enfin, tout ce que je ne fis pas. Que vous dirai-je, Monsieur, je mis tout cela sur le compte des truffes, et je suis réellement persuadée qu'elles m'avaient donné une prédisposition dangereuse, et si je n'y renonce pas (ce qui eut été trop rigoureux), du moins, je n'en mange jamais sans que le plaisir qu'elles me causent ne soit mêlé d'un peu de défiance.

The mushroom was also equally well known as the truffle to the ancient Romans for its aphrodisiacal qualities. Thus Martial says:

> Quum sit anus conjux et sint tibi mortua membra,
> Nil aliud bulbis quam sater esse potes.[1]
> If envious age relax the nuptial knot
> Thy food be mushrooms and thy feast shalot.

This bulb was believed by the ancients to be so decided a stimulant that it was always served up, together with pepper and pine-nuts, at the wedding dinner.

An immoderate use of chocolate was, in the seventeenth century, considered so powerful an aphrodisiac that Jean Franco Raucher strenuously enforced the necessity of forbidding the monks to drink it, adding that if such an interdiction had been laid upon it at an earlier period the scandal with which that sacred order had been assailed would have been prevented. It is a singular fact that, fearful of losing their character, or, what, perhaps, was dearer to them, their chocolate,

---

[1] Martial, *Epigram.*, Lib. XIII, epig. 34. [D]

the worthy cenobites were so diligent in suppressing Raucher's work that four copies only of it are said to be in existence.[1]

The history of the middle ages abounds with complaints of the lubricity, gluttony, and drunkenness of the monks, vices which are described as being their ruin, in the following pithy distich:

> Sunt tria nigrorum quae vestant res monachorum,
> Renes et venter et pocula sumpta frequenter.[2]
> Three things to ruin monks combine—
> Venery, gluttony, and wine.

A monk who was a great enemy to adultery was one day preaching against it, and grew so warm in his argument, and took so much pains to convince his congregation of his own abhorrence of it, that at last he broke out in the following solemn declaration:

Yea, my brethren, I had rather, for the good of my soul, have to do with ten maids every month, than, in ten years, to touch one married woman!

The celebrity they acquired in the field of Venus may readily be imagined from a quatrain[3] that was affixed in a conspicuous part of the Church of St Hyacinthe, and which, translated, runs thus:

> You ladies who for pregnancy do wish
> To great St Hyacinthe your prayers apply,
> And what his Saintship cannot accomplish
> *The monks within will surely satisfy.*[4]

---

[1] Rare foods (that is, foods difficult of access, or expensive) have often maintained an aphrodisiac reputation. Such was the potato at its first introduction in England. Havelock Ellis says: 'Thus the potato, when first introduced from America, had the reputation of being a powerful aphrodisiac, and the Elizabethan dramatists contain many references to this supposed virtue. As we know, potatoes, even when taken in the largest doses, have not the slightest aphrodisiac effect, and the Irish peasantry, whose diet consists very largely of potatoes, are regarded as possessing an unusually small measure of sexual feeling.' (*Studies in the Psychology of Sex*, Random House, New York, 1936. Vol. 3, Part 1, p. 173.)

[2] Ducange, *Glossaire*. [D]

[3] J. H. Meibomius, *De flagrorum usu in Re medica et Venerea*, Paris, 1792, p. 125. [D]

[4] Tales such as these have been current all over the world for centuries. A few Oriental examples are to be found in *Eastern Love* (an anthology), translated by E. Powys Mathers, privately printed for subscribers only, London, John Rodker,

It would have been well had these holy men been contented with these comparatively venial indulgences. The following macaronic epigram, however, shows that they were but too much addicted to the *Amour Socratique*:

> Let a friar of some order tecum pernoctare
> Either thy wife or thy daughter hic vult violare.
> Or thy son he will prefer, sicut fortem fortis,
> God give such a friar pain in Inferni portis.[1]

But the open violation of their monastic vows, especially that of chastity, sometimes subjected monks to very severe punishment, a singular instance of which is recorded by Thévenot.[2]

To these poor monks may, however, be applied the sly remark of Hume upon a similar act of cruelty perpetuated, though for a far more innocent cause, by Geoffry, the father of Henry II, upon the prior and chapter of Seez in Normandy, viz. that 'of the pain and danger they might justly complain, yet since they had vowed chastity, he deprived them of a superfluous treasure'.[3]

If the properties of ambergris be less potent than those of phosphorus they are certainly less fatal. According to Boswell,[4] three grains of the former suffice to produce a marked acceleration of the pulse, a considerable development of muscular strength, a greater activity in the intellectual faculties, and a disposition to cheerfulness and venereal desires. The same author also says that it is a medicine which can, for a short time, restore an effete old man to juvenility.[5] The ancients reposed great confidence in the virtues of this drug, employing it as a renovator of the vital powers and organs whose energy had been exhausted by age or by excess; and throughout the East this perfume still maintains a reputation for life-preserving qualities.

1927 (12 vols.). And they have been especially prevalent in Europe since the time of Boccaccio and the early Italian novelists, and the rise of the anti-clerical movement. Needless to say, many of them are without foundation in fact.

[1] See *Macaronéana*, par M. Octave Delepierre, Paris, 1852, p. 3. [D]

[2] Thévenot, *Portraits des Vies des Hommes Illustrés*, Vol. I, p. 23, fol. edit. [D]

[3] Hume's *Hist. of England*, Vol. I, p. 348. [D]

[4] *Dissertatio Inauguralis de Ambra*, § iv, p. 36. [D]

[5] Medicamentum quod non solum potenter stimulat, sed vel effoetum senem, pro brevi tempore, ad juventutem iterum restituit. Ibid., § viii, p. 44. [D]

Madame Du Barry,[1] the infamous mistress of Louis XV, is reported to have availed herself of its aphrodisiacal qualities in order to stimulate the jaded appetite of her royal paramour.

L'attachement du roi pour Madame Du Barry[2] lui est venu des efforts prodigieux qu'elle lui fit faire au moyen d'un baptême (lavement) ambré dont elle se parfuma intérieurement tous les jours. On ajoute qu'elle joignit à cela un secret dont on ne se sert pas encore en bonne société.

Piquant as is this anecdote, the key to it is equally so.

Les mouches cantarides, i diabolini l'essence de giroflée, les baptêmes ambrés, etc., sont des inventions de notre siècle dont la débilité eût été incurable sans ces secours. L'auteur ne peut rendre *le secret de la mauvaise société*, dont se sert la Comtesse, sans blesser la bonne, tout ce qu'il peut dire décemment est que ce secret est un diminutif des erreurs philosophiques.[3]

The old pharmacopoeia are amply furnished with formulae of which amber constitutes the base. These recipes are generally designated by names which, to a certain extent, indicate the particular use to which they are destined by their makers; thus, France formerly boasted her *Tablettes de Magnanimité*, or *Electuaire Satyrion*, and *Une poudre de joie*. Troches, or odoriferous lozenges, to which the ancients gave the

---

[1] Née dans une condition obscure, vouée au libertinage dès sa plus tendre jeunesse, autant par goût que par état, Mme Du Barry ne put offrir à son august amant, malgré la fleur de la jeunesse et les brillants appas dont elle étoit encore pourvue, que les restes de la plus vile canaille, de la prostitution.' *Vie privée des maitresses de Louis XV*, p. 153.—'You are no doubt curious to hear an opinion of Madame Du Barry's beauty from the lips of one who has seen her both in her days of prosperity and after her downfall. She was a person of small, almost diminutive stature, extremely frail and delicate in feature, which saved her from being vulgar; but even from the first, she always wore that peculiarly *fane* look which she owed to a youth of dissipation, a maturity of unbounded indulgence. At the period of my visit she was about thirty-six years of age, but, from her child-like form and delicacy of countenance, appeared much younger, and her *gambades* and unrestrained gestures of supreme delight on having, as she said, *quelqu'un à qui parler*, did not seem displaced. Although alone, and evidently not in expectation of visitors, her toilet was brilliant and recherché, the result of the necessity of killing time.' *Talleyrand Papers*. [D]

[2] *Espion de la Cour*. [D]

[3] *Gazetier Cuirasse*, ou Anecdotes Scandaleuses de la Cour de France. [D]

pretty name of *Avunculae Cypriae*, were, and perhaps are still, sold in Paris under that of *Seraglio Pastilles*. Ambergris forms the basis of these, as it also does of the Indian pastilles called *Cachunde*, and which were equally in repute. Zactus Lusitanus[1] stated that they were composed of bole Tuccinum, musk, ambergris, aloes-wood, red and yellow sanders (*pterocarpus santalinus*), mastic, sweet-flag (*colamus aromaticus*), galanga, cinnamon, rhubarb, Indian myrobalon, absynth, and of some pounded precious stones, which however, impart no additional quality to the composition. Speaking of this composition, the *Encyclopaedia Parthensis* describes it as

a medicine highly celebrated among the Chinese and Indians; it is composed of ambergris and several other aromatic ingredients, perfumes, medicinal earths and precious stones. It imparts a sweetness to the breath, is a valuable medicine in all nervous complaints, and is esteemed as a prolonger of life and an exciter to venery.[2]

Rivière[3] gives us the following formula for a potion whose virtue is indisputable:

Take of amber, half a drachm; musk, two scruples, aloes, one drachm and a half; pound them all together, pour upon the mass a sufficient quantity of spirits of wine so that the liquor may cover it to the height of about five fingers' breadth; expose it to sand heat, filter and distil it, close it hermetically, and administer it in broth in the dose of three or five drops. This liquor is also advantageous when mixed with syrup, prepared as follows:—Take of cinnamon water, four ounces: orange and rose water, each six ounces, and sugar candy q.s.

Musk taken internally is said by many physicians to be almost equal to ambergris for its aphrodisiacal qualities. Externally applied, this substance produces very singular phenomena. Borelli details the case of a man 'qui s'étant frotté le penis avec du musc avant de se livrer à l'exercice des fonctions génitales, resta uni avec sa femme sans pouvoir

---

[1] In his *Praxis Medica Admiranda*, wherein he also gives the formula of an electuary *ad excitandum tentiginem nulli secundum*, p. 295, Observ., XCI, as well as a recipe for pills *ad coitus ignaviam*, CXIII, p. 297. [D]

[2] *Encyclopaedia Parthensis*, Article, Cachunde. [D]

[3] See his *Premier Traité de l'homme et de son essentielle anatomie, avec les éléments et ce qui est en eux, de ses maladies, médecine et absolus remèdes*, etc., Paris, 1588. [D]

s'en séparer. Il fallait, dans cette position lui donner une quantité de lavements afin de ramollir les parties qui s'étaient extraordinairement tuméfiées.'[1] Diermerbreek and Schurigius give similar instances. The effects of musk are, therefore, also equal to those produced by certain plants, as recorded by Theophrastus: 'Esse herbas quae vel ad *sexagesimum coitum* vim praestant sed at demum secernitur sanguis.'[2] Weickard says that by means of this drug he resuscitated the genital power in a man who had nearly completed his eightieth year.

But, of all aphrodisiacs, the most certain and terrible in its effects are cantharides, commonly known as Spanish flies. That they exercise a powerful and energetic action upon the organization and stimulate, to the utmost, the venereal desire, is but too true. The effects, however, which these insects, when applied as a blister upon the skin, are known to produce are insignificant when compared with their intense action upon the stomach when taken internally; nor is it the stomach only which is affected by them: the bladder experiences an irritation exceeding even that caused by the severest strangury. To these succeed perforation of the stomach, ulcers throughout the entire length of the intestinal canal, dysentery, and, lastly, death in the midst of intolerable agonies. Medical works abound with observations concerning the fatal effects of cantharides when unduly administered, whether from ignorance or for exciting the venereal appetite. Two cases are recorded by Pabrol in his *Observations Anatomiques*.

Paré also relates that a courtesan, having sprinkled the meat given by her to one of her lovers with pounded cantharides, the wretched youth was seized with a violent priapism and loss of blood at the anus, of which he died.

Ferdinand the Catholic, of Castile, owed his death to the effects of a philter administered to him by his queen, Germaine de Foix, in the hope of enabling him to beget an heir to the crowns of Aragon, Navarre, and Naples. Says Mignot:[3]

Plusieurs dames attachées à la Reine, lui indiquèrent un breuvage qu'il fallait, disoit-on, donner à Ferdinand pour ranimer ses forces. Cette

[1] *Cent.*, II. [D]
[2] See Celius, Lib. XIV, cap. 3. [D]
[3] *Histoire de Ferdinand et Isabelle*, Tom. II, 326. Paris, 1766. [D]

princesse fit composer ce rémède, sous ses yeux, et le présenta au roi qui désirait, plus qu'elle, d'avoir un fils. Depuis ce jour, la santé de Ferdinand s'affaiblit, au point qu'il ne la recouvra jamais.

The life of the celebrated Wallenstein, one of the heroes of the Thirty Years War, was for a long time endangered from the effects of a potion administered to him by his countess.

De retour dans sa patrie, il [Wallenstein] fit inspirer une vive passion à une riche veuve de la famille de Wiezkova, et eut l'adresse de se faire préférer à des rivaux d'un rang plus élevé; mais cette union fut troublée par l'extrême jalousie de sa femme; on prétend même qu'elle fit usage de philtres qui pensèrent compromettre la santé de son mari.[1]

Cardinal Dubois,[2] the favourite and Minister of Philip, Duke of Orléans, Regent of France, during the minority of Louis XV, gives the following amusing account of a love-potion, to the powerful effects of which he considered himself indebted for his existence.

An old bachelor, of Brivas, had engaged to marry a young lady of only sixteen years of age. The night before the wedding he assembled the wise heads of his family for the purpose of consulting upon the best means of enabling him to perform his part creditably in the approaching amorous conflict. Opinions were divided; some maintained that nature was adequate to the occasion at any age, while others recommended a certain preparation in the Pharmacopoeia, which would amply supply the defect of youth in a sexaginary husband. The old gentleman chose, without hesitation, the surest and speediest of these two chances of success. The prescription was sent to the shop of my worthy father, who was an apothecary in the town, and he accordingly immediately set to work, and made up a draught which would have awakened desire even in Methuselah himself. This valuable philter was not to be sent to the party till the next day. It was late, and my

---

[1] *Biographie Universelle*, Art. Wallenstein. [D]

[2] Detested by the Parisians, Dubois was the object of innumerable caricatures, of which the most *sanglante* was one representing him 'à genoux aux pieds d'une fille de joie qui prenait de ce sale écoulement qui afflige les femmes, tous les mois, pour lui en rougir sa calotte et le faire Cardinal'. See *Erotika Biblion*, Paris, 1792, p. 25. [D]
A comparatively modern edition of the *Erotika Biblion*, with an excellent bibliography and a reliable text edited by Guillaume, was published at Paris, 1910, by the Bibliothèque des Curieux. There have been reprints of this text until the early 1920's.

mother [continues the Cardinal] desired her husband to retire to rest and he, tired out with his day's work, quickly undressed himself, blew out his candle, and deposited himself, like a loving husband, by the side of his dear spouse. Awakening in the middle of the night, he complained of being excessively thirsty, and his better half, roused from her slumbers, got up in the dark and groping about for something wherewith to quench his thirst, her hand encounted the invigorating philter, which it truly proved to be, for I came into the world precisely nine months after that memorable night.[1]

Although love-potions and philters, as well as the other preparations had recourse to, for animating and arousing the organs for reproduction frequently owe, as we have shown, their advantages to cantharides, and are but too often productive of terrible effects, yet it cannot be denied that when administered by a skilful, cautious, and experienced physician they have restored the desired vigour when all other means have failed.

The flesh of the Schinck (*scincus*), an amphibious animal of the lizard species, and sometimes of the land lizard, or crocodile, is said, when reduced to powder and drunk with sweet wine, to act miraculously in exciting the venereal action; it is also prepared for the same object in the form of the electuary known by the name of Diasatyrion. Aelius recommends that in order to cause the erection of the virile organ the flesh of this animal should be taken from the vicinity of its genital apparatus.[2] It is a well-known fact that the Egyptian peasants carried their lizards to Cairo, whence they were forwarded, via Alexandria, to Venice and Marseilles. This species of lizard, which feeds upon aromatic plants, was also used as an aphrodisiac by the Arabs, and the well-known anti-poisonous quality of its flesh has caused it, in more ancient times, to be employed as an ingredient in the far-famed Mithridates, or antidote to poison. Browne informs us[3] 'that in Africa, no part of the Materia Medica is so much in requisition as those which stimulate to veneral pleasure. The *Lacerta scincus* in powder, and a thousand other articles of the same kind, are in continual demand.' The plant Chervri (*sandix ceropolium*) is also accounted as capable of exciting amorous propensities, so much so that Tiberius, the

---

[1] *Mémoires du Cardinal Dubois*, Vol. I., p. 3. [D]
[2] Aelius Tetrabilis, I, *Disc.*, Chaps. 32 and 33. [D]
[3] Browne's *Travels in Africa*, p. 343. [D]

Roman emperor, the most lascivious, perhaps, of men, is said to have exacted a certain quantity of it from the Germans, by way of tribute, for the purpose of rendering himself vigorous with his women and catamites; and Venette says that the Swedish ladies give it to their husbands when they find them flag in their matrimonial duties.[1]

But it was upon the plant called Satyrion (*orchis mascula*) that those who required aphrodisiacal remedies rested their most sanguine hopes. This plant, Theophrastus assures us, possesses so wonderful a property of exciting to venery that a mere application of it to the parts of generation will enable a man to accomplish the act of love twelve times successively. Speaking of this plant, Venette[2] says that the herb which the Indian King Androphyl sent to King Antiochus was so efficacious in exciting men to amorous enjoyment as to surpass in that quality, all other plants, the Indian who was the bearer of it assuring the king 'qu'elle lui avait donné de la vigueur pour soixante-dix embrassements', but he owned 'qu'aux derniers efforts ce qu'il rendait n'était plus de semence'.

Matthoile, however, observing that those persons who made use of it did not appear much given to lasciviousness, concluded that we had lost the true satyrion of the ancients; but it is nevertheless certain, notwithstanding so adverse an opinion, that this plant long preserved its reputation and was recommended by all botanists for its aphrodisiac potency. Of all the species of this plant the one popularly known as dog-stones is reputed to possess the greatest virtue.

The Turks have also their Satyrion (*orchis morio*) which grows upon the mountains near Constantinople, and which they make use of to repair their strength and stimulate them to the generative act. From this root is made the salep of which the inhabitants of Turkey, Persia, and Syria are extremely fond, being looked upon as one of the greatest restoratives and provocatives to venery in the whole vegetable world. But besides the aphrodisiacal qualities attributed to this plant by the above people, they give it credit for other ones, which good opinion experience has confirmed, and therefore whenever they undertake a long voyage they never omit to carry it with them as a specific against all diseases. Modern practitioners likewise commend its restorative,

---

[1] *La génération de l'homme, ou tableau de l'amour conjugal*, Tom. I, p. 276. [D]
[2] Ibid., p. 232. [D]

mucilaginous, and demulcent qualities as rendering it of considerable utility, particularly in sea scurvy, diarrhoea, dysentery, and stone or gravel. In addition to this property, salep also possesses the very singular one of concealing the taste of sea water, hence to prevent the dreadful calamity of perishing by thirst at sea it has been proposed that the powder of this plant should form part of the provisions of every ship's company.

Borax is likewise considered to possess peculiar aphrodisiacal qualities. 'Il pénètre', says Venette, 'toutes les parties de notre corps et en ouvre tous les vaisseaux, et par la ténuité de sa substance, *il conduit aux parties génitales* tout ce qui est capable de nous servir de matière à la semence.'[1]

The plant Rocket (*brasica eruca*) has likewise been especially celebrated by the ancient poets for possessing the virtue of restoring vigour to the sexual organs, on which account it was consecrated to and sown around the statue of Priapus; thus Columella says:

> Et quae frugifero seritur vicina Priapo
> Excitet ut veneri tardos eruca maritos.[2]
> Th'eruca, Priapus, near thee we sow
> To rouse to duty husbands who are slow.

Virgil attributes to it the same quality, designing it as—

> . . . Et venerem revocans eruca morantem.[3]
> Th'eruca, plant which gives to jaded appetite the spur.

Lobel[4] gives an amusing account of the effects of this plant upon certain monks in the garden of whose monastery it was sown, an infusion of it being daily doled out to them under the impression that its cheering and exhilarating qualities would rouse them from the state of inactivity and sluggishness so common to the inmates of such establishments. But alas! the continual use of it produced an effect far more powerful than had been contemplated by the worthy itinerant monk who had recommended it, for the poor cenobites were so

---

[1] Venette, *Génération de l'homme*, Tom. I, p. 279. [D]

[2] *De cultu hortorum*, v. 108. [D]. Available in the Loeb Series, with translation and Latin text.

[3] *Moretum*, v. 85. [D]

[4] *Mag. Nat.*, Lib. VII. [D]

stimulated by its aphrodisiacal virtues that, transgressing alike their monastic wall and vows, they sought relief for their amorous desires in the fond embraces of the women residing in the neighbourhood.

Salt, Mala Bacchica,[1] Cubebs, Surag,[2] and Radix Chinae (bark) were also regarded by ancient physicians as powerful aphrodisiacs. Gomez[3] asserts of the first of these substances, that women who much indulge in it are thereby rendered more salacious, and that for this reason Venus is said to have arisen from the sea; whence the epigram:

> Unde tot in Veneta scortorum millia cur sunt?
> In promptu causa est. Venus orta mari.

> In Venice why so many punks abound?
> The reason sure is easy to be found:
> Because, as learned sages all agree,
> Fair Venus' birth-place was the *salt, salt sea.*

To the last of the above-mentioned plants Baptista Porta ascribes the most wonderful powers, his words being:

Planta quae non solum edentibus, sed et genitale languentibus tantum valet, ut coire summe desiderant, quoties fere velint, possint; alios *duodecies* profecisse, alios ad *sexaginta vices* pervenisse, refert.[4]

Certain condiments are also aphrodisiacal, acting, as they undoubtedly do, as powerful stimulants. Thus Tourtelle and Peyrible assure us that pepper is a provocative to venereal pleasures, while Gesner and Chappel cured an atony of the virile member of three or four years' duration by repeated immersions of that organ in a strong infusion of mustard seed.

The principal ingredient of the *bhang*[5] so much used by the Indians,

---

[1] Mala Bacchica tanta olim in amoribus praevalerunt, ut coronae ex illis statuae Bacchi ponerentur. [D]

[2] Surag radis ad coitum summe facit: *si quis comedat aut infusionem bibat, membrum subite erigitur. Leo Afric.,* Lib. IX, cap. ult., p. 302. [D]

[3] Gomez (Ferdinand) of Ciudad Real, a celebrated physician, born 1388, died 1457. [D]

[4] *Mag. Nat.,* Lib. VII, c. 16. [D]

[5] Bhang is fairly frequently alluded to in the *Arabian Nights.* See Burton's translation, in the original 16 vol. Benares edition, or in the 16 (or sometimes 17) vol. Burton Club facsimile reprints. The 12 vol. Smithers edition is somewhat abridged and expurgated and therefore of less use to the enquirer.

as well as of the *maslac* of the Turks, is a species of the hemp plant. The Indians, says Acosta,[1] masticate the seeds and leaves of several species of that plant in order to increase their vigour in the venereal congress, and very frequently combine with it ambergris, musk, and sugar, preparing it in the form of an electuary. It has been remarked, moreover, that even in our own climate the caged birds that are fed with hemp seed are the most amorously inclined.

According to Browne,[2] whole fields are in Africa sown with *hashish*, the *bhang* of the East Indies, for the purpose of being used as a stimulant to amorous dalliance. It is used in a variety of forms, but in none, it is supposed, more effectually than what, in Arabic, is called Maijûn, a kind of electuary, in which both men and women indulge to excess.

It is said that the Chinese, domesticated at Batavia, avail themselves of a certain electuary for the purpose of stimulating their appetite for sexual intercourse. This preparation, called by them Affion, is chiefly composed of opium, and it is asserted that its effect is so violent that a brutal passion supervenes and continues throughout the night, the female being obliged to flee from the too energetic embraces of her lover.[3]

Narcotics in general, and especially opium, have been considered as direct aphrodisiacs, an opinion which if well founded would enable us to account more easily for those agreeable sensations by which the use of these substances is followed. But it is very probable that narcotics act upon the genital organs in no other way than they do upon the other ones: that is to say, they certainly stimulate them but only proportionately to the increase of force in the circulation of the blood and to the power or tone of the muscular fibre. It is also very probable that the voluptuous impressions superinduced by them depend upon the circumstances under which those persons are, who habitually indulge in them, and that they are connected with other impressions or with particular ideas which awaken them. If, for instance, in a Sultan reclining upon his sofa the intoxication of opium is accompanied by images of the most ravishing delight, and if it occasions in him that

---

[1] *Tractado de las drogas y medicinas de las Indias Orientales*, Chap. LXI, p. 360. Burgos, 1578. [D]

[2] *Travels in Africa*, p. 341. [D]

[3] Lignac, *A physical view of man and woman in a state of marriage*. Vol. I, p. 190. [D]

sweet and lively emotion which the anticipation of those delights awakens throughout the whole nervous system, the same inebriation is associated in the mind of a Janizary or a Spahi with ideas of blood and carnage, with paroxysms, the brutal fury of which has, certainly, nothing in common with the tender emotions of love. It is in vain to allege in proof of the aphrodisiacal qualities of opium the state of erection in which the genital members of Turks are found when lying dead on a field of battle,[1] for this state depends upon, or is caused by, the violent spasm or universal convulsive movements with which the body is seized in the moment of death: the same phenomenon frequently appears in persons who suffer hanging.[2] In warm countries it is the concomitant of death from convulsive diseases, and in our own climate it has been observed in persons who have died from apoplectic attacks.

The power which certain odours possess of exciting venereal desires admits not the slightest doubt, at least as far as the inferior animals are concerned. Nearly all the mammifera exhale or emit, in the rutting season, peculiar emanations serving to announce from afar to the male the presence of the female and to excite in him sexual desire. Facts have been observed with respect to insects even, which cannot be otherwise accounted for than by odorous effluvia. If, for instance, the female of the bombyx butterfly be placed in a box accurately closed it will not be long before several males will be seen flying around the prison, and which could not possibly have known by means of their visual organs the presence of their captive Dulcinea.[3] Now the question is, does

[1] Turcae ad Levenzinum contra Comitem Ludovicum Souches pugnantes, opio exaltati turpiter caesi, et octo mille numero occisi, *mentulas rigidas*, tulere. Christen., *Opium Hist.* [D]

[2] As has already been mentioned, Bloch discusses this in his *History of English Sexual Morals*, London, 1936 (and reprints). Havelock Ellis mentions it, and the Marquis de Sade includes descriptions in his *Nouvelle Justine, ou les Malheurs de la Vertu*, En Hollande, 1797. The same episodes appear in the earlier version of *Justine* published in 1791, and lately reprinted by J.-J. Pauvert, Paris, 1957 (with an excellent Introduction by Georges Bataille). This version has been translated into English and published by the Olympia Press, Paris, but importation into English-speaking countries is forbidden for obvious reasons. An earlier English translation issued from Paris by Isidore Liseux is complete but not very readable.

[3] See especially Havelock Ellis, *Studies in the Psychology of Sex*, Random House, New York, 1939, Vol. II, Part I, pp. 57, 80, and 98—*Sexual Selection in Man*.

anything analogous take place in our own species? Many authors assert that there does, and among them Virey, who, speaking of such exhalations, says:

L'extrême propreté des hommes et des femmes, l'habitude de se baigner et de changer souvent de linge *font disparaître* les odeurs génitales[1]. . . . On doit aussi remarquer que la haire des Cénobites, la robe des Capucins, le froc des moines, les vêtements rudes et malpropres portent à de fortes tentations, à cause de la qualité stimulante et de la sueur fétide dont étaient bientôt empreintes toutes ces sortes d'habillements.'[2]

Cabanis[3] made the following observation:

Odours act powerfully upon the nervous system, they prepare it for all the pleasurable sensations; they communicate to it that slight disturbance or commotion which appears as if inseparable from emotions of delight, all which may be accounted for by their exercising a special action upon those organs whence originate the most rapturous pleasure of which our nature is susceptible. In infancy its influence is almost nothing, in old age it is weak, its true epoch being that of youth, that of love.

It is certain that among most nations, and from the remotest antiquity, voluptuous women strengthened their amorous propensities by the use of various perfumes, but particularly of musk, to which has been attributed the power of exciting nocturnal emissions. The great Henry IV, of France, no novice in love-affairs, was opposed to the use of odours, maintaining that the parts of generation should be allowed to retain their natural scent, which, in his opinion, was more effectual than all the perfumes ever manufactured by art.[4]

Another aphrodisiacal remedy, which for a long time enjoyed a great reputation, was the penis of the stag, which was supposed to

[1] It was, perhaps, the knowledge of this fact that suggested to La Fontaine the lines:

'Un muletier à ce jeu
    Vaut trois rois.'

'To play at which game, I'm sure it is clear
    Three kings are no match for one muleteer.' [D]

[2] *Histoire Naturelle du Genre Humain.* Tom. II, p. 123. [D]

[3] Cabanis, *Rapport, &c.,* Tom. II, p. 89. [D]

[4] His wife, Queen Marguerite de Navarre, found it quite natural for a lady to mention to her lover that she had not washed her hands for a week!

possess the virtue of furnishing a man with an abundance of seminal fluid. Perhaps the reason why the ancients attributed this property to the genital member of that animal was from the supposition that it was the receptacle of the bile; that the abundance and acrid quality of this fluid caused lasciviousness, and that the stag being transported by an erotic furor during the rutting season, he was the most salacious of animals, and consequently that the genital organ of this quadruped would, when applied to man's generative apparatus, impart thereto considerable heat and irritation. A somewhat similar opinion respecting the horse appears to have obtained among the Tartars if we may judge from the following account given by Foucher d'Obsonville:[1]

Les palefreniers amènent un cheval de sept à huit ans, mais nerveux, bien nourri et en bon état. On lui présente une jument comme pour la saillir, et cependant on le retient de façon à bien irriter ses idées. Enfin, dans le moment où il semble qu'il va être libre de s'élancer dessus, l'on fait adroitement passer la verge dans un cordon dont le nœud coulant est rapproché du ventre; ensuite, saisissant l'instant où l'animal paraît dans sa plus forte érection, deux hommes, qui tiennent les extremités du cordon, le tirent avec force et, sur-le-champ, le membre est séparé du corps au-dessus du noeud coulant. Par ce moyen, les esprits sont retenus et fixés dans cette partie, laquelle reste gonflée; aussitôt, on la lave et la fait cuire avec divers aromatiques et épiceries aphrodisiaques.

The means of procuring the vigour necessary for sexual delights has also been sought for in certain preparations celebrated by the alchemists. Struck by the splendour of gold, its incorruptibility, and other rare qualities, some physicians imagined that this metal might introduce into the animal economy an inexhaustible source of strength and vitality; while empirics, abusing the credulity of the wealthy and the voluptuous, made them pay exorbitantly for aphrodisiacal preparations in which they assured their dupes that gold, under different forms, was an ingredient. Among innumerable other instances is that of a French lady who to procure herself an heir strove to reanimate an exhausted constitution by taking daily in soup what she was made to believe was potable gold, to the value of fifty francs, a fraud to expose which it suffices to say that the largest dose of perchloride of gold that can be safely administered is one-sixth of a grain. The tincture of gold known

[1] *Essais philosophiques sur les mœurs de divers animaux étrangers.* [D]

by the name of *Mademoiselle Grimaldi's potable gold* enjoyed a wonderful reputation towards the close of the eighteenth century as an efficacious restorative and stimulant; and numerous instances of its all but miraculous powers were confidently adduced. Dr Samuel Johnson, indeed, in a note upon a well-known passage in Shakespeare,[1] denies the possibility of making gold potable: 'There has long', he observes, 'prevailed an opinion that a solution of gold has great medicinal virtues, and that the incorruptibility of gold might be communicated to the body impregnated with it. Some have pretended to make gold *potable*, among other frauds practised upon credulity.'

So far back, however, as the seventeenth century the Abbé Guence showed that it was feasible, and even described the process minutely; and it is now known to every chemist that gold is susceptible of entering into immediate combination with chlorine by the agency of heat, that it may even be dissolved in water charged with chlorine, and that various methods exist of obtaining chlorate of gold, a combination which is often successfully employed in the treatment of syphilitic cases. Ether, naphtha, and essential oils take gold from its solvent, and form liquors which have been called *potable* gold.

Even the Christian Church itself possessed, in its early times, aphrodisiacs peculiarly its own. Says Voltaire:[2]

On trouve dans la lettre à Maître Acacius Lampirius (Literae virorum obscurorum) une raillerie assez forte sur la conjuration qu'on employait pour se faire aimer des filles. Le secret consistoit à prendre un cheveu de la fille, on le plaçoit d'abord dans son haut-de-chausses; on faisoit une confession générale et on faisoit dire trois messes, pendant les quelles on mettoit le cheveu autour de son col; on allumait un cierge béni au dernier Evangile et on prononçait cette formule. 'O, Viergel je te conjure par la vertu du Dieu tout-puissant, par les neuf chœurs des anges, par la vertu gosdrienne, amène-moi ici cette fille, en chair et en os, afin que *je la saboule* à mon plaisir."

---

[1] 'The care on thee depending
 Hath fed upon the body of my father,
 Therefore, thou, best of gold, art worst of gold;
 Other less fine in carat is more precious,
 Preserving life in *medicine potable*.'
 Henry IV, Part II, Act iv, sc. iv. [D]
[2] *Lettres sur François Rabelais*, Let. II. [D].

Bourchard, Bishop of Worms, has transmitted to us[1] an account of certain aphrodisiacal charms practised by the women of his time, the disgusting obscenity of which is such that we cannot venture upon translating the passage.

Remedies taken internally are not the only ones which stimulate man to sexual intercourse. External applications materially contribute to that end, and liniments have been composed wherewith to anoint the parts of generation. These washes are made of honey, liquid storax, oil and fresh butter, or the fat of the wild goose, together with a small quantity of spurge, pyrethrum, ginger or pepper to insure the remedy's penetrating: a few grains of ambergris, musk or cinnamon are to be added by way of perfume.

Remedies for the same purpose may also be applied to men's testicles especially; as, according to the opinion of Galen, those parts are the second source of heat, which they communicate to the whole of the body; for, besides the power of engendering, they also elaborate a spirituous humour or fluid which renders man robust, hardy, and courageous. The best application of this kind is that composed of cinnamon powder, gilliflower, ginger, and rose water, together with theriac, the crumb of bread, and red wine.

In addition to the means already mentioned for restoring vigour to the generative organs, two others may be reckoned which have been successfully resorted to for bracing them in such persons whose reproductive faculties lie dormant rather than extinct: These two methods are known as flagellation and urtication.[2]

Flagellation was recommended by several of the ancient physicians as an effectual remedy in many disorders, and this upon the physiological axiom of Hippocrates—*ubi stimulus, ibi affluxus.* Seneca considers it as able to remove the quartan ague. Jerome Mercurialis speaks of it as employed by many physicians in order to impart embonpoint to thin, meagre persons; and Galen informs us that slave merchants used it as a means of clearing the complexion of their slaves and plumping them up. Alaedeus, of Padua, recommends flagellation with green nettles, that is urtication, to be performed on the limbs of

[1] *De Poenitentia Decretorum,* Lib. XIX. [D]

[2] See Millingen's *Curiosities of Medical Experience,* art. 'Flagellation', Vol. II, p. 47 et seq. [D]

young children for the purpose of hastening the eruption of the small pox. Thomas Campanella[1] attributes to flagellation the virtue of curing intestinal obstructions and adduces in proof of his assertion, the case of the Prince of Venosa, one of the best musicians of his time, who would not go to stool without being previously flogged by a valet kept expressly for that purpose.

Even at a later period the same opinion obtained as to the efficacy of flagellation, it being supposed by many physicians to reanimate the torpid circulation of the capillary and cutaneous vessels, to increase muscular energy, to promote absorption, and to favour the necessary secretions of our nature.[2] As an erotic stimulant, more particularly, it may be observed that, considering the many intimate and sympathetic relations existing between the nervous branches of the extremity of the spinal marrow, it is impossible to doubt that flagellation exercised upon the buttocks and the adjacent parts has a powerful effect upon the organs of generation.

Meibomius,[3] the great advocate for the use of this remedy, remarks that stripes inflicted upon the back and loins are of great utility in exciting the venereal appetite because they create warmth in those parts whose office it is to elaborate the semen and to convey it to the generative organs. He therefore considered it by no means wonderful that the miserable victims of debauchery and lasciviousness, as well as those whose powers have been exhausted by age or excess, should have recourse to flagellation as a remedy. He observes that its effect is very likely to be that of renewed warmth in the now frigid parts, and of furnishing heat to the semen, an effect in producing which the pain

---

[1] *Medic.*, Lib. III, art 12. [D]

[2] See Richter, *Opuscula medica*, Col. I, p. 273. 'Qui novit ex stimulantium fonte, cardiaca, aphrodisiaca, diaphoretica, diuretica aliaque non infimi ordinis medicamenta peti, perspicit plenius quam larga verberibus bene merendi sit, uti praesertim in tempore nervorum, paralysi, impotentia ad Venerem et naturalium excretionum eluxit.' [D]

[3] Author of the work entitled, *De flagrorum usu in re venerea*. Lug. Bat., 16, 3. with the motto:

'Delicias pariunt Veneri crudelia flagra
Dum nocet, illa juvat, dum juvat, ecce nocet.'
'Lo! cruel stripes the sweets of love ensure,
And painful pleasures pleasing pains procure.' [D]

itself materially contributes by the blood and heat which is thereby drawn down to the part until they are communicated to the reproductive organs, the erotic passion being thus raised, even in spite of Nature herself, beyond her powers. A similar view is taken by a modern writer whose opinion is

that the effect of flagellation may be easily referred to the powerful sympathy which exists between the nerves of the lower part of the spinal marrow and other organs. Artificial excitement appears in some degree natural; it is observed in several animals, especially in the feline race. Even snails plunge into each other a bony, prickly spur, that arises from their throats, and which, like the sting of the wasp, frequently breaks off, and is left in the wound.[1]

After the appearance of the Abbé Boileau's *Histoire de la Flagellation* the Jesuits condemned several propositions found either in the work or in others approved by him. The following is one:

Necesse est cum musculi lumbares virgis aut flagellis diverberantur, spiritus vitales revelli, adeoque salaces motus ob vicinam partium genitalium et testium excitari, qui venereis ac illecebris cerebrum mentemque fascinant ac virtutem castitatis ad extremas angustias redigunt.

From out of almost innumerable instances of the efficacy of flagellation as an aphrodisiac, the following are selected.

Cornelius Gallus, the friend of Virgil, Horace, Tibullus, and Catullus, and who, according to Pliny, died the most delightful of deaths by expiring in the embraces of the fondest object of his affections,[2] was solely indebted for the delicious transports he enjoyed with her to the scourge with which her severe father chastised her for the faults that originated in too warm a temperament, a punishment which,

---

[1] Millingen, *Curiosities of Medical Experience*, Vol. II, p. 52. [D]. See also Remy de Gourmont, *Physique de l'Amour*, translated into English by Ezra Pound, New York, Wiley Book Co., 1940 (originally published by the Casanova Society, London). Reprinted, London, 1958, by Neville Spearman.

[2] To this personage may justly be applied the French epitaph upon one who died under similar circumstances:

> 'Je suis mort de l'amour entrepris
> Entre les jambes d'une dame,
> Bien heureux d'avoir rendu l'âme,
> Au même lieu où je l'ai pris.' [D]

instead of counteracting, furthered the wishes of the voluptuous Roman. Titus Aetherius also lost his life at the moment of orgasm.

Jean Pic de Mirandole relates[1] the case of a person known to him who, being a great libertine, could not consummate the act of love without being flagellated until the blood came, and that, therefore, providing himself for the occasion with a whip steeped in vinegar, he presented it to his *inamorata*, begging her not to spare him, for 'plus on le fouettait, plus il y trouvait des délices, la douleur et la volupté marchant, dans cet homme, d'un pas égal'.

Meibomius mentions the case of a citizen of Lübeck, who, being accused and convicted of adultery, was sentenced to be banished. A woman of pleasure with whom this man had been for a long time intimate, appeared before the judges as a witness on his behalf. This woman swore that the man was never able to consummate the act of love with her unless he had been previously flogged—an operation which it was also necessary to repeat before each successive indulgence.

That this was a means employed by Abelard in his commerce with Héloise appears from the following passages in two of his letters to her:[2]

Stripes which, whenever inflicted by love, not by fury but affection transcended, in sweetness, every unguent.

Thou knowest to what shameful excesses my unbridled lust had delivered up our bodies, so that no sense of decency, no reverence for God, could, even in the season of our Lord's passion, or during any other holy festival, drag me forth from out that cesspool of filthy mire; but that even with threats and scourges I often compelled thee who wast, by nature, the weaker vessel, to comply, notwithstanding thy unwillingness and remonstrances.[3]

The renowned Tamerlane, the mighty conqueror of Asia, required a like stimulus,[4] the more so perhaps from the circumstance of his being a monorchis.[5]

---

[1] See his work, *Contra Astrologos*, Lib. III, cap. 27. [D]

[2] *Petri Aboelardi Abbatis Rugensis et Heloissae Abbatissae Paracletensis Epistolae,* Epist. I, p. 10. [D]

[3] Ibid., Epist. III, p. 81. [D]

[4] See Meibomius, p. 43, note a. Edit. Paris 1792, 12mo. [D]

[5] Name given to persons having only one testicle. [D]

The Abbé Boileau, in his well-known and entertaining *Histoire des Flagellants*, partly attributes the gross licentiousness of that period to the strange practice then in vogue of doing penance by being scourged in public; and his brother, the celebrated poet and critic, defending the Abbé against the animadversions of the Jesuits, remarks very forcibly:

> Non, le livre des Flagellans
> N'a jamais condamné, lisez-le bien, mes pères,
>   Ces rigidités salutaires
>   Que, pour ravir le Ciel, saintement violents,
> Exercent sur leur corps, tant de Chrétiens austères:
>   Il blâme seulement ces abus odieux
>   D'étaler et d'offrir aux yeux
> Ce que leur doit toujours cacher la bienveillance,
>   Et combat vivement la fausse piété,
>   Qui sous couleur d'éteindre en nous la volupté
> Par l'austérité même, et par la pénitence
>   Sait allumer le feu de la lubricité.[1]

Flagellation, indeed, as well as the custom of wearing the hair-shirt, so common with the monks, and even with religious lay Catholics, was, by the stimulus it imparted to the skin, and hence to the internal, viscera, much more likely to increase the energy of the physiological functions, and *thus excite the commission of the very acts they are intended to suppress.*

The Abbé Chuppé d'Auteroche, member of the Académie des Sciences, and who died in California a few days after the observation of the Transit of Venus in 1760, remarks that the stripes given to persons frequenting the vapour baths in Russia impart activity to the fluids and elasticity to the organs and give additional stimulus to the venereal appetite.[2]

M. Serrurier records the following curious case:

One of my schoolfellows, who found an indescribable pleasure in being flogged, purposely and wilfully neglected his duty in order to draw upon himself the correction, which never failed to produce an emission of semen. As may easily be imagined he soon began the practice of masturbation, in which he indulged to so frightful an extent that rapid consumption ensued,

---

[1] *Œuvres*, Tom. I, p. 283. Ed. 1714. [D]
[2] *Travels in Siberia in 1661*, Tom. I, p. 319. [D]

and he died, a most horrible and disgusting object, affording a melancholy example of that fatal vice.[1]

The case of Jean Jacques Rousseau is well known. When a child he was by no means displeased with the corrections administered to him by a lady considerably his elder, he even frequently sought for a whipping at her hands, especially after he perceived that the flagellation developed in him the manifest token of virility. But he must be allowed to give his own account of it:

Assez long temps, Madame Lambercier s'en tint à la menace, et cette menace d'un châtiment tout nouveau pour moi me semblait très effrayante, mais après l'exécution, je le trouvai moins terrible à l'épreuve que l'attente ne l'avait été, et ce qu'il y a de plus bizarre est que ce châtiment m'affectionna davantage à elle qui me l'avait imposé. Il fallait même toute la vérité de cette affection et toute ma douceur naturelle pour m'empêcher de chercher le retour du même traitement en le méritant, car j'avais trouvé dans la douleur, dans la honte même, un mélange de sensualité qui m'avait laissé plus de désir que de crainte de l'éprouver derechef, par la même main. Il est vrai que comme il se mêlait, sans doute, à cela quelque instinct précoce du sexe, le même châtiment reçu de son frère, ne m'eût point du tout, paru plaisant.[2]

As flagellation is practised by striking the skin with a rod formed of twigs, until the heat and redness become more intense, so if the twigs be replaced by fresh nettles, the operation will become—*urtication*.[3]

---

[1] *Dictionnaire des Sciences Médicales*. Art. Pollution. [D]

[2] *Confessions*, Tom. I. [D]. A complete English translation is available in Dent's Everyman's Library, London (New York, Dutton), in two volumes. Perhaps the best English translation is that by J. M. Cohen, specially made for E. V. Rieu's invaluable series of 'Penguin Classics', and published from Harmondsworth by Penguin Books.

[3] Flagellation is mentioned in Brantôme, *Vies des Dames Galantes*. See the English translation by Francis Macnamara, *Lives of Gallant Ladies*, London, Pushkin Press, 1943, p. 195. A new translation is that by Alec Brown, Elek Books, London, 1960. The translation by Alfred Allinson, made for Carrington of Paris, and later reprinted by the Fortune Press, London, and Liveright, New York, is not quite so good.

There is a lengthy description of flagellation for sexual purposes in Cleland's *Fanny Hill*, originally published at London by G. Fenton in two volumes in 1747 or 1748 (the date is uncertain). There were reprints, but the book was first openly published in London in this century in 1963 almost simultaneously by Luxor Press and Mayflower Books.

The employment of urtication is of great antiquity, for Celsus as well as Aretaeus mentions the use of it, it being in those times a popular remedy. That the Romans had frequent recourse to it in order to arouse the sexual appetite is proved by the following passage from Petronius Arbiter:

Oenothea semiebria ad me respiciens;—Perficienda sunt, inquit, mysteria *ut recipas nervos*.

Simulque profert scorteum fascinum quod, ut olio et minuto pipere, atque *urticae* trito circumdedit semine, paulatim coepit insere ano meo. Hoc credelissima anus spargit subinde femina mea Nasturcii[1] succum cum abrotono miscet, perfusis que inguinibus meis, viridis urticae fascem comprehendit omnes que infra umbilicum coepit lenta manu caedere.[2]

Menghus Faventinus assures us that nettles have 'une propriété merveilleuse pour allonger, tendre, grossir et ériger le membre viril qui, par une parcimonie de la nature, feroit craindre la stérilité'.

Urtication appears to have been well known in France during the time of Rabelais, who, alluding to this mode of procuring the vigour necessary for amorous conflict, says 'se frotter le cul au panicaut [a species of thistle] vrai moyen d'avoir au cul passion'.

> Une femme en mélancholie
> Pour faute d'occupation,
> Frottez-moi le cul d'ortie
> Elle aura au cul passion.[3]

The irritation caused by nettles produces effects analogous to those which are observed in persons affected with the itch, the ringworm, and leprosy. The lubricity of those unfortunates is sometimes uncontrollable; they suffer violent priapisms, which are followed by ejaculation, whenever a severe itching forces them to scratch themselves with a kind of furor or madness.

'From a medical point of view,' observes Dr Millingen, 'urtication, or

---

[1] *De Nasturcio mira refert Dioscoridas*, I, 2, c. 185. [D]

[2] *Satyricon*, Caput XXXVIII. [D]. This quotation can be found, in English, in *The Complete Works of Petronius*, done into English by Jack Lindsay, New York, Wiley Book Co., 1944, p. 135. A reprint of Lindsay's *Satyricon* is published by Elek Books, London, 1960. The pagination differs.

[3] *Ducatiana* II, b. 505. [D]

stinging with nettles, is a practice not sufficiently appreciated. In many instances, especially in cases of paralysis, it is more efficacious than blistering or stimulating frictions. Its effects, though perhaps less permanent, are general and diffused over the limb. This process has been found effectual in restoring *heat to the lower extremities,* and a case of obstinate lethargy was cured by Corvisart by a repeated urtication of the whole body. During the action of the stimulus, the patient, who was a young man, would open his eyes and laugh, but then sink again into a profound sleep. In three weeks, however, his perfect cure was effected.'[1]

In 1783 Dr James Graham, an humble imitator of the celebrated Cagliostro, commenced giving his sanitary lectures, which he illustrated by the dazzling presence of his Goddess of Health, a character which, for a short time, was sustained by Emma, afterwards the celebrated Lady Hamilton, wife of Sir William Hamilton, English Ambassador at the Court of Naples, and the *chère amie* of the immortal Nelson.

After describing various aphrodisiacal remedies, the lecturer thus proceeds:

But, gentlemen, if all the above means and methods, which I have thus faithfully, ingenuously, and with the frankest and most unreserved liberality, recommended, fail, suffer me, with great cordiality, and assurance of success, to recommend my celestial, or medico, magnetico, musico, electrical bed, which I have, with so much study and at so vast an expense, constructed, not alone to insure the removal of barrenness, when conception is at all in the nature of things possible, but likewise to improve, exalt and invigorate the bodily, and through them, the mental faculties of the human species. This bed, whose seemingly *magical* influences are now celebrated from pole to pole, and from the rising to the setting sun! is indeed *unique* in science! and unquestionably the first and the only one that ever was mentioned, erected, or even, perhaps, thought of, in the world; and I will now conclude the lecture with giving you a slight descriptive sketch of the structure of the bed, and the nature of those influences with which it glows—which it breathes forth, and which it animates, regenerates, and transports those happy, happy, persons who have the honour and the paradisiacal blessedness of reposing on it.

The Grand Celestial State Bed! then, gentlemen, which is twelve feet long by nine wide, is supported by forty pillars of brilliant glass, of great

¹ *Curiosities of Medical Experience,* Vol. II, p. 55. [D]

strength and of the most exquisite workmanship, in regard to shape, cutting and engravings; sweetly delicate and richly variegated colours, and the most brilliant polish! They are, moreover, invisibly incrusted with a certain transparent varnish in order to render the insulation still more complete; and that otherwise, properly assisted, we may have, in even the most unfavourable weather, abundance of the electrical fire.

The sublime, the magnificent, and, I may say, the super-celestial dome of the bed, which contains the odoriferous, balmy and ethereal spices, odours and essences, and which is the grand magazine or reservoir of those vivifying and invigorating influences which are exhaled and dispersed by the breathing of the music, and by the attenuating, repelling, and accelerating force of the electrical fire—is very curiously inlaid or wholly covered on the under side with brilliant plates of looking-glass, so disposed as to reflect the various attractive charms of the happy recumbent couple, in the most flattering, most agreeable and most enchanting style.

On the top or summit of the dome, are placed, in the most loving attitudes, two exquisite figures, representing the marriage of Cupid and Psyche, with a fine figure of Hymen behind, and over them, with his torch flaming with electrical fire in one hand and with the other, supporting a celestial crown, sparkling, likewise, with the effulgent fire over a pair of real living turtle-doves, who, on a little bed of roses, coo and bill under the superanimating impulses of the genial fire! The other elegant groups of figures which sport on the top of the dome—the Cupids, the Loves, and the Graces! besides festoons of the freshest and most beautiful flowers, have each of them musical instruments in their hands, which by the exquisite and most expensive mechanism, are made to breathe forth sounds corresponding with the appearance of the several instruments—flutes, guitars, violins, clarionets, trumpets, horns, oboes, kettle-drums, &c. On the posts or pillars, too, which support the grand dome are groups of figures, musical instruments, organ-pipes, &c. which in sweet concert with the other instruments, at the commencement of the tender dalliance of the happy pair, breathe forth celestial sounds! lulling them in visions of elysian joys! opening new sources of pleasure and 'untwisting all the chains which tie the hidden soul of harmony!' At the head of the bed in the full centre front, appears, sparkling with electrical fire, through a glory of burnished and effulgent gold, the great, first, ever operating commandment, *Be Fruitful, Multiply and Replenish the Earth*! Under this is a most elegant and sweet-toned organ, in the front of which is a fine landscape of moving figures on the earth, birds flying, swans &c., gliding on the waters, a fine procession, too, is seen, village nymphs strewing flowers before priests, brides,

bridegrooms and their attendants, who, all entering into the temple of
Hymen, disappear from the delightful eye. The painting and embellishment
of this front are most masterly, and reflect the highest honour on the artists
by whom they were executed; and the whole view is terminated with
fountains, waterfalls, shepherds, shepherdesses, and other peasants, as
pastoral sports and rural employment, and by a little church, the dial of
which points out truly and distinctly the hour.

In the celestial bed no feather bed is employed; sometimes mattresses
filled with sweet new wheat or cut straw, with the grain in the ears, and
mingled with balm, rose leaves, lavender flowers, and oriental spices, and,
at other times, springy hair mattresses are used. Neither will you find upon
the celestial bed linen sheets; our sheets are of the richest and softest silk or
satin; of various colours suited to the complexion of the lady who is to
repose on them. Pale green, for example, rose colour, sky blue, black, white,
purple, azure, mazarin blue, &c., and they are sweetly perfumed in the
oriental manner, with otto and odour of roses, jessamine, tuberose, rich
gums, fragrant balsams, oriental spices, &c.; in short, everything is done to
assist the ethereal, magnetic, musical and electric influences, and to make
the lady look as lovely as possible in the eyes of her husband and he, in hers.
But to return, in order that I might have for the important purposes, the
strongest and springy hair, I procured, at a vast expense, the tails of English
stallions which when twisted, baked, and then untwisted and properly
prepared, is elastic to the highest degree.

But the chief elastic principle of my celestial bed is produced by artificial
loadstones. About fifteen hundred pounds' weight of artificial and com-
pound magnets are so disposed and arranged as to be continually pouring
forth in an ever-flowing circle inconceivable and irresistibly powerful tides
of the magnet effluxion, which is well known to have a very strong affinity
with the electric fire.

Such is a slight and inadequate sketch of the grand celestial bed, which,
being thus completely insulated,—highly saturated with the most genial
floods or electrical fire!—fully impregnated moreover, with the balmy
vivifying effluvia of restorative balsamic medicines and of soft, fragrant
oriental gums, balsams and quintescence, and pervaded at the same time
with full springing tides of the invigorating influences of music and magnets
both real and artificial, gives such elastic vigour to the nerves, on the one
hand, of the male, and on the other, such retentive firmness to the female;
and, moreover, all the faculties of the soul being so fully expanded, and so
highly illuminated, that it is impossible, in the nature of things, but that
strong, beautiful, brilliant, nay, double-distilled children, if I may use the
expression, must infallibly be begotten.

A digression may, perhaps, be here pardonable, in order to give some notice of the latter and last days of the beautiful, highly accomplished, and fascinating woman mentioned above.

She had been presented to Nelson by her husband, who had previously told her that he was about to introduce her to a little *thread-paper* of a man, who could not boast of being very handsome, but who would become, some day, one of the greatest men that England ever produced. After the battle of the Nile he again visited Naples, and was now little better than a perfect wreck. At Calvi, in 1794, he had lost an eye. At Teneriffe his right arm was shattered and amputated close to the shoulder. At the battle of the Nile he was severely wounded in the head. Incessant anxiety and watchfulness for his country's honour and welfare had blanched his brow, and shattered the 'little thread-paper of a man' at the outset, till, on his return in triumph to his mistress, he seemed to be on the verge of an early grave.

Yet she proved herself a true woman, if an erring one, in her reception of the man she loved, and unhesitatingly and unequivocally forsook her all to attend upon and worship him.

Not far from Merton turnpike stood the house of Nelson and his mistress. It was left with all its liabilities to Lady Hamilton, but she was obliged to take a hasty departure, and, harassed by creditors, in sickness of heart and without funds, the unhappy woman escaped to Calais.

Now for the sad, sad finale. From the portal of a house, as cheerless and dreary as can be imagined, in the month of January, with a black silk petticoat stretched on a white curtain thrown over her coffin for a pall, and a half-pay Irish dragoon to act as chaplain over the grave, which was in a timber-yard, were the remains of Nelson's much adored friend removed to their final resting place under the escort of a *sergent de ville.*

She died without the common necessaries of life, and was buried at the expense of the town, notwithstanding Nelson's last words: '*Blackwood, take care of my poor Lady Hamilton!'*

'Whatever the errors of Lady Hamilton may have been,' says Doran, 'let us not forget that without her aid, as Nelson said, the battle of the Nile would never have been fought, and that in spite of her sacrifices and services, England left her to starve, because the government was too virtuous to acknowledge the benefits rendered to her country by a lady with too loose a zone.'

The remarks of honest old Burton[1] upon aphrodisiacs, though quaint, are so judicious and pertinent that we cannot better conclude this part of our essay than by quoting them:

The last battering engines are philters, amulets, charms, images, and such unlawful means: if they cannot prevail of themselves by the help of bawds, panders and their adherents, they will fly for succour to the devil himself. I know there be those that deny the devil can do any such thing, and that there is no other fascination than that which comes by the eyes . . . It was given out, of old, that a Thessalian wench had bewitched King Philip to dote upon her, and by philters enforced his love, but when Olympias, his queen, saw the maid of an excellent beauty, well brought up, and qualified: these, quoth she, were the philters which inveigled King Philip; those the true charms, as Henry to Rosamond:[2]

> One accent from thy lips the blood more warms
> Than all their philters, exorcisms, and charms. (*Drayton*)

With this alone Lucretia brags, in Aretine, she could do more than all philosophers, astrologers, alchymists, necromancers, witches, and the rest of the crew. As for herbs and philters, (saith she), I could never skill of them. *The sole philter that ever I used was kissing and embracing, by which alone I made men rave like beasts stupefied, and compelled them to worship me like an idol.*[3]

ANTI-APHRODISIACS

The means best calculated to produce effects contrary to those just treated of are of several kinds, but such as are derived from hygiene are

[1] *Anatomy of Melancholy*, Part 3, sect. 2, memb. 2. subs. 5. [D]

[2] *Pornodidascalus seu Colloquium Muliebre Petri Aretini* ingeniossimi et fere incomparabilis virtutum et vitiorum demonstratoris: *De Astu nefario, horrendisque dolis, quibus impudicae mulieres juventuti incautae insidiantur.—Francofurti. Anno 1623.* [D]

[3] Verum omni ista scienca (magica) [says Lucretia] nunquam potui movere cor hominis sola vero saliva mea (id est amplexu et basiis) inungens tam furiose furere tam bestialiter obstupefiere plurimos coegi ut instar idiol me Amoresque meos adorarint.—pp. 47–8. [D]

entitled to be considered as the most powerful. Previously, however, to describing the medicinal substances that may be efficaciously employed in moderating, or rather checking, too violent a propensity to venery, some notice must be taken of the diet adapted to ensure such a result.

The use of milk, vegetables, such as lettuce, water-purslain, cucumbers, etc., and especially of fruit in which the acid principle predominates, slackens the movement of the heart and of the sanguineous system; it diminishes the animal heat, the chief source of which is in the activity of the circulation; it produces a feeling of tranquillity and of coolness; the respiration, being more slow, occasions the absorption of a less quantity of oxygen, added to which, as a less quantity of reparative materials is contained in this description of aliments, there result a less active nutrition, the loss of embonpoint, and the complete prostration of every principle of irritability; in short, it is of all diets the one least capable of furnishing fuel to the passions. For common drink mere water, and, if the impulse of passion should increase, a small quantity of nitre, vinegar, or vitriolic acid may occasionally be added to the water to make it more cooling.

Other means conducive to the same end are a laborious life, much bodily exercise, little sleep, and a spare diet, so that the fluids may be more easily conducted to other parts, and that there may not be produced a greater quantity than is requisite for the support of the body. Equally valuable

> When there's a young and sweating devil
> That commonly rebels,

will be found what Shakespeare recommends:

> A sequester from liberty, fasting and prayer,
> Much castigation, exercise devout.[1]

Should the desire of committing excesses rise to any height, immediate recourse must be had to some serious and mind-absorbing occupation, less nutritious food and drink should be taken, all dishes peculiarly stimulating to the palate avoided, as well as the use of wine and other spirituous liquors.

[1] *Othello*, Act iii, sc. iv. [D]

A cool regimen in every respect was particularly insisted upon by the ancients: hence Plato and Aristotle recommended the custom of going barefoot as a means of checking the stimulus to carnal desire, a suggestion which appears to have been acted upon by some of the monkish orders. The cold bath was considered equally efficacious, while some, among whom may be reckoned Pliny and Galen, advised thin sheets of lead to be worn on the calves of the legs and near the kidneys.

The first and most important of the hygienic means consists in shunning every species of excitement and in having little or no communication with the other sex, and the earlier such restraint is imposed, the better. 'He that is chaste and continent, not to impair his strength, or terrified by contagion, will hardly be heroically virtuous. Adjourn not that virtue until those years when Cato could lend out his wife, and impotent satyrs write satires against lust—but be chaste in thy flaming days, when Alexander dared not trust his eyes upon the fair sisters of Darius, and when so many men think that there is no other way than that of Origen.'[1,2]

The next means is that of carefully abstaining from the perusal of all publications calculated to inflame the passions, by which publications are meant not obscene books only. With respect to these, indeed a great error obtains, for the persons most anxious to peruse them are, for the most part, old worn-out debauchees, men whose generative powers are comparatively feeble, if not altogether destroyed, and who unfortunately for themselves, require this unnatural and detestable kind of stimulus, while, on the contrary, young men and those in middle life, who had not drawn too largely upon their constitution, and for whom the allurements of nature are themselves a sufficient provocative, regard such publications with horror and disgust. It is not, therefore, we repeat, works of this description which we allude to,

---

[1] Sir Thos. Browne's Works, Vol. III, p. 89. Bohn's Edit. [D]

[2] Origen, one of the Fathers of the Church, born in A.D. 185, is a melancholy proof how far the reason may be perverted by erroneous views in religious matters; for according to Fulgos, 'ut corpus ab omni venerea labe mundum servaret, omnique suspicione careret, sectis genitalibus membris, eunuchum se fecit'. He, however, lived long enough to condemn his error. See his fifteenth sermon upon St Matthew, cap. 19, v. 12; his work against Celsus, Lib. 7, and his seventh treatise upon the eighteenth and nineteenth chapters of St Matthew. [D]

but those the perusal of which is more dangerous during the period of the passions—novels, more especially such as, under the pretext of describing the working of the human heart, draw the most seducing and inflammatory pictures of illicit love, and throw the veil of sentimental philosophy over the orgies of debauchery and licentiousness. Nothing is more perilous to youth, especially of the female sex, than this description of books. Their style is chaste, not one word is found that can offend the ear, while the mind of the unsuspecting reader is often tainted and corrupted by the most impure ideas and descriptions clothed in the most elegant phraseology. How admirably does Voltaire stigmatize this attention to a mere superficial (if the epitaph be allowed) purity! Says he:

> Plus les mœurs sont dépravés, plus les expressions deviennent mesurées: on croit de gagner en langage ce qu'on a perdu en vertu. La pudeur s'est enfuite des cœurs et s'est réfugiée sur les lèvres.

There are two kinds of study particularly adapted to preserve the mind and the affections from the assaults of vice and libidinousness. The first of these is *Mathematics*, whose efficacy in this respect has been proved by frequent experience. The Venetian lady mentioned by Rousseau in his *Confessions* was not ignorant of this their power, when, seeing the singular effect which her charms had produced upon the, as yet, youthful philosopher, said to him: '*Gianetto, lascia le donne e studia la matematica.*' 'James, give up the ladies and apply yourself to mathematics.' It will, indeed, be found that in all ages mathematicians have been little disposed or addicted to love, and the most celebrated among them, Sir Isaac Newton, is reputed to have lived without ever having had sexual intercourse. The intense mental application required by philosophical abstraction forcibly determines the nervous fluid towards the intellectual organs, and hinders it from being directed towards those of reproduction.

After the study of Mathematics comes that of *Natural History*, which will be found to be almost equally beneficial, requiring, as it does, the unremitting attention of the student, his perambulation in the open country, and the personal observation of all animated objects.

This peculiar influence of the above-mentioned studies ought particularly to engage the attention of persons who superintend the education of youth; there being no doubt that the effervescence of youthful passions may, to a great extent, be allayed by directing the juvenile mind to either of those studies, according as the constitution exhibits greater or less ardour and precocity. Sometimes, however, there are found idiosyncrasies which bid defiance to remedies of this description, but, nevertheless, yield to the force of medicine: of such, the following is an instance:

A man, by profession a musician, of an athletic figure and sanguine complexion, with red hair, and a very warm temperament, was so tormented with erotic desires that the venereal act, repeated several times in the course of a few hours, failed to satisfy him. Disgusted with himself, and fearing, as a religious man, the punishment with which concupiscence is threatened in the Gospel, he applied to a medical practitioner, who prescribed bleeding with the use of sedatives and refrigerants, together with a light diet. Having found no relief from this course of treatment, he was then recommended to have recourse to wedlock, and, in consequence, married a robust and healthy young woman, the daughter of a farmer. At first, the change appeared to benefit him but, in a short time, he tired his wife out by his excessive lubricity, and relapsed into his former satyriasis. His medical friend now recommended frequent fasting, together with prayer, but these also failing of effect, the unhappy man proposed to submit to castration, an operation which was judged to be highly improper, considering the great risks the patient must necessarily incur. The latter, however, still persisted that his wish should be complied with, when, fortunately, a case having occurred in Paris, in which a person afflicted with nephritic pains occasioned by the presence of a calculus, was cured by a preparation of nitre, at the expense, however, of being for ever incapacitated for the pleasures of love. The hint was taken and doses of nitre dissolved in *aqua nymphae* were given night and morning, during the space of eight days, and with such success that, at the end of that time, he could scarcely satisfy the moderate claims of his wife.[1]

Some physicians place great confidence in the medicines called refrigerants. The most favourite of these are infusions from the leaves of flowers of the white water-lily (*nymphea alba*), sorrel, lettuce, perhaps, also from mallows, violets and endive (*cichorium*), oily seeds, and waters distilled from lettuce, water-lily, cucumbers, purslain, and endives. In equal esteem are the syrups of orgeat, lemons, and vinegar,

---

[1] Baldassar Timoeus, *Cas. med.*, Lib. XIX. Salacitas nitro curata. [D]

to which may be added cherry-laurel water, when given in proper and gradually increasing doses. Hemlock, camphor, and agnus-castus have likewise been much recommended as moderators of the sexual appetite.

According to Pliny[1] the *nymphea alba* was considered so powerful that those who take it for twelve days successively will then find themselves incapable of propagating their species, and if it be used for forty days the amorous propensity will be entirely extinguished.

With respect to hemlock, it is too dangerous a medicine to repose confidence in.

The ancients had a high opinion of camphor, a reputation which this drug preserved until a comparatively late period, for Scaliger informs us that in the seventeenth century monks were compelled to smell and masticate it for the purpose of extinguishing concupiscence; and it was a favourite maxim of the medical school of Salernum[2] that

> Camphora per nares castrat odore mares.
> Camphor if smell'd
> A man will geld.

This fatal property, however, has been denied by modern medical authorities, and apparently with reason, if the fact be true that such workmen as are employed in extracting this useful vegetable product, and who may be said to live constantly in a highly camphorated atmosphere, do not find themselves in the least degree incapacitated for gratifying the calls of *l'amour physique.*

There is no doubt, on the other hand, that camphor has been successfully employed in cases of nymphomania, and several medical writers have asserted its efficacy in neutralizing the properties of cantharides, adducing instances which would appear to prove its sedative power: the following one is related by Groenvelt:[3]

[1] *Historie Mundi*, Lib. XXVI, c. 7. [D]

[2] The medical school of Salerno (*latine Salernum*) was founded by Robert Guiscard at the end of the eleventh century: and about the year 1100 a collection of medical aphorisms was composed in Latin verse by a certain John of Milan, and published under the title of *Medicina Salertina*. Of this poem, which originally consisted of 1239 verses, only 373, or about a third, are extant. These were published at Paris in 1625 by Réné Moreau; in 1653 it was travestied by L. Martin; paraphrased by Bruzen de la Martinière in 1743, and by Dr Levacher de la Feuverie in 1782. [D]

[3] *De tuto cantharidum in medicina usu interno.* [D]

A young man who had taken a large dose of cantharides in some wine felt, at first, a sort of violent itching, accompanied by great irritation in the bladder, and soon after he suffered greatly from extreme heat, together with an intolerable strangury. Bleeding, emulsions, injections, and opium preparations afforded not the slightest relief. Groenvelt prescribed two scruples of camphor in two boluses. The first dose partly mitigated the pains, and the second one removed them entirely. The remedies which were first administered had, no doubt, weakened the inflammation, and the strangury being no longer kept up by the spasmodic state of the urinary apparatus, camphor sufficed to effect a cure. Burton asserts the value of camphor as an anti-aphrodisiac, and says that when fastened to the parts of generation, or carried in the breeches, it renders the virile member flaccid.

Agnus castus, so called from the down on its surface resembling that upon the skin of a lamb, and from its supposed anti-aphrodisiacal qualities, was in great repute among the Athenians, whose women, during the celebration of the Thesmophoria or feasts and sacrifices in honour of Ceres, abstained for some days from all pleasure of love, separating themselves entirely for that time from the men. It was usual with them during the solemnities to strew their beds with *agnus castus*, fleabane, and other herbs such as were supposed to have the power of expelling amorous inclinations. Arnaud de Villeneuve[1] exaggerates, almost to a ridiculous degree, the virtue of the *agnus castus*, asserting, as he does, that the surest way to preserve chastity is to carry about the person a knife with a handle made of its wood. It was also, and perhaps is still, much used by the monks, who made an emulsion of its seeds steeped in Nenuphar water, and of which they daily drank a portion, wearing at the same time round their loins a girdle made of its branches. Lettuce has also the reputation of being anti-aphrodisiacal. Lobel instances the case of an English nobleman who had long been desirous of having an heir to his estates, but all in vain. Being, however, at length advised to discontinue eating lettuces, of which he was particularly fond, his wishes were gratified by his being blessed with numerous offspring.

[1] Arnaud de Villeneuve was one of the luminaries of the thirteenth century, being distinguished for his profound knowledge of medicine, chemistry, astrology, and theology. He discovered the sulphuric, muriatic, and nitric acids, and was the first to compose alcohol and the essence of terebinth or turpentine.

The desire for coition was also supposed to be diminished by drinking a decoction of the pounded leaves of the willow. Vervain, dried coriander, and also mustard, drunk in a fluid state, were said to prevent the erection of the penis. Alexander Benedictus declares that a topaz having been previously rubbed against the right testicle of a wolf, then steeped in oil or in rose-water and worn as a ring, induces a disgust for venereal pleasures, as does also, if we may credit the same sapient physiologist, a powder made of dried frog. The two following prescriptions are said to be of great efficacy:

De verbena in potu, et non erigitur virga sex diebus. Utere mentha sicca cum aceto: genitalia illinita succo hyoscyami aut cicutae coitus appetitum sedant.

It has even been asserted that coffee possessed the same property. In the year 1695 it was maintained, in a thesis at the Ecole de Médecine at Paris, that the daily use of coffee deprived both man and woman of the generative power. M. Hecquet[1] relates the following anecdote as a proof of such effect:

A Queen of Persia, seeing some grooms using all their efforts to throw a horse upon the ground, enquired the reason of the trouble they were thus taking. Her attendants gave her to understand as delicately as they could, that it was for the purpose of castrating him.

'How unnecessary is so much trouble,' said her majesty, 'they have only to give him coffee, and their object will be fully and easily attained.'[2]

Most probably the queen spoke from her own experience of its anti-aphrodisiacal effects upon her royal consort.

There are some diseases which are considered as anti-aphrodisiacal on account of the decided aversion which the patient who is afflicted with them feels for the pleasures of sexual union. Thus a species of epidemic leprosy is common among the Cossacks of the Jaik, which is attended by pains in the joints and a disgust for copulation, a disgust the more extraordinary not only because exanthematous diseases in general excite a desire for the above act but also inasmuch as this malady, in particular, usually attacks persons in the prime of their

[1] *Traité des dispenses du carême.* [D]
[2] 'Any man', said Abernethy, the celebrated and eccentric surgeon, 'that drinks coffee and soda water, and smokes cigars, may lie with my wife.' [D]

youth. Another disease analogous to the one just mentioned, the Plica-Polonica, rages, during the autumnal season, in Poland, Lithuania, and Tartary. It is said to have been introduced into the first of these countries by the Tartars, who had it originally from India. One of the most singular phenomena attending this disorder, and which evidently proves the close sympathy existing between the head and the organs of generation, is that when the patient is bald the Plica not unfrequently fastens upon the sexual parts, and acquires such a length as to descend below the calves of the legs. The mode of treatment, that of mercury and sudorifics, proves the mucous character of the disorder, and, consequently, accounts for its well-known tendency to strike the whole animal economy with that prostration of strength which produces a total indifference to the sex.

Continual exercise on horseback was considered by Hippocrates[1] as anti-aphrodisiacal and Van Sweiten, commenting upon that opinion, justly observes that the continual joltings caused by so violent an exercise, added to the compression produced upon the parts of generation by the weight of the body, was by no means unlikely to produce a local relaxation of those organs to such an extent as to prevent erection altogether.

If whatever opposes an obstacle to the gratification of the sexual appetite may be considered as having a place among the anti-aphrodisiacs, certain mechanical processes may be ranked as such. Of these, *fibulation*, from the Latin word *fibula* (a buckle or ring), was the very reverse of circumcision, since the operation consisted in drawing the prepuce over the glans and preventing its return by the insertion of a ring.[2]

The *fibula* (buckle) is so called because it serves to fix together and to reunite parts which are separated. It was formerly a surgical instrument which, besides the use now particularly in question, served also to keep closed the lips of any extensive wounds. It is mentioned as being so applied by Oribuse,[3] and by Scribonius Largus.[4] Employed, therefore, as it was for various uses, the *fibula* appears to have different

---

[1] *De Aer: Aqua et Locis*, Cap. X. [D]
[2] Comment in Boerh, *Aphor.*, Vol. III, sec. 1063. [D]
[3] *De Machinis*, C. IV. [D]
[4] No. 206. [D]

shapes, now but little known to us. Rhodius[1] has treated of all those mentioned in the writings of antiquity.[2]

Mensius thinks that the custom of infibulating may be traced back to the time of the siege of Troy, for the singer Demodocus, who was left with Clytemnestra by Agamemnon,[3] appears to that critic to have been a eunuch, or at least to have been infibulated.[4]

Among the ancients, as well as among many modern nations, the laws of chastity and the restraints of honour appeared scarcely sufficient to hinder the sexes from uniting, in spite of all the obstacles opposed by a vigilant watch and strict seclusion.[5] Indeed, what Roman virgin could entertain very strict ideas of modesty while she saw the goddess of love honoured in the temple, or the amours of Venus and Mars celebrated, while the poor cuckolded Vulcan, after seizing the amorous couple in his net, was only thereby exposed to the ridicule of the Olympic Divinities. There can be little doubt but that excess of this description bastardized and corrupted the ancient Greeks and Romans, and that recourse was necessarily had to the *fibula* when the deities themselves set the example. Of what use, indeed, could be the moral lessons of a Plato or a Socrates, even when enforced by infibulation, if vice was thus sanctioned by divine example? The only aim of such a state of things was to vanquish obstacles. The art of eluding nature was studied, marriage was despised, notwithstanding the edicts of Augustus against bachelors; the depopulated republic wallowed in the most abandoned lust, and, as a natural consequence, the individual members of it became corrupted and enervated from their very infancy.

The infibulation of boys, sometimes on account of their voice, and not unfrequently to prevent masturbation, was performed by having the prepuce drawn over the glans; it was then pierced, and a thick thread was passed through it, remaining there until the cicatrizing of the hole; when that took place, a rather large ring was then substituted, which was not removed except with the permission of the party

---

[1] *Exercitatio de acia*, Cap. 4, et seq. [D]

[2] See *Male Infibulation*, by E. J. Dingwall, London, Baillière, which is a very complete study of the subject, and now a volume of some rarity. Dingwall also contributed an article to *Encyclopaedia Sexualis*, New York, Dingwall-Rock, 1936.

[3] *Odyssey*, VIII, line 477. [D]

[4] Introd. to *Hesiod*, Cap. VI, p. 14. Edit. Plautin, 1603 in voce αοιδος. [D]

[5] *Annals of Gallantry*. [D]

ordering the operation.[1] The Romans infibulated their singers in order to preserve their voices:

> Si gaudet cantu; *nullius fibula* durat
> Vocem vendentis praetoribus.[2]

But should the dame in music take delight,
The public singer is disabled quite;
In vain the praetor guards him all he can,
She slips the buckle (*fibula*) and enjoys her man.

They even subjected to the same operation most of their actors:

> Solvitur his magno comoedi fibula. Sunt, quae
> Chrysogonum cantare vetent.[3]

Take from Chrysogonus the power to sing,
Loose, at vast prices, the comedian's ring.

> Dic mihi, simpliciter, comoedis et citharoedis,
> Fibula, quid praestas? . . . carius ut futuunt.[4]

Tell me, clasp! frankly, of what advantage are you to actresses and lute players? To enhance their favours.

> Menophili, penem, tam grandis fibula vestit
> Ut sit comoedis omnibus, una satis
> Hunc ego credideram (nam saepe lavamur in unum)
> Sollicitum voci parcere, Flacce, suae;
> Dum ludit media populo spectante palaestra,
> Delapsa est misero, fibula; verpus erat.'[5]

Nor were dancers and gladiators exempted from the same operation, especially the latter, in order that they might preserve all the vigour required in their horrible and degrading occupation.

The best description of the *fibula* is that given by Holiday:

The fibula does not strictly signifie a button, but also a buckle or clasp, or such like stay. In this place, the poet expresses by it the instrument of servilitie applied to those that were employed to sing upon the stage; the Praetor who set forth playes for the delight of the people, buying youths

---

[1] Celsus has described the operation in detail. *Medicina*, Lib. VII, c. 25. [D]
[2] juvenal, *Sat.* VI, v. 379–80. [D]
[3] Ibid., v. 73–4. [D]
[4] Martialis, Lib. XIV, *Ep.* 215. [D]
[5] Martialis, Lib. VII. *Ep.* 81. [D]

for that purpose, and that they might not, by lust, spoil their voice, their overseers closed their shame with a case of metal having a sharp spike of the same metal passing by the side of it, and sometimes used one of another form; or by a nearer crueltie, they thrust a brazen or silver wire through that part which the Jew did lose in circumcision.

The form of the first, and also another fashion, the curious reader may here see (being without any immodestie) as they are represented by Pignerius, *de servis*, p. 82. But whatsoever the fashion or invention was, the trust was but fond that was committed to them, seeing that the art of lust and gold could make them as vain as the Italian engines of jealousy in this day. Thus, 'O Lentulus,' says the poet, speaking figuratively to some noble-man, 'it is that thou art married; but it is some musician's or fencer's bastard that is born under thy lordly canopie.'[1]

Winkelman furnishes us with a description of an infibulated musician,[2] it being a small bronze statue representing a naked deformed individual, as thin as a skeleton, and carrying a ring in his *enormi mentula*. Martial, who laughs at everything, speaks of these singers sometimes breaking their ring, and says that it becomes necessary to send them to a fibula-maker in order to have the damage repaired:[3]

> Et cujus refibulavit turgidum, faber, penem,
> Il di cui turgido membro abbia il fabro fibbiato.

The practice of infibulation was very common in India, from religious motives. As a proof of their sanctity, many of the Santons, or Mohammedan saints, as well as other devout persons, bonzes, fakirs, and the like, devoted themselves to perpetual virginity. Whether it was with the intention of placing themselves beyond the possibility of breaking their vow, or of giving evidence of their constancy, certain it is that they loaded their prepuce with an enormous fibula, or ring; and in their warm climate, where nudity does not shock ideas of propriety or decency, devout women not unfrequently repaired to these *soi-disant* saints, to admire and venerate such efforts of virtue and self-denial; they are even reported to have knelt down, and, in that humiliating posture, to have kissed the preputial ring, no doubt with the vain hope of thereby obtaining indulgences. In some places these

---

[1] Holiday's Juvenal, *Sat.* VI, illustr. 11, note '*Unbutton a Comedian*'. [D]
[2] *Monumenti Antichi inediti.* Rome, 1767, fol., IV, c. 8, p. 247, fig. 188. [D]
[3] Martial, Lib. IX, *Epig.* 28, v. 12. [D]

martyrs fasten their fibula with a lock, the key of which they deposit with the magistrate of the town or village. But, Nature insisting upon her rights, is often too strong for this self-violence, nor can desire, or the not-to-be-mistaken symptom of it, be opposed, or even prevented from being gratified; and since the lock, which obstructs the extremity of the prepuce only, cannot hinder a kind of erection, nor, indeed, of effusion of the seminal fluid, it cannot do more than oppose the introduction of the male organ into the receptacle destined for it.

Another description of fakirs were formerly to be seen in India, especially in its southern peninsula, whose custom it was to traverse the country in a state of nudity, and who had been rendered impotent by the following regimen. The children destined for this penitential state are taken away from their parents at the age of six or seven years, and made to eat, daily, a quantity of the young leaves of a tree called *Mairkousie.* At first the dose given them is not larger than a filbert. This regimen must be persisted in until the party reaches the age of five and twenty years, the dose being increased till, at the maximum, it is as large as a duck's egg. During all this time the devotee is subjected to no other regimen, except a light purge, once in six months, by means of *Kadoukaie,* or the black mirobolan. Although rendered completely impotent by this mode of treatment, so far from their physical strength and beauty of form being diminished or deteriorated thereby, they are, on the contrary, improved by it; the enjoyment of constant good health is likewise almost an invariable consequence.

Infibulation is not confined to the male sex exclusively, for it is practised on girls and women in India, Persia, and the East. Generally, and most commonly, it consists of joining together the lips of the female sexual organ, or closing the labia of the vagina by a suture made with waxed thread, a small aperture being left for the egress of the urine and the menstrua.

Linschet witnessed the operation at Pegu, as did also Schultz; Browne saw it performed, at Darfour, on females from eleven to twelve years of age.[1] At the time of marriage a cut of the bistouri dissevers the parts which have been closed by the effects of the suture. Sometimes jealousy contents itself by passing a ring through the parts. Women, as well as girls, are subjected to this disgusting operation, the only

[1] *Travels in Africa and Egypt.* [D]

difference being that the ring of the latter cannot be removed, while that of the former has a kind of lock, the key of which is in the husband's possession. Pallas informs us that the beautiful nation of the Tcherkesses, or Circassians, carefully preserve the virginity of their girls by means of a leathern girdle, or rather corslet made of skin, and sewn immediately upon the naked body. The husband alone has the right of severing this corslet, which he does on the nuptial night.

When the violation of virgin chastity and conjugal fidelity became more frequent fathers and husbands had recourse, even in Europe, to a mechanical contrivance for the purpose of preserving intact the honour of the family. This was a kind of padlock which shut up all access to the seat of voluptuousness. The invention is attributed to one Francesco di Carrera, an imperial judge of Padua, who lived about the close of the fifteenth century. The machine itself was called the *Girdle of Chastity*.[1] Francesco's acts of cruelty brought him to the scaffold, where he was strangled in 1405 by a decree of the Senate of Venice. One of the principal accusations brought against him was the employment of the Girdle of Chastity for his mistresses, and it is said by Misson[2] that a box filled with these articles was for a long time preserved in the palace of St Mark, at Venice. Rabelais speaks of these girdles, which he calls *Ceintures à la Bergamasque*. 'Nay,' says he, Pantagruel, 'may that Nick in the dark cellar, who hath no white in his eye, carry me quiet away with him, if, in that case, whenever I go abroad from the palace of my domestic residence, I do not, with as much circumspection as they use to ring mares in our country, to keep them from being sallied by stoned horses, clap a Bergamesco lock upon my wife.' Brantôme has the following notice of these chastity preservers:

Du temps du roi Henri il y eut un certain Quincaillier qui apporta une douzaine de certains engins à la foire de St Germain pour brider le cas des femmes. Ces sortes de cadenas estoient en usage à Venise dès devant l'année 1522, estoient faits de fer et centuroient comme une ceinture, et

[1] See the detailed study by E. J. Dingwall, *The Girdle of Chastity*, London, Routledge. An article by the same author is included in the previously cited *Encyclopaedia Sexualis*, New York, Dingwall-Rock.

[2] 'There [in the arsenal] are also various whimsical bolts and locks with which he [Carrera] used to keep his concubines confined.' *Travels in Italy*. See *The World*, Vol. 18, p. 154. [D]

venoient à se prendre par le bas et se fermer à clef, si subtilement faits, qu'il n'estoit pas possible que la femme en estant bridée une fois, s'en peust jamais prévaloir pour ce doux plaisir, n'ayant que quelques petits trous menus pour servir à pisser.[1]

An endeavour was made to introduce these Bernasco padlocks into France during the reign of Henry II, and a shop was opened by an Italian at the fair of St Germain, where they were publicly sold, and in such numbers that the French gallants, becoming alarmed, threatened to throw the vendor into the Seine if he did not pack up his merchandise and decamp, which he immediately did for fear that the menace might be put in execution.

Voltaire describes the Cadenas as originating with Pluto, who, jealous of his wife Proserpine, was advised:

Qu'un cadenas, de la structure nouvelle
Fut le garant de sa fidélité,
A la vertu par la force asservie,
Plus ne sera l'amant favorisé.
En un moment, feux, enclumes, fourneaux
Sont préparés aux gouffres infernaux.
Tisiphone, de ces lieux, serrurière,
Au cadenas met la main, la première,
Elle l'achève et des mains de Pluton
Proserpine reçut ce triste don.
Or ce secret aux enfers inventé
Chez les humains tôt après fut porté
Et depuis ce temps dans Venise et dans Rome
Il n'est pédant, bourgeois, ou gentilhomme
Qui pour garder l'honneur de sa maison
De cadenas n'ait sa provision.[2]

This sage advice, a loud applause
From all the damned assembly draws;
And straight, by order of the State,
Was registered on brass by fate;

[1] Brantôme, *Dames Galantes*. [D]. English translation by Francis Macnamara, London, Pushkin Press, 1943. Another, and absolutely complete, translation by Alec Brown, London, Elek Books, 1960.

[2] *Le Cadenas*. This poem was composed by the author when he was only eighteen years of age and it was occasioned by a lady who was in the circumstances here spoken of. [D]

That moment, in the shades below,
They anvils beat and bellows blow,
Tisiphone, the blacksmith's trade
Well understood; the locks she made:
Proserpina, from Pluto's hand
Receiving, wore it by command.
This lock, which hell could frame alone,
Soon to the human race was known;
In Venice, Rome, and all about it
No gentleman or cit's without it.[1]

We shall close this essay with the amusing summary of anti-aphrodisiacal remedies, as given by Rabelais.[2] The physician Rondibilis remarks to Panurge:

You say that you feel in you the pricking stings of sensuality, by which you are stirred up to venery. I find in our faculty of medicine, and we have founded our opinion therein upon the deliberate resolution and final decision of the ancient Platonics, that carnal concupiscence is cooled and quelled five several ways:—

Firstly. By the means of wine. I shall easily believe that, quoth Friar John, for when I am well whittled with the juice of the grape, I care for nothing else, so I may sleep. When I, quoth Rondibilis, say that wine abateth lust, my meaning is, wine immoderately taken; for by intemperance, proceeding from the excessive drinking of strong liquor, there is brought upon the body of such a swill-down bouser, a chillness in the blood, a slackening in the sinews, a dissipation of the generative seed, a numbness and hebetation of the senses, with a perversive wryness and convulsion of the muscles, all which are great lets and impediments to the act of generation. Hence it is that Bacchus, the god of bibbers, tipplers, and drunkards is most commonly painted beardless and clad in a woman's habit, as a person altogether effeminate, or like a libbed eunuch. Wine, nevertheless, taken moderately, worketh quite contrary effects, as is implied by the old proverb, which saith,—That Venus taketh cold, when not accompanied

[1] Dr Smollett's translation. Vol. XXXII. [D]

[2] Much better translations of Rabelais are: *The Complete Works of Rabelais*, translated by Jacques Le Clercq, New York, Limited Editions Club, 1936. Reprinted in the *Modern Library* series by Random House, 1944. Also that made specially by J. M. Cohen for the *Penguin Classics*, Harmondsworth, Penguin Books, 1955, and reprints. Both are unexpurgated and eminently readable, and render Rabelais much more accurately than previous translations.

by Ceres and Bacchus.[1] This opinion is of great antiquity as appeareth by the testimony of Diodorus the Sicilian, and confirmed by Pausanias, and it is usually held among the Lampsacians, that Don Priapus was the son of Bacchus and Venus.

Secondly, the fervency of lust is abated by certain drugs, plants, herbs and roots, which make the taker cold, maleficiated, unfit for and unable to perform the act of generation; as hath often been experimented by the water-lily, Heraclea, Agnus-Castus, willow-twigs, hemp-stalks, woodbine, honeysuckle, tamarisk, chastetree, mandrake, bennet keebugloss, the skin of a hippopotamus, and many other such, which by convenient doses proportioned to the peccant humour and constitution of the patient, being duly and seasonably received within the body—what by their elementary virtues on the one side, and peculiar properties on the other, do either benumb, mortify and bedumpse with cold, the prolific semence, or scatter and disperse the spirits which ought to have gone along with, and conducted the sperm to the places destined and appointed for its reception—or lastly, shut up, stop and obstruct the way, passages and conduits, through which the seed should have been expelled, evacuated, and ejected. We have nevertheless, of those ingredients which, being of a contrary operation, heat the blood, bind the nerves, unite the spirits, quicken the senses, strengthen the muscles and thereby rouse up, provoke, excite and enable a man to the vigorous accomplishment of the feat of amorous dalliance. I have no need of those, quoth Panurge, God be thanked and you my good master. Howsoever, I pray you, take no exception or offence at these my words; for what I have said was not out of any ill-will I did bear to you, the Lord, he knows.

Thirdly. The ardour of lechery is very much subdued and abated by frequent labour and continual toiling. For by painful exercises and laborious working so great a dissolution is brought upon the whole body, that the blood which runneth alongst the channels of the veins thereof for the nourishment and alimentation of each of its members, had neither time, leisure, nor power to afford the seminal resudation or superfluity of the third concoction, which nature most carefully reserves for the conservation of the individual, whose preservation she more heedfully regardeth than the propagation of the species and the multiplication of the human kind. Whence it is that Diana is said to be chaste, because she is never idle, but always busied about hunting. For the same reason was a camp, or leaguer of old called—Castrum,[2] as if they would have said—Castum; because the

---

[1] Sine Baccho et Ceres friget Venus. [D]

[2] *'Castrum quasi Castum, Castra'*, says Isidorus in his *Etymologies*, Lib. IX, 'sunt ubi miles steterit: dicta autem, castra, quasi, casta, eo quod ibi castraretur libido.' *A castle* from *castrating of lust*. [D]

soldiers, wrestlers, runners, throwers of the bar, and other such like athletic champions, as are usually seen in a military circumvallation, do incessantly travail and turmoil, and are in a perpetual stir and agitation. To this purpose also, Hippocrates writeth in his book, *De Aere, Aqua et Locis:*—That in his time there were people in Scythia as impotent as eunuchs in the discharge of a venerean exploit; because that, without any cessation, pause or respite, they were never from off horseback, or otherwise assiduously employed in some troublesome and molesting drudgery.

On the other part, in opposition and repugnancy hereto, the philosophers say, That idleness is the mother of luxury. When it was asked of Ovid, Why Aegisthus became an adulterer? he made no other answer than this, Because he was idle.[1] Who were able to rid the world of loitering and idleness might easily disappoint Cupid[2] of all his designes, aims, engines and devices and so disable and appal him, that his bow, quiver, and darts should from thenceforth be a mere needless load and burthen to him; for that it could not then lie in his power to strike or wound any of either sex with all the arms he had. He is not, I believe, so expert an archer as that he can hit the cranes flying in the air, or yet the young stags skipping through the thicket, as the Parthians knew well how to do; that is to say, people moiling, stirring and hurrying up and down, restless and without repose. He must have those hushed, still, quiet, lying at a stay, lither and full of ease, whom he is able to pierce with all his arrows. In confirmation thereof, Theophrastus being asked on a time, What kind of beast or thing he judged a toyish, wanton love to be? he made answer, That it was a passion of idle and sluggish spirits. From which pretty description of tickling-tricks, that of Diogenes, the Cynic, was not very discrepant when he defined lechery—The occupation of folk destitute of all other occupation. For this cause the Sicyonian sculptor Canachus,[3] being desirous to give us to understand that slowth, drowsiness, negligence, and laziness, were the prime guardians and governesses of ribaldry, made the statue of Venus, not standing, as other stone-cutters had used to do, but sitting.

Fourthly. The tickling pricks of incontinency are blunted by an eager study; for from thence proceedeth an incredible resolution of the spirits, that oftentimes there do not remain so many behind as may suffice to push and thrust forwards the generative resudation to the places thereto appropriated, and therewithal inflate the cavernous nerve, whose office is to

---

[1] Quaeritur Aegystus quare sit factus adulter
  In promptu causa est: desidiosus.—*De Remed. Amoris.* [D]
[2] 'Otia si tollas, periere Cupidinis artes.' [D]
[3] See Pausanias's *Corinthians.* [D]

ejaculate the moisture for the propagation of human progeny. Lest you should think it is not so, be pleased but to contemplate a little the form, fashion, and carriage of a man exceeding earnestly set upon some learned meditation and deeply plunged therein, and you shall see how all the arteries of his brains are stretched forth, and bent like the string of a cross-bow, the more promptly, dexterously and copiously to suppeditate, furnish and supply him with store of spirits, sufficient to replenish and fill up the ventricles, seats, tunnels, mansions, receptacles and cellules of common sense—of the imagination, apprehension, and fancy—of the ratiocination, arguing and resolution—as likewise, of the memory, recordation, and remembrance; and with great alacrity, nimbleness, and agility, to run, pass and course from one to the other, through those pipes, windings, and conduits, which to skilful anatomists are perceivable at the end of the wonderful net, where all the arteries close in a terminating point; which arteries taking their rise and origin from the left capsule of the heart, bring, through several circuits, ambages, and anfractuosities, the vital spirits, to subtilize and refine them in the aetherial purity of animal spirits. Nay, in such a studiously meditating, musing person, you may espy so extravagant raptures of one, as it were out of himself, that all his natural faculties for that time will seem to be suspended from each their proper charge and office, and his exterior senses to be at a stand. In a word, you cannot choose than think, that he is by an extraordinary ecstasy quite transported out of what he was or should be; and that Socrates did not speak improperly when he said, That philosophy was nothing else but a meditation upon death. This possibly is the reason why Democritus[1] deprived himself of the sense of seeing, prizing, at a much lower rate, the loss of his sight, than the diminution of his contemplation which he had frequently found disturbed by the vagrant flying-out strayings of his unsettled and roving eyes. Therefore is it that Pallas, the goddess of wisdom, tutoress and guardianess of such as are diligently studious and painfully industrious, is and hath been still accounted a virgin. The Muses upon the same consideration are esteemed perpetual maids: and the Graces, for the same reason, have been held to continue in a sempiternal pudicity.

I remember to have read that Cupid,[2] on a time, being asked by his

---

[1] Vide Cicero, Lib. V, *Tusc. Questions* and Plutarch's *Treatise of Curiosity*. It must, however, be observed, that this story is wholly incredible, inasmuch as the same writers affirm that Democritus employed his leisure in writing books and in dissecting the bodies of animals, neither of which could very well be effected without the eyes. [D]

[2] In Lucian, in the Dialogue entitled 'Venus and Cupid'. [D]

mother Venus, why he did not assault and set upon the Muses, his answer was, that he found them so fair, so neat, so wise, so learned, so modest, so discreet, so courteous, so virtuous, and so continually busied and employed, —one in the speculation of the stars,—another in the supputation of numbers—the third in the dimension of geometrical quantities,—the fourth in the composition of heroic poems,—the fifth in the jovial interludes of a comic strain,—the sixth in the stately gravity of the tragic vein,—the seventh in the melodious disposition of musical airs,—the eighth in the completest manner of writing histories and books on all sorts of subjects, and,—the ninth in the mysteries, secrets, and curiosities of all sciences, faculties, disciplines and arts whatsoever, whether liberal or mechanic,— that approaching near unto them he unbent his bow, shut his quiver, and extinguished his torch, through mere shame and fear that by mischance he might do them any hurt or prejudice. Which done, he thereafter put off the fillet wherewith his eyes were bound, to look them in the face, and to hear their melody and poetic odes. There took he the greatest pleasure in the world, that many times he was transported with their beauty and pretty behaviour, and charmed asleep by their harmony, so far was he from assaulting them or interrupting their studies. Under this article may be comprised what Hippocrates wrote in the afore-cited treatise concerning the Scythians, as also that in a book of his intituled, Of Breeding and Production, where he hath affirmed all such men to be unfit for generation as have their parotid arteries cut—whose situation is behind the ears—for the reason given already, when I was speaking of the resolution of the spirits, and of that spiritual blood, whereof the arteries are the sole and proper receptacles; and that likewise he doth maintain a large portion of the parastatic liquor to issue and descend from the brains and back-bone.

Fifthly. By the too frequent reiteration of the act of venery. There did I wait for you, quoth Panurge, and shall willingly apply it to myself, whilst any one that pleaseth may, for me, make use of any of the four preceding. That is the very same thing, quoth Friar John, which Father Scyllion,[1]

[1] The story itself is the same as that related by Poggio (Bracciolini) of a hermit of Pisa. 'Eremita', says he, 'qui Pisis morabutur, tempore Petri Gambacurtae, meretricem noctu in suam cellulam deduxit, vigesiesque ea nocte mulierem cognovit; semper cum moveret clunes, ut crimen fugeret luxuriae, vulgaribus verbis dicens: "domati, carne cattizella": hoc est, doma te, miserima caro!' [D]

An English translation from the *Facetiae* of Poggio was published at Paris by Isidore Liseux. Some of the tales are amusing, but the volume as a whole is incredibly boring. They are what today would be called a collection of mildly smutty jokes, useful for reference but not for entertainment.

Prior of St Victor, at Marseilles, calleth maceration and taming of the flesh. I am of the same opinion, and so was the hermit of Saint Radegonde, a little above Chinon; for, quoth he, the hermits of Thebaide can no way more aptly or expediently macerate and bring down the pride of their bodies, daunt and mortify their lecherous sensuality, or depress and overcome the stubbornness and rebellion of the flesh, than by dufling and fanfreluching five and twenty or thirty times a day.

ESSAY 2

Ancient Phallic Worship:
Remarks upon the Symbols of Reproductive Powers

F R O M the investigations and researches of the learned there appears to be no doubt but that the most ancient of all superstitions was that in which Nature was contemplated chiefly under the attribute or property of fecundity; the symbols of the reproductive power being those under which its prolific potencies were exhibited. It is not because modern fastidiousness affects to consider those symbols as indecent, and even obscene, that we should therefore suppose them to have been so regarded by the ancients: on the contrary, the view of them awakened no impure ideas in the minds of the latter, being regarded by them as the most sacred objects of worship.[1] The ancients, indeed, did not look upon the pleasures of love with the same eye as the moderns do: the

[1] See, especially, Hans Licht: *Sexual Life in Ancient Greece.* Translated from the German by J. H. Freese, M.A., and edited by Lawrence H. Dawson. London, Routledge, 1932 (and many reprints). The volume contains 31 plates.

The original German edition is: *Sittengeschichte Griechenlands,* and was published in three volumes at Dresden and Zürich by the Paul Aretz Verlag (1925-8). This edition was profusely illustrated, and includes representations of the phallus as a tribute (at Brea in Thracia), religious prostitution, a comedian with phallus, herms, satyrs, amulets, etc. The text of the English edition, while very useful, has been abridged and toned down; and the illustrations to the London edition are poor when compared with the original. Hans Licht is a pseudonym for Dr Paul Hans Brandt.

Apropos the above remark of Davenport, Licht says: '. . . the Greeks, the healthiest and most aesthetically perfect people hitherto known to the world, soon felt a covering of the sexual parts, while the body was otherwise uncovered, to be unnatural, and recognized that such a covering only had meaning if one had ascribed a moral and inferior value to their functions. But just the opposite was

tender union of the sexes excited their veneration, because religion appeared to consecrate it, inasmuch as their mythology presented to them all Olympus as more occupied with amatory delights than with the government of the universe.[1]

The reflecting men of those times, more simple, but, it must be confessed, more profound than those of our own day, could not see any moral turpitude in actions regarded by them as the design of Nature, and as the acme of felicity. For this reason it is that we find not only ancient writers expressing themselves freely upon subjects regarded by us as indecent, but even sculptors and painters equally unrestrained in this particular.[2]

The statesman took advantage of these religious impressions: whatever tended to increase population being held in honour. Those images and priapi so frequently found in the temples of the ancients, and even in their houses, and which we consider as objects of indecent lewdness, were, in their eyes, but so many sacred motives exciting them to propagate their species.

In order to represent by a physical object the reproductive power of the sun in springtime, as well as the action of that power on all sentient beings, the ancients adopted that symbol of the male gender which the Greeks, who derived it from the Egyptians, called—phallus. This worship was so general as to have spread itself over a large portion of the habitual globe, for it flourished for many ages in Egypt and Syria,

indeed the case, so that far from being ashamed of these organs, the Greeks rather regarded them with pious awe and treated them with an almost religious reverence as the mystical instruments of propagation, as the symbols of nature, life-producing and inexhaustibly fruitful.' (op. cit.)

[1] The best *recueil* and *critique* of the Greek Myths is: *The Greek Myths* by Robert Graves, London, Penguin Books, 1955 (2 vols. specially written for Penguin Books).

[2] This remark applies not only to ancient Greece and Rome, but also to the civilizations of India, China, etc., and to countless primitive communities. Japanese bridal books may perhaps legitimately be included in this category, although the prime reason for these superbly painted scrolls was the education of the uninitiated in the variety of coital posture and technique.

For some beautiful plates—many in colour—of the paintings and statuary at Pompeii, see: *Roma Amor* (An Essay on Erotic Elements in Etruscan and Roman Art) by Prof. Jean Marcadé; Geneva, Nagel; London, Charles Skilton, 1961. The plates are complete and entirely 'unexpurgated'.

Persia, Asia Minor, Greece and Italy: it was, and still is, in vigour in India and many parts of Africa, and was even found in America on its discovery by the Spaniards. Thus Garcilaso de la Vega informs us[1] that in the public squares of Panuco (a Mexican town) *bas-reliefs* were found which, like those of India, represented in various ways the sexual union; while at Tlascala, another town of that country, the reproductive act was worshipped under the joint symbol of the generative organs, male and female.

A more surprising fact is that this worship has, as will be shown hereafter, been perpetuated to a very late date among the Christians of Europe.

In its origin the phallus, or emblem of the generative and procreative powers of Nature, appears to have been of a very simple and inoffensive character—although it was afterwards made subservient to the grossest and most superstitious purposes.

In India this worship is everywhere to be found accompanying the triune God, called by the Hindoos, *Trimourti* or *Trinity,* and the significant form of the single obelisk or pillar called the *linga* or *lingham;*[2] and it should be observed, in justice to the Hindoos, that it is some comparative and negative praise to them that this emblem, under which they express the elements and operations of nature, is not externally indecorous. Unlike the abominable realities of Egypt, Greece, and Rome, we see this Indian phallic emblem in the Hindoo religious exhibitions, without offence, nor know, until information be extorted, that we are contemplating a symbol whose prototype is obscene.

Besides the lingham, the equally significant *yoni* or *cteis* is to be seen, being the female organ of generation. It is sometimes single, often in conjunction, for the Indians, believing that the emblem of fecundity might be rendered more energetic by combining the organs of both sexes, did so unite them, giving to this double symbol the name of

[1] Garcilaso de la Vega, *Historia de los Incas,* Cap. VI. [D]

[2] In the church of St Peter's, at Rome, is kept, *en secret,* a large stone emblem of the creative power, of a very peculiar shape, on which is engraved $Z \epsilon \upsilon \varsigma \ \Sigma \omega \tau \eta \rho$. Only persons who have great interest can get a sight of it. Is it from this stone having some peculiar virtue that those *preux chevaliers,* the cardinals, keep it so closely? Perhaps they choose to monopolize the use of it? I never saw it, but I know that it was at St Peter's—HIGGINS [D]. The more usual spelling of *lingham* is: *lingam.*

pulleiar, confounded by some writers with the lingham itself. This pulleiar is highly venerated by the sectarian worshippers of Siva (the third god of the Trimourti), who hang it round their neck as a charm or amulet, or, enclosing it in a small box, fasten it upon their arm. The Indians have also a little jewel called *taly,* worn, in like manner, by females round their necks as a charm. It is presented to them on their wedding day by their husbands, who receive it from the hands of the Brahmins. Upon these jewels is engraved the representation, either of the lingham or of the pulleiar. The following anecdote connected with this custom is given by M. Sonnerat.[1]

A Capuchin missionary had a serious dispute with the Jesuits residing at Pondicherry, which was referred for decision to the judicial courts. The disciples of Loyola, who can be toleration itself when toleration furthers their crafty and ambitious views, had declined all interference with the above custom. M. Tournon, the Pope's legate apostolic, who regarded the matter as one not to be trifled with, and with whom, moreover, the Jesuits were no favourites, strictly prohibited the *taly,* enjoining all female converts to substitute in its place either a cross or a medal of the Virgin. The Indian women, strongly attached to their ancient customs, refused obedience. The missionaries, apprehensive of losing the fruits of their zealous labours, and seeing the number of their neophytes daily diminishing, entered into a compromise by adopting a *mezzo-termine* with the females in question, and it was agreed that a cross should be engraved upon the *taly,* an arrangement by which the symbol of Christian salvation was coupled with that of the male and female *pudenda.*

The deep and enthusiastic veneration felt by the Hindoos for this worship is naturally explained by their intense anxiety and desire for having children who might perform those ceremonies to their *manes* which they firmly and piously believe will have the effect of mitigating their punishment in the world to come. They worship the lingham, therefore, for the sake of having progeny, and husbands, whose wives are barren, send them to adore that symbol, and, if report be true, the ladies take especial care not to disappoint the wish of their dear spouses.

It is probable that the introduction of this worship is due to the Indians who founded the seat of Siva, imagining, as they no doubt did,

[1] *Voyage aux Indes Orientales et à la Chine, par Sonnerat, depuis 1774 jusqu'en 1781;* Tome I, liv. 2. [D]

that the most effectual means of propagating it would be by presenting their deity under the form of that organ by which the reproduction of the human race is effected.

Nothing can be a greater proof of the high antiquity of the Indians than this worship, it being certain that the Egyptians did not establish it, as well as the dogma of metempsychosis, among themselves, until after they had travelled in India.

Phalli, usually in lead, have been found in the river Rhône. These were most likely signs and tokens belonging to some secret society probably of a licentious character. Similar ones are in the *Forgeais* collection, and were engraved in the *Plombs Historiés* of that antiquarian.

According to an ingenious writer,[1] who is of opinion that the Indians sent, at a very remote period, colonists to Ireland, the round towers, so numerous in that island, are no other than ancient phallic temples erected in honour of the fructifying power of Nature emanating, as it was supposed to do, from the sun, under the name of Sol, Phoebus, Apollo, Abad, or Budh.[2]

Alluding to these towers, Mr O'Brien observes: 'The Eastern votaries, suiting the action to the idea, and [in order] that their vivid imaginations might be still more enlivened by the very *form* of the *temple*, actually constructed its architecture after the model of the *membrum virile*, which, obscenity apart, is the divinity-formed and indispensable medium selected by God himself for human propagation and sexual prolificacy.' There is every reason to believe that our *maypole* is a relic of ancient phallic worship.

The manners of the ancient Hebrews seem to have differed little, if at all, in this respect, from those of the nations surrounding them: thus, David, dancing with all his might before the ark, lifted up his ephod and exhibited his nakedness to 'the eyes of the handmaids of his servants'. No blame is attached to the king for such gross indecency during a

[1] Henry O'Brien, *Round Towers of Ireland*, London, 1834, Chap. VIII. [D]

[2] Apropos the Irish, George Ryley Scott, in *Phallic Worship*, Luxor Press, London, says: 'It has been asserted that Cromcruach, the principal deity of the ancient Irish, was a phallic god, but I can find no conclusive or substantial evidence as to the truth of this. Long before the introduction of Christianity, however, Ireland was the seat of the Druid sun, stone and serpent-worship. It is to the prohibition of serpent worship in Ireland that the legend of St Patrick relates' (p. 237).

public and religious ceremony; while Michal, his wife, was punished with barrenness for expressing her disapprobation of his conduct.[1] This example attests the great respect entertained by the Hebrews for the organs of generation;[2] but we have a further proof of this reverence for them in the fact that, when taking a solemn oath, they placed their hand upon them in token of its inviolability: When Abraham, addressing 'his oldest servant of his house, that ruled over all that he had', is made to say: 'Put I pray thee, thy hand under my thigh, and I will make thee swear, by the Lord, the God of heaven, and the God of the earth, that thou shalt not take a wife unto my son of the daughters of the Canaanites,'[3] and when Jacob, at the point of death 'called his son Joseph, and said unto him, If now I have found grace in thy sight, put, I pray thee, thy hand under my thigh, and deal kindly and truly with me; bury me not, I pray thee, in Egypt',[4] the Hebrew text has been incorrectly translated in both these instances; for, according to learned commentators, it is not the *thigh*, but the *phallus* that is meant; such tact having, in the opinion of the Rabbins, been introduced for the purpose of doing honour to circumcision.

This custom obtains in Egypt even in our own day, for many

---

[1] II *Samuel*, VI, v. 20–3. [D]

[2] The indispensable and inseparable appendages to the male organ have thus been eulogized by Giov. Francesco Lazzarelli in his poem entitled *La Cicceide*, p. 120: *Le Prerogativi de 'Testicoli.* [D]

The effect of Judeo-Christian moral concepts is evident in Davenport, for he does not think of saying: 'for such *supposed* gross indecency'—or 'for what to our mistaken modern conceptions might be termed gross indecency'. Havelock Ellis and René Guyon had few precursors. It remained for such as the Marquis de Sade to treat of such matters rationally. But it seems that Davenport remained ignorant of the long and frequently very reasonable philosophical and moral discussions to be found in Sade's writing.

The works of Havelock Ellis are well enough known (see, in this connection, *The Evolution of Modesty* in the *Studies in the Psychology of Sex*). Two of Guyon's books are translated into English: *Sex Life and Sex Ethics*, London, John Lane, 1933 (later reprinted), and *Sexual Freedom*, London, John Lane, 1939, also reprinted. An uncompleted series of articles was also written by Guyon for the *Journal of Sex Education*, London, 1948–52, and would have been completed had the journal been continued after the death of its editor, the late Norman Haire, CH.M., M.B.

[3] *Genesis*, XXIV, v. 2, 3. [D]

[4] *Genesis*, XLVII, v. 29. [D]

travellers assert that the Arabs, when desirous of saluting or making a promise with great solemnity, place their hand upon the part in question.[1] A case in point is related in a letter of the Adjutant-General Julian to a member of the Institute of Egypt.[2] An Egyptian who had been arrested as a spy and brought before the General, finding that all his asseverations of innocence could not be understood, 'leva sa chemise bleue, et prenant son phallus à la poignée, resta un moment dans l'attitude théatrale d'un dieu jurant par le Styx. Sa physionomie semblait me dire: *Après le serment terrible que je fais pour vous prouver mon innocence, osez-vous en douter?* Son geste me rappela que du temps d'Abraham on jurait vérité en portant la main aux organes de la génération.' The vast antiquity of this custom among the ancient Egyptians is proved by the figure, in Caylus, Vol. VI, Plate I, fig. 4, representing Osiris grasping his phallus while taking an oath.

A custom greatly resembling this manner of swearing existed also in the north of Europe, as is proved by an ancient law still extant: thus, one of the articles of the Welsh laws enacted by *Hoel the Good*, provides that in cases of rape if the woman wishes to prosecute the offender, she must, when swearing to the identity of the criminal, lay her right hand upon the relics of the saints and grasp with her left one the peccant member of the party accused.[3]

It may be mentioned, *en passant*, that the low Irish in Dublin, and

---

[1] Amongst the Arabs, the left hand, which was used for holding the penis during urination, was never used for handling food. Thus, Burton says: 'Cutting off the right hand is the Koranic punishment [Chap. V] for one who robs an article worth four dinars, about forty francs . . .' (Sir Richard F. Burton, *Arabian Nights*, unexpurgated edition, privately printed for the Kamashastra Society, London and Benares, 1885, Vol. I, p. 274, note 2.)

[2] *Mémoires sur l'Egypte*, publiés pendant les Campagnes de Bonaparte, Partie 2, p. 193. [D]

A similar episode in which a terrified sailor publicly exposes his uncircumcised penis in a public square in order to prove his Christianity (and therefore a case of mistaken identity) is told by the Marquis de Sade with an almost Rabelaisian flair in his *Historiettes Contes et Fabliaux* (Publiés sur le texte authentique . . . avec un avant-propos par Maurice Heine), Paris, Simon Kra, 1927.

[3] The Latin text of the law is as follows: 'Si mulier stuprata lege cum illo agere velit, membro virili sinistra prenso et dextra reliquos sanctorum imposita, juret super illas quod is per vim se, isto membro, vitiaverit.'—*Voyage dans le Département du Finistère*, Tom. III, p. 233. [D]

the London costermongers, often make use of an expression which, whether connected or not with the custom above noted, offers for our consideration a curious coincidence at least. If extra force is to accompany an assertion, it is very common for the vulgar to say in conclusion: '*S'elp my taters!*' or '*So help me* TESTES'[1]—equal to saying, 'I swear by my member.' That the word 'taters' is a corruption of, and vulgarism for, '*testes*' we see very readily in the expression '*strain my taters*'—i.e. to pass urine or make water.

The Greeks had consecrated the same symbols of universal fecundity in their mysteries, the phallus and the cteis being publicly exhibited in the sanctuary of Eleusis. The *membrum virile* or *active* principle of generation was carried to the temple of Bacchus and there crowned with a garland by one of the most respectable matrons of the town or city. The Egyptian Osiris, and the female *pudenda*, or symbol of the *passive* principle of generation, were, in like manner, carried in procession to the temple of Libera or Proserpine.

The worship of Priapus among the Romans was derived from the Egyptians, who, under the form of Apis, the sacred bull, worshipped the generative power of Nature;[2] and, as the syllable *pri* or *pre* signifies, in the Oriental tongue, principle, production, or natural or original source, the word *Priapus* may be translated *principle of production* or *fecundation of Apis*. The same symbol also bore among the Romans the names of *Tutunus*, *Mutinus*, and *Fascinum*. Among the many places where this divinity was worshipped, Lampsacus,[3] in Asia Minor, was

[1] In Northumberland and Durham, certainly up to the early 1930's, it was not uncommon to hear, amongst the working classes, the expression: 'Sw'elp me taties!' (May my potatoes help me!), meaning 'By my balls!' or 'May my balls help me!'—a further corruption in which the testes had become likened to, and euphemized as, potatoes. A similar expression in the same area was 'By me onions!'. These expressions were chiefly confined to the old, and used but little by the young —and then in burlesque fashion. It seemed that most people were not aware of the origin of such phrases and seemed to think that they came from the early music-hall stage, where indeed they may, on occasion, have been employed.

[2] See Sir J. G. Frazer, *The Golden Bough*, abridged edition, London, Macmillan, 1922 (and reprints), p. 365, where Diodorus Siculus is quoted. Also pp. 476, 501.

[3] Hunc locum tibi dedico consacroque, Priape,
　　Quae domus tua, Lampsaci est, quaque silva, Priape.
　　Nam te praecipue in suis urbibus colit, ora
　　Hellespontia, caeteris ostreosior oris.
　　　　　　　　　　　　　　　Catullus, *Carm.* xviii. [D]

the most noted on account of the obscene rites there practised. The Priapi were of different forms; some having only a human head and the phallus; some with the head of Pan or of a faun—that is, with the head and ears of a goat. Others, with their indecent attribute, were placed in the public roads, and were then confounded with the divinities *Mercury* and *Terminus*, who preside over boundaries. Scaliger says that he saw at Rome, in the palace of a cardinal,[1] a similar statue whose phallus had served as a signpost.[2] All the human parts of these priapi were invariably painted red.

When furnished with arms, which he was when representing Terminus, Priapus held in one hand a reaping hook, and, like Osiris, grasped with the other the characteristic feature of his divinity, which was always of a monstrous size and in a state of erection.

In the towns Priapus had public chapels, whither such devotees as were suffering from maladies concerned with his attributes repaired for the purpose of offering to him *ex-votos* representing the parts afflicted; these ex-votos being sometimes paintings and, at others,

This poem is not included in the Loeb edition of *Catullus, Tibullus,* etc. (translated by F. W. Cornish; London, Heinemann; New York, G. P. Putnam's Sons, 1921). It is translated literally (and anonymously) by Sir Richard F. Burton in: *Priapeia* . . . Now First Done into English Prose from the original Latin . . . The Erotica Biblion Society, Athens (i.e. London), 1888. Edition limited to 250 copies. The translation is:

> This grove I dedicate and consecrate to thee,
> Priapus, who hast thy home and woodlands at Lampsacus; for the
> coast of the Hellespont, richer than all others in oysters,
> especially worships thee in its cities.

As Burton says, this epithet is particularly Catullian, and appropriate to the coasts favoured by Priapus, owing to the fact that oysters were, and are, considered an incentive to lust: 'She knows no difference 'twixt head and privities who devours immense oysters at midnight', i.e. 'the half-drunken dame is equally inclined for coition or coynte-licking'. Cf. *Valer. Max.* II, I, 5: *Sen. Ep.* 83.

None of the editions of the *Priapeia* are easily come by, although perhaps the French translation, with Latin text, is more available than others: *L'Œuvre Priapique des Anciens et des Modernes* . . . Paris, *Bibliothèque des Curieux,* 1914. (Contains also *L'Hermaphrodite* de Panormita, *L'Hecatelegium* (extraits) de Pacifico Massimi, and the *Priapées* de Maynard.

[1] From possessing such an article of *virtu,* his eminence must surely have been of the opinion of Cardinal Bembo—*that there is no sin below the navel.* [D]

[2] Falce minax et parte tui majore, Priape,
   Ad fontem quaeso, dic mihi, qua sit iter.—*Priapeia.* [D]

little figures made of wax or of wood, and, occasionally, even, of marble.

Females as superstitious as they were lascivious might be seen offering in public to Priapus as many garlands as they had lovers. These they would hang upon the enormous phallus of the idol,[1] which was often hidden from sight by the number suspended by only one woman.

Others offered to the god as many phalli, made of the wood of the willow tree, as they had vanquished men in a single night.

St Augustine informs us that it was considered by the Roman ladies as a very proper and pious custom to require young brides to seat themselves upon the monstrous and obscene member of Priapus. And Lactantius says: 'Shall I speak of that *Mutinus*, upon the extremity of which brides are accustomed to seat themselves in order that the god may appear to have been the first to receive the sacrifice of their modesty?'[2]

These facts prove that the worship of Priapus had greatly degenerated with the Romans, since, losing sight altogether of the object typified, they attached themselves to the symbol alone, in which they could see only what was indecent; and hence religion became a pretext for libertinism.[3]

Respected so long as the Roman manners preserved their pristine simplicity, but degraded[4] and vilified in proportion as the morals of the people became corrupted, the very sanctuary itself of Priapus failed to protect him from obloquy and ridicule. Christian writers added their indignant invectives to the biting sarcasms of the poets, and the worship of Priapus would have been annihilated had not superstition

---

[1] Which was always represented in a state of erection, and with a frequently exaggerated upward curve, rather tending to imitate a coat-peg.

[2] See St Augustine, *Civ. Dei*, Lib. VI, cap. 9, and Lactantius, *De falsa religione*, Lib I. [D]. St Augustine's *City of God* (De Civitate Dei) is obtainable in an English translation in the Everyman Library (London, *Dent*, 2 vols.).

[3] See Plate 1, fig. 4, in the original edition. This is the well-known phallus, found at Pompeii over a baker's door, with the appended motto 'Hic habitat felicitas'.

[4] Thus his statue was placed in orchards as a scarecrow to drive away superstitious thieves, as well as children and birds:

> Pomarii tutela diligens *rubro*
> Priape, furibus minare mutino.—*Priapeia*, Carm. 73. [D]

and the force of habit, that most indestructible of all human affections, come to the rescue. These two powerful levers of mankind triumphed over reason and Christianity, and succeeded, notwithstanding the strenuous and continued efforts of the latter, in maintaining in some degree the worship of that filthy deity; for the Christian priests, while opposing *à l'outrance*, the superstitions and impure practices already adverted to, did not do so as regarded the other customs equally repugnant to decency and religion. Less austere to these, and consulting their own interests, they turned to their profit the ancient worship established by the Romans and strengthened by habit: they appropriated to themselves what they could not destroy, and, in order to attract to their side the votaries of Priapus, they made a Christian of him.

But besides the lingham of the Indians, the phallus of the Greeks, and the priapus of the Romans, the cross (T), although generally thought to be exclusively emblematical of eternal life, has also, on account of its fancied similarity to the *membrum virile*, been considered by many as typical of the reproductive powers of Nature. It was known as such to the Indians, being as common in their country as in Egypt or Europe. 'Let not the piety of the Catholic Christian', says the Rev. Mr Maurice, 'be offended at the preceding assertion that the Cross was one of the most usual symbols among the hieroglyphics of Egypt and India. Equally honoured in the Gentile and the Pagan world, this Christian emblem of universal nature, of that world to whose four corners its diverging radii pointed, decorated the hands of most of the sculptured images in the former country [Egypt], and the latter [India] stamped its form upon the most majestic of the shrines of their deities.'[1]

It is well known that the cross was regarded by the ancient Egyptians as the emblem of fruitfulness. Thus the Rev. Mr Maurice describes a statue bearing a kind of cross in its hand as the symbol of fertility, or, in other words, of the procreative and generative powers.[2] The cross T so common upon Egyptian monuments was known to the Buddhists and to the Lama of Thibet 700 years before Christ. The Lama takes his name from the *Lamah*, which is an object of profound veneration with

[1] *Ind. Antiq.*, Vol. II, p. 361. [D]
[2] *Ind. Antiq.*, Vol. I, p. 247. [D]

his followers: 'Ce qui est remarquable', says M. Avril, 'c'est que le grand prêtre des Tartares porte le nom de Lama qui, en langue Tartare, désigne *la Croix*; et les Bogdoi qui conquirent la Chine en 1664, et qui sont soumis au Dalai-Lama dans les choses de la religion, ont toujours des croix sur eux, qu'ils appellent *lamas*.'[1]

The letter *Tau*, T, being the last one of the ancient alphabets, was made to typify, not only the end, boundary, or terminus of districts, but also the generative power of the eternal transmigratory life, and was used indiscriminately with the phallus; it was, in fact, the phallus.[2] Speaking of this emblem, Payne Knight[3] observes: 'One of the most remarkable of those symbols of generation is a cross in the form of the letter T, which thus served as the emblem of *creation* and *generation* before the church adopted it as the sign of salvation, a lucky coincidence of ideas which, without doubt, facilitated the reception of it among the faithful.' And again: 'The male organs of generation are sometimes represented by signs of the same sort, which might properly be called symbols of symbols. One of the most remarkable of these is the Cross in the form of the letter T, which thus served as the emblem of creation and generation.'

The famous *Crux Ansata*,[4] which may be seen on all the monuments of Egypt, is what is alluded to by the Prophet Ezekiel,[5] and is affirmed by the learned L. A. Crozius to be nothing else than the triple phallus mentioned by Plutarch.[6]

We shall now proceed to notice a few of the traces of phallic worship as were still to be found lingering in some parts of Europe so late as the eighteenth century, a tenacity of existence by no means surprising

---

[1] *Voyage dans la Chine*, par Avril, Liv. III, p. 194. [D]

[2] Higgins, *Anacalypsis*, Vol. I, p. 269. [D]

[3] See Richard Payne Knight: *An Account of the Remains of the Worship of Priapus lately existing at Isernia* . . . etc., London, 1786. This was privately reprinted in a very limited edition by John Camden Hotten, London, 1865. It has again been reprinted in a *de luxe* edition, for private subscribers only, by Charles Skilton, London, 1952.

[4] For some ingenious and learned observations on the Tau, or Crux Ansata, see: *Classical Journal*, No. 39, p. 182. [D]

[5] Chap. IX, v. 3.

[6] For a description of some of the above-mentioned crosses, see Plate V [in the original edition], also *Voyage dans la basse et la haute-Egypte pendant les campagnes de Bonaparte, 1802 et 1829*, par Denon—Planches 48, 78. [D]

if it be considered that of all the human affections none is more dangerous to oppose, none more difficult to eradicate, than habit. Accordingly
it will be found that the above superstition has maintained itself in
countries where Christianity was established, and that, bidding defiance
to the severe precepts of that pure faith, it successfully resisted for at
least seventeen centuries every effort made to extirpate it by the
Christian clergy, backed by the civil power. Its triumph was, however,
by no means complete, for this worship was constrained to yield to
circumstances and to use a disguise by adopting the forms and
designations peculiar to Christianity, a mask which on the other hand,
favoured not a little its preservation.

Hence it was that the names of certain legendary saints were given
to the ancient God of Lampsacus,[1] the said names having some relation
either to the act over which that deity presided, or to his most prominent attributes.

The first Bishop of Lyon was honoured throughout Provence,
Languedoc, and the Lyonnais as a saint, and as his name happened to
be Pothin, Photin, or Fotin, commonly pronounced by the lower
orders *Foutin*,[2] these people, who are very apt to judge of the nature of
things by the sound of the words by which they are designated, thought
St Foutin worthy of replacing St Priapus, and accordingly conferred
upon him the prerogatives of his predecessor.

---

[1] This city was the birthplace of the deity Priapus, whose orgies were there
constantly celebrated. Alexander the Great, in his Persian expedition, resolved to
destroy Lampsacus on account of its many vices, or rather from a jealousy of its
adherence to Persia; but it was saved by the artifice of the philosopher Anaxamenes,
who, having heard that the king had sworn to refuse whatever he should ask him,
begged him to destroy the city. [D]

[2] *Foutin*, which would suggest that the word came from the French verb *foutre*
(to fuck), which, as in the English, means 'to sow seed'. An amusing story relative
to the supposed virtues of a similar saint is told in *Eastern Love*, an anthology
translated by E. Powys Mathers. (Edition limited to 1000 numbered sets and
printed for subscribers only. London, John Rodker, 1927–9. 12 vols. See Vol. 6:
Gallant Tales from the Chinese.) The tale concerns the devotions paid before an
idol by barren women, and how the monks effectively remedy their condition.
Payne Knight says the name 'Foutin' is said to be a corruption of Gotinus or
Photinus, the first Bishop of Lyons, but even if this is true the above explanation of
the corruption holds good (*Worship of Priapus*, London, 1865, reprinted 1952,
pp. 139–40).

St Foutin de Varailles had particular reverence paid to him in Provence, nor is this to be wondered at, since the power was attributed to him of rendering barren women fruitful, stimulating flagging husbands, and curing secret maladies. It was consequently the custom to lay upon his altar, as was formerly done upon that of the god Priapus, small votive offerings, made of wax, and representing the weak or otherwise afflicted parts. Sanci says: 'To this saint are offered waxen models of the *pudenda* of both sexes. They are strewn in great numbers over the floor of the chapel, and should a gust of wind cause them to rustle against one another, it occasioned a serious interruption to the devotions paid to the saint. I was very much scandalized,' continues he, 'when passing through the town, I found the name of *Foutin* very common among the men. My landlord's daughter had for godmother a young lady whose name was Foutine.'

The same saint was similarly honoured at Embrun. When the Protestants took that town in 1585 they found among the relics of the principal church, the *phallus* of St Foutin. The devotees of that town, in imitation of pagan ones, made libations to this obscene idol. They poured wine over the extremity of the phallus, which was dyed red by it. This wine, being afterwards collected, and allowed to turn sour, was called *the holy vinegar*, and according to the author from whom this account is taken,[1] was applied by women to a most extraordinary purpose; but what that purpose was we are not informed, and can therefore only guess at it.

At Orange there was also a phallus much venerated by the inhabitants of that town. Larger than the one at Embrun, it was, moreover, covered with leather, and furnished with its appendages. When in 1562 the Protestants destroyed the Church of St Eutropius in this town, they seized the enormous phallus and burned it in the market place. Similar phalli were to be found at Poligny, Vendre in the Bourbonnais, and at Auxerre.

The inhabitants of Puy-en-Velay, even to this day, speak of their *St Foutin*, who, in times not far remote from our own, was invoked by barren women, who, under the notion of giving a greater efficacy to their prayers, scraped the phallus of the saint, and, mixing the

[1] *Journal d'Henri III*, par l'Etoile. Tome 5. [D]

particles so abraded in water, devoutly swallowed them in the hope of thereby being rendered fruitful.[1]

It is no doubt to one of these phallic saints that Count de Gebelin refers when, speaking of the goat *Mendès*, he says: 'I have read somewhere that in the south of France there existed not long ago a custom resembling the one mentioned; the women of that part of the country devoutly frequented a temple containing a statue of the saint, and which statue they embraced, expecting that their barrenness would be removed by the operation.'[2]

In the neighbourhood of Brest stood the chapel of the famous St Guignole, or Guingalais, whose phallic symbol consisted of a long wooden beam which passed right through the body of the saint, and the fore-part of which was strikingly characteristic. The devotees of this place, like those of Puy-en-Velay, most devoutly rasped the extremity of this miraculous symbol for the purpose of drinking the scrapings mixed with water—as an antidote against sterility. And when, by the frequent repetition of this operation, the beam was worn away, a blow with a mallet in the rear of the saint propelled it immediately in front. Thus, although it was being continually scraped, it appeared never to diminish, a miracle due exclusively to the mallet.

Antwerp was the Lampsacus of Belgium, Priapus being the tutelary god of that city. *Ters* was the name given to him by the inhabitants who held this divinity in the greatest veneration. Females were accustomed to invoke him on the most trivial occasions, a custom which Goropius informs us continued as late as the sixteenth century.[3]

So inveterate was this superstition that Godefroy de Bouillon, marquis of the city and illustrious leader of the first crusade, in order to

---

[1] Of the occurrence of miracles there remains no doubt, and Aldous Huxley (*The Perennial Philosophy*, London, Chatto, 1946, p. 299) says: 'The miracles which are at present in greatest demand, and of which there is the steadiest supply, are those of psychic healing.' The researches of J. B. Rhine (*The Reach of the Mind*, Pelican Books, 1954, and *New World of the Mind*, London, Faber, 1954, esp. pp. 215–17) throw much scientific light upon the matter. It is likely that manifestations of healing by psycho-kinesis are assisted in 'those of less faith' through some such procedure as that practised by the women of Puy-en-Velay.

[2] *Histoire Religieuse du Calendrier*, p. 420. [D]

[3] Johannis Goropii Becani, *Origines Antwerpianae*, 1569, Lib. I, pp. 26 and 101. [D]

eradicate it, or to replace it by ceremonies of the Christian Church, sent to Antwerp, from Jerusalem, as a present of inestimable value, *the foreskin of Jesus Christ*.[1] This precious relic, however, found but little favour with the Belgian ladies, and utterly failed to supersede their beloved *Fascinum*.[2]

In the kingdom of Naples, in the town of Trani, the capital of the province of that name, there was carried in procession, during the carnival, an old wooden statue representing an entire Priapus, in the ancient proportions; that is to say that the distinguishing characteristic of that god was very disproportioned to the rest of the idol's body, reaching, as it did, to the height of his chin. The people called this figure *il Santo Membro*, the holy member. This ancient ceremony, evidently a remains of the feasts of Bacchus, called by the Greeks *Dionysiacs*, and by the Romans *Liberalia*, existed as late as the commencement of the eighteenth century, when it was abolished by Joseph Davanzati, archbishop of that town.

Sir William Hamilton's account of the worship paid to St Cosmo and St Damianus is very curious:

On the 27th September, at Isernia, one of the most ancient cities of the kingdom of Naples, situated in the province called the Contado di Molise, and adjoining the Aruzzo, an annual fair is held which lasts three days. On one of the days of the fair the relics of Sts Cosmo and Damianus are exposed. In the city and at the fair, *ex-votos* of wax, representing the male parts of generation, of various dimensions, sometimes even the length of a palm, are publicly exposed for sale. There was also waxen vows that represent other parts of the body mixed with them, but of those there are few in comparison with the number of the Priapi.

The distributors of these vows carry a basket full of them in one hand, and hold a plate in the other, to receive the money, crying out, 'Saints Cosmo and Damianus!' If you ask the price of one, the answer is, '*più ci metti, più meriti*'; the more you give, the more the merit. The vows are chiefly presented by the female sex, and they are seldom such as represent

[1] The foreskins, still extant, of the Saviour are reckoned to be twelve in number. One was in the possession of the monks of Coulombs; another at the Abbey of Charroux; a third at Hildesheim, in Germany; a fourth at Rome, in the Church of St Jean-de-Latran; a fifth at Antwerp; a sixth at Puy-en-Velay, in the Church of Notre-Dame, etc. So much for relics! [D]

[2] Dulaure, *Singularités Historiques de Paris*, p. 77. Paris, 1825.

legs, arms, &c., but most commonly the male parts of generation. The person who was at the *fête*, in the year 1780, and who gave me this account (the authenticity of which has since been confirmed to me by the governor of Isernia) told me also that he heard a woman say, at the time she presented a vow, '*Santo Cosmo, benedetto, cosi le voglio,*' 'Blessed St Cosmo, let it be like this!' The vow is never presented without being accompanied by a piece of money, and is always kissed by the devotee at the moment of presentation.[1]

But, as might naturally be expected, this does not suffice to fructify barren women; and consequently another ceremony, one which is doubtless much more efficacious, was required.

The parties who resorted to this fair slept for two nights, some in the Church of the Capuchin Friars, and the others in that of the Cordeliers, and when these two churches were found to be insufficient to contain the whole of such devotees, the Church of the Hermitage of St Cosmo received the surplus.

In the three edifices the women were, during the two nights, separated from the men, the latter lying under the vestibule, and the women in the church. These, whether in the church of the Capuchins, or in that of the Cordeliers, were under the protection of the Father Guardian, the Vicar, and a Monk of Merit. In the Hermitage it was the Hermit himself who watched over them.

From this it may easily be imagined how the miracle was effected without troubling St Cosmo and St Damianus at all in the matter, as well as that the virtue possessed by these two saints was extended even to young maidens and widows.

---

[1] *Letter of Sir W. Hamilton,* prefixed to Payne Knight's *Worship of Priapus.*

[D]

ESSAY 3

Anaphrodisia : or Absence of the Reproductive Powers

A DESCRIPTION of the symbols under which the *reproductive power* was anciently worshipped having been given in the preceding essay, the present one will contain some account of the *negation* or *absence*[1] of that faculty, whether total or partial, as known under the names of *impotence*[2] and *sterility*.

Potency, or power as regards the generative act, may be defined as the aptitude or ability to beget, and impotence, the negation or absence of that power.[3]

The canon law distinguished three kinds of impotence—viz. that which proceeds from frigidity; that which is caused by sorcery (ligature or 'point-tying'),[4] and that which, proceeding from some defect of conformation, is properly designated as *impotentia coeundi*. The different kinds of impotence may thus be classed: 1. Those which

---

[1] The italics, quite unnecessary, are those of Davenport.

[2] Davenport always uses the word 'impotency', which in each case I have supplanted with the modern usage: 'impotence'.

[3] Scarcely correct. Potency is not necessarily the 'ability to beget', but rather the ability to achieve and maintain a durable erection for the satisfactory performance of coitus. And absence of the 'ability to beget' is not necessarily impotence, but may be *infertility*—which can easily exist alongside a firm erection with ejaculation.

[4] 'Point-tying' applies to the knotting of the 'points' which tied the 'cod-piece' in earlier days, and is a euphemism for impotence. To untie the cod-piece is synonymous with unbuttoning the 'fly'. The old French work, *Les Quinze Joyes de Mariage*, opens thus: 'The first joy of Marriage is when the young man is in his first youth, when he is fresh, nimble and merry and careth for naught save the untyleing his cod-piece point . . .' (Paris, 1595).

are proper to men; 2. Those proper to women; and 3. Those common to both sexes.[1]

The causes of impotence proper to man are natural frigidity, defect of conformation, and accident.

The causes of impotence proper to women[2] are all such obstacles as arise *ex clausura uteri aut nimia arctitudine.*

The causes common to both men and women are the defect of puberty and imperfect conformation.[3]

Impotence may also be divided into natural and accidental; the former being that which a person is born with, or which proceeds *ex vitio naturalis temperamenti vel partium genitalium*; and the latter that which arises from some accident, as *ex casu vel morbo.*[4]

Another definition of impotence in man is the *non posse seminare in vase idoneo*; three things being considered as indispensable to his due performance of the sexual act: 1. *Ut arriget* or erection; 2. *Ut vas foemineum resaret*, or intromission, and 3. *Ut in vase seminat*, or emission.

Sterility must not be confounded with impotence. Many women are barren, but very few are impotent.[5] While, on the contrary, many men are impotent who ought not, on that account, to be regarded as barren. In either sex impotence is present when from whatever cause an individual cannot concur in sexual contact. Sterility exists when the

[1] Regarding impotence, Kinsey says: 'Early erectal impotence occurs in only a few cases (0·4 per cent of the males under twenty-five, and less than 1 per cent of the males under thirty-five years of age). In only a small proportion of these is it a lifelong and complete incapacity.' (Kinsey, Pomeroy and Martin, *Sexual Behaviour in the Human Male*, W. B. Saunders, Philadelphia and London, 1948, page 237.) Kinsey also says: 'Impotence in a male under fifty-five years of age is almost always the product of psychologic conflict . . .' (op. cit., p. 323).

[2] Woman is never, correctly, impotent, as, barring an abnormal obstruction to the vaginal entrance, she is always capable of coitus, even should she be incapable of orgasm. As for frigidity in men, this is so rare as to be negligible.

[3] Mentioned by Kinsey and others, but, as all are agreed, extremely rare.

[4] Loss of the penis, during war (due to fragments of shrapnel, etc.), is not unknown, as also loss of erectile power due to damage to the nerve centres in the spine—regarding the emotional conflict due to this last, the American film director, Elia Kazan, produced an excellent film concerning the subject, *The Men.*

[5] See Th. Van de Velde, *Fertility and Sterility in Marriage*, London, Heinemann, 1931, reprinted 1934.

contact, after having been regularly accomplished, is followed by no productive result.

With the exception of those pathological cases in which deformities are sometimes (but very rarely) met with, it may be affirmed that woman is never impotent, for her organization opposes it. Radical impotence, in fact, results in the female from the complete absence, or the occlusion simply, of the vagina. Now, these cases are extremely rare, and may therefore be considered as exceptions or as real monstrosities.

As the causes of sterility in women are numerous and of various kinds, we shall briefly enumerate them.

The absence of ovaries or their diseased state are the radical cause of sterility. These causes may be suspected but not cured. When there is no uterus, fecundation and pregnancy are not impossible, since extra-uterine pregnancies are occasionally observed; that is to say, cases in which the product of conception has escaped the uterus, and proceeded to establish itself in some point of the lower belly. Neither is the vagina indispensable, for cases are cited of the contraction of this organ accompanied by rectovaginal fistula, in which fecundation is effected, although the fecundating fluid had been confined to the rectum.[1]

Female masturbation is another rife cause of barrenness in women.[2] If it be true that the number of eggs is limited, and that there are not more than from fifteen to twenty in each ovary, it is evident that sterility must ensue when these fifteen or twenty eggs have been detached without fecundation. If, on the contrary, new eggs are continually secreted by the ovaries, it is equally evident that the secretory action must, sooner or later, become exhausted by the over-excitement caused by the indulgence above-mentioned.

Another very great cause of sterility, and which must be of frequent occurrence, is found in the obstructed or choked-up state of the Fallopian tubes. These passages, which establish the communication between ovary and uterus, may be obstructed by inflammation, either

---

[1] Anal intercourse between male and female, although a criminal offence in the law of the country, is much more common than is generally supposed.

[2] One can only point out that this statement, and what follows, is sheer nonsense. Masturbation is harmless in either sex.

acute or chronic, to which they may be subject in all diseases of the abdomen, as well as by frequent excitement.

Morgagni speaks of certain women of the town in whom the Fallopian tubes were completely obliterated by the thickening of the parietes or sides, an evident consequence of the continual orgasm in which they were kept by immoderate indulgence in coitus.[1]

The absence of menstruation almost always induces barrenness. Cases are, notwithstanding, reported in which women have their menses during pregnancy, but these are exceptions which, so far from invalidating the rule, confirm it.

Polypi, or the development of fibrous bodies in the uterus, present an equal obstacle to fecundation, their presence having the effect of perverting the physiological functions of the uterus, nor does their removal always cause sterility to disappear.

Impotence in women can only result from the absence of the vagina, or from its excessive narrowness which does not allow of the approach of the male, although instances have occurred of fecundation being effected without the introduction of the male organ. Thus cases have been found of women who have been fecundated, and have even arrived at the term of pregnancy, having been obliged to submit to a surgical operation for the removal of the hymen, which membrane had not been broken in the acts which had nevertheless effected the fecundation. Lastly, the excessive length, when it does exist, of the clitoris, also opposes the conjugal act by the difficulty it presents to the introduction of the fecundating organ.[2] The only remedy to be employed in

[1] As is well enough known nowadays, prostitutes merely feign excitement and orgasm whilst engaging with their clients, reserving true abandon and participation for their lover. Unlike the nymphomaniac they are not in a frequent and immoderate state of excitement.

[2] For sizes of the clitoris (illustrated by life-size sectional drawings), see fig. 116 of *Human Sex Anatomy*, by R. L. Dickinson, M.D., F.A.C.S., 2nd edition, London, Baillière, Tindall & Cox, 1949. A vaginal *fossa*, causing difficulty in penile penetration, is also illustrated in life-size line-drawing section in figs. 94b and 95 of the same Hand Atlas. Sizes of the clitoris, projections, and other illustrative information are to be found on pp. 1108–10, and elsewhere, in *Sex Variants*, A study of Homosexual Patterns, by George W. Henry, M.D., New York, Paul B. Hoeber Inc., 2 vols., 1941. 1 vol. edition, same pagination, 1948. The single-volume edition was published in England (also same pagination) by Cassell & Co., London, 1950.

this case consists in amputation, an operation which has been frequently performed.

The organ in question is known to resemble, in a very great degree, the virile member,[1] both in external form and internal structure, to be susceptible of erection and relaxation and endowed with exquisite sensibility. It has been seen equal to the penis in volume. A remarkable instance is given by Home.[2] It occurred in a negress who was purchased by General Melville, in the island of Dominica, in the West Indies, about the year 1744. She was of the Mandango nation, twenty-four years of age, her breasts were very flat, she had a rough voice and a masculine countenance. The clitoris was two inches long, and in thickness resembled a common-sized thumb. When viewed at some distance the end appeared round and of a red colour, but upon closer examination was found to be more pointed than that of a penis, and having neither prepuce nor perforation; when handled it became half erected, and was in that state fully three inches long and much thicker than before: when she voided her urine she was obliged to lift it up, as it completely covered the orifice of the urethra. The other parts of the female organs were found to be in a natural state. Columbus quotes the existence of a woman who had a clitoris as long as the little finger. Haller speaks of another in whom this organ was seven inches in length. Some have even been said to be of the monstrous length of twelve inches.[3]

These are the enormous dimensions which sometimes deceive as to the real character of the sex, and which have occasioned the belief in the existence of real hermaphrodites. Women so formed have also a great disposition to usurp the virile functions; they preserve scarcely anything of their sex except their habits and manners. Their

[1] For which reason it has been utilized as copulator by those Lesbians in whom it has been above the average. See R. L. Dickinson, op. cit., and G. W. Henry, op. cit. See also Kinsey, et al., *Sexual Behaviour in the Human Female*, London and Philadelphia, W. B. Saunders, 1953, p. 575. When normal in size, Lesbians still utilize its sensibility for mutual masturbation.

[2] See *Lectures on Comparative Anatomy* by Sir Everard Home, Bart. Vol. III, p. 166, London, 1823. [D]

[3] This seems an impossibility. A length of six inches has rarely been noted, even in a pseudo-hermaphrodite (true hermaphrodism, being, of course, a myth).

stature is in general tall, their limbs muscular, their face masculine, and their deportment bold and manly. In a word they completely justify the words of Martial:

Mentiturque virum prodigiosa Venus.[1]

In the case of man's impotence it often happens, on the contrary, that, with organs to all appearance perfectly formed, he is, nevertheless, impotent.

If the woman be organized for receiving, the man is formed for imparting. Now, in the majority of cases, his impotence is such that although he seems to be provided with abundant stores, he is precluded from offering them:

. . . . *Si*
Coneris, jacet exiguus cum ramice nervus
Et quamvis tota palpetur nocte, jacebit.[2]

Such, in fact, is the great difficulty of those individuals who have abused their organs and destroyed their sensibility.[3] The erectile tissue whose turgescence is indispensable no longer admits into its vascular *plexus* or network a quantity of fluid sufficient to give the organ the power of penetrating—*jacet exiguus*—and, although it may be supposed that the seminal glands perform their functions perfectly well, and secrete abundantly the fluid peculiar to them, the copulative organ remains paralysed. This is the impotence which is brought on by old age, and which Ariosto has so forcibly described in the following lines, wherein he relates the futile attempts made upon Angelica by the Hermit:

---

[1] Misquoted by Davenport as: Martial, Lib. I, Epigram 91. In all the editions I have consulted this Epigram is numbered 90. The lines are neatly translated by Sedley:
Didst act of man th'inimitable part.
[2] Juvenal, *Sat.*, *X*, v. 205–6. [D]
[3] A rather careless statement, badly phrased, and applicable only to an extreme and unusual minority of individuals. As Stekel says: 'Never was a more contemptible falsehood uttered than the one which states that regular and frequent sexual intercourse undermines one's vital strength. . . . It is only persons who have an active sexual impulse and who also exercise it who attain advanced age.' (W. Stekel, *Impotence in the Male*, 2 vols., New York, Liveright, 1939; London, John Lane, 1940. See Vol. I, p. 43. See also Vol. I, p. 46.)

Egli l'abbraccia, ed a piacer la tocca:
Ed ella dorme, e non più fare ischermo:
Or le baccia il bel petto, ora la bocca,
Non è, ch'l veggia, in quel loco aspro ed ermo.
Ma nel incontro, il suo destrier trabocca
Che al desio non risponde, il corpo infermo:

.   .   .   .

Tutte le vie, tutti i modi tenta,
Ma quel pigre rozzo non però salta
Indarno el fren gli scoute e li tormenta
E non può far che tenga la testa alta.[1]

At other times the impotence of the man is independent of the secretion of the fecundating fluid and even of the erection, both of which are regular. In such case it is caused either by the gland[2] not being properly perforated, or by a contraction of the urethral canal, which contraction arrests the seminal fluid at the moment of expulsion, causing it to flow back towards the bladder, or else intercepting the continuous stream and allowing it to run by driblets only. The former of these imperfections technically called *Hypospadiaeos* is a vice of conformation in which the penis, instead of being perforated at the summit of the gland, presents its opening at a greater or less distance from the gland, at the lower part of the urethra or at the *perinaeum*.

As might be expected, impotence, when precocious, influences in no small degree the moral character. Cabanis knew three men who, in the vigour of age, had suddenly become impotent, although in other respects they were in good health, much engaged in business, and had but little reason to be affected by the loss of pleasures in which they indulged but rarely, and with great moderation; yet their character became gloomy and irascible, and their mental powers appeared to diminish daily.[3] The celebrated Ribeiro Sanchez, a pupil of Boerhaave, observes in his *Traité des maladies Vénériennes chroniques* that these diseases particularly dispose those subject to them to superstitious terrors.

---

[1] *Orlando Furioso*, Can. I, stanz. 49, 60. [D]

[2] i.e. Glans penis. It is incorrect to speak of impotence in such cases. It is simply a matter of deformation of the penis. In hypospadias (as we spell it now), the urethral fissure opens on the underside of the penis, some distance from the glans.

[3] *Rapport*, Tom. I, p. 335. [D]

Impotence may, however, equally proceed from moral as from physical causes. In this case it consists in the total privation of the sensibility peculiar to the reproductive organs. This insensibility is by no means infrequent in persons whose mental powers are continually in action, as the following case will show:

A celebrated mathematician of a very robust constitution, having married a young and pretty woman, lived several years with her, but had not the happiness of becoming a father. Far from being insensible to the charms of his fair wife, on the contrary he frequently felt impelled to gratify his passion, but the conjugal act, complete in every other respect, was never crowned by the emission of the seminal fluid. The interval of time which occurred between the commencement of his labour of love and the end was always sufficiently long to allow his mind, which had for a moment been abstracted by his pleasure, to be brought back to the constant objects of his meditation—that is, to geometrical problems or algebraical formulae. At the very moment even of the orgasm, the intellectual powers resumed their empire and all genital sensation vanished. Peirible, his medical adviser, recommended Madame *** never to suffer the attentions of her husband until he was *half-seas-over*,[1] this appearing to him the only practical means of withdrawing her learned spouse from the influence of the divine Urania and subjecting him more immediately to that of the seductive goddess of Paphos. The advice proved judicious. Monsieur *** became the father of several fine and healthy boys and girls, thus furnishing another proof of the truth of the maxim, '*Sine Cerere et Baccho friget Venus.*'

But that impotence arising from the predominance of the intellect is the least formidable of all. The one most to be dreaded is that which

[1] Apropos the administration of alcohol, Kenneth Walker says:

'Taken in large amounts alcohol diminishes desire, but in small amounts it may act as an aphrodisiac. Alcohol is particularly useful in the treatment of the patient of nervous temperament, who, having failed in the past, is very apprehensive of renewing attempts at intercourse.' (*Sexual Disorders in the Male*, by Kenneth Walker & Eric B. Strauss. Hamish Hamilton Medical Books, London, 1944, pp. 118–20.)

Perhaps Oblivon (methylpentynol) might be temporarily used to achieve a relaxed state and the diminution of anxiety—reinforced by practice in the art of relaxing.

results from the excessive and premature exercise of the reproductive functions, for, as has been well observed, 'the too frequent indulgence of a natural propensity at first increases the concomitant desire and makes its gratification a part of the periodical circle of action; but by degrees the over-excitement of the organs, abating their tone and vitality, unfits them for the discharge of their office, the accompanying pleasures are blunted, and give place to satiety and disgust'.[1]

Such unfortunate persons as are the victims of this kind of anaphrodisia become old long before their natural time, and have all their generative apparatus blasted with impotence. Their testicles withered and dried up secrete nothing but a serous fluid void of all virtue; the erectile tissue no longer admits into its plexus the quantum of blood necessary for turgescence, the principal organ of the reproductive act remains in a state of flaccidity, insensible to the reiterated and most stimulating solicitations; the muscles destined to favour erection are stricken with paralysis, and the violence of their desires, joined to the want of power to gratify them, drives the unhappy victim to acts of the most revolting lubricity and thence to despair.

An instance of this kind occurred in the case of a young man, the son of an opulent family. He had arrived at puberty, but from the early age of ten had been accustomed to indulge in indecent familiarities with young girls, who had gratified him by lascivious manipulations; the consequence was an entire loss of the erectile power. Travelling being recommended, he proceeded to France where he consulted, but without avail, several celebrated physicians. He then went to the waters of Spa, and there his case was attentively and anxiously considered by Van-Hers.

The sensibility and weakness of the genital member were so great that on the slightest touch, and without any sensation or desire to sexual intercourse, the young man emitted a fluid similar to whey. This secretion continued night and day, every time that he made water, or

---

[1] Sir Charles Morgan, *Philos. of Morals*, p. 25. [D]
Frank Harris, as a student in America, suffered from the same nonsensical delusions regarding the 'excessive and premature' exercise of the sexual functions (see *My Life and Loves*, Vol. 1, in the privately printed editions—either Harris's own edition, or the Paris, Obelisk Press, reprints. The work was also re-issued by W. H. Allen in London, 1964).

upon the slightest friction of his linen. After various remedies being proposed, without any beneficial results, Van-Hers considered the disease as incurable; but, as the patient would not coincide in his opinion and was very rich, he continued his travels in France, Italy, and Germany, in the hope of recovering his powers of virility. He failed not, as usual, to meet with physicians who, from mercenary motives, held out to him the most illusory prospects of a perfect cure. At length, after six years passed in travelling and in vain attempts to regain the generative faculty, he returned to the candid and able physician from whom he had the truth, and whose opinion he was now convinced was but too well founded. As may be supposed, Van-Hers perceived no new circumstance to justify an alteration in his view of the case and the unfortunate young man returned home, deeply deploring the advantages of a fortune which had made him the victim of a precocious abuse of pleasures to which he must now bid adieu for ever.[1]

Too great a warmth of passion[2] may not only defeat its own object, but also produce a temporary impotence. A lover, after having with all the ardour of affection longed for the enjoyment of his mistress, finds himself at the moment of fruition incapable of consummating his happiness. The only remedy for this misfortune is to allay the over-excitement and to restrain the exuberance of the imagination. It would be madness to persist in endeavouring to obtain a victory which must be certain, as soon as the heat of the animal spirits being abated, a portion of them proceeds to animate the agents of voluptuous passion. The following are cases of this description:

A young man whose wife's relations had promised him a considerable estate as soon as she proved pregnant, fatigued himself to no purpose by continued devotions at the shrine of love; his over-anxiety defeating the very object he so ardently desired to accomplish. In despair at the failure of his repeated efforts, he was, at length, on the point of believing his wife to be barren, when, following the advice of a judicious physician, he absented

---

[1] From: *Nosographie philosophique.* [D]

[2] This fact has been repeatedly stressed by all modern writers on the causes and cure of impotence, and is probably quite a common situation, especially amongst the young and inexperienced. The way to potency under such circumstances is achieved by employment of the 'law of reversed effort'.

himself from home for a fortnight, and upon his return proved by the success which attended his amorous labours, that absence is sometimes the best doctor.

A noble Venetian, aged twenty years, was married to a very handsome lady, with whom he cohabited with a good deal of vigour, but never could emit semen in the coition, whereas in his dreams he could discharge very freely. This misfortune very much afflicted him and his family; and as no remedy could be found at home, the Venetian ambassadors residing at the different courts of Europe were desired to consult some of the most eminent physicians in the cities where they resided, to account for the causes, and to find a cure for this extraordinary complaint of the difference of states when in sleep and when actually in coition.

I was of the opinion that it consisted altogether in the urethra being closely shut by the vigour of the erection in coition, which found so great a resistance that the powers that throw the seed out of the *vesiculae seminales* could not overcome it; whereas, in dreams, the pressure on the urethra being much less, an evacuation was effected.

The method of cure was not less successful than obvious from the foregoing account: for gentle evacuations and a slender diet brought about and fully completed their desires.[1]

Cabanis is of the opinion that debility of the stomach almost always produces a similar state in the organs of generation:

L'énergie ou la débilité de l'estomac produit, presque toujours, un état analogue dans ceux de la génération. J'ai soigné un jeune homme chez qui la paralysie accidentelle de ces derniers avait été produite par certains vices de la digestion stomachique; et qui reprit la vigueur de son âge, aussitôt qu'il eût récouvré la puissance de digérer.[a]

Old Montaigne's advice in cases similar to those cited above is worthy of notice:

As to what concerns married people having the year before them, they ought never to compel, or so much as to attempt the feat, if they do not find

[1] *Medical Essays* published by a society in Edinburgh, Vol. I, p. 270. Case reported by W. Cockburn, M.D. [D].—The cure seems to have been by suggestion, for the presence of ejaculation in dreams, and not during actual coitus, would seem to suggest a psychic block during the waking state, completely preventing orgasm and ejaculation. A further proof that a neurosis may be cured by other means than psychoanalysis.

[a] Cabanis, *Rapport*, Tome II, p. 422. [D]

themselves very ready. And it is better to fail of indecently handling the nuptial sheets, and of paying the ceremony due to the wedding night, when man perceives himself full of agitation and trembling, expecting another opportunity at a better and more private leisure, when his fancy shall be better composed, than to make himself perpetually miserable for having misbehaved himself, and being baffled at the first result. Till possession be taken, a man that knows himself subject to his infirmity, should leisurely and by degrees make certain little trials and light offers, without attempting at once to force an absolute conquest over his own mutinous and indisposed faculties; such as know their members to be naturally obedient to their desires, need to take no other care than to counterplot their fancies. The indocile and the rude liberty of this scurvy member is sufficiently remarkable by its importunate, unruly, and unseasonable tumidity and impatience at such times as we have nothing for it to do, and by its most unseasonable stupidity and disobedience when we stand most in need of its vigour, so imperiously contesting the authority of the will, and with so much obstinacy denying all solicitations of hand and fancy.[1] And yet, though his rebellion is so universally complained of, and that proofs are not wanting to condemn him, if he had, nevertheless, asked me to plead his cause, I should, peradventure, bring the rest of his fellow-members into suspicion of complotting the mischief against him, out of pure envy of the importance and ravishing pleasure peculiar to his employment, so as to have, by confederacy, armed the whole world against him, by malevolently charging him alone with their common offence.[2]

Too great warmth of clothing round the parts of generation, or too great pressure upon them, may be reckoned as causes of impotence. The custom of wearing breeches was considered by Hippocrates[3] as a predisposing cause of the impotence so common among the ancient Scythians.[4] Hunter was also of the opinion that this article of

---

[1] The advice to the impotent to proceed slowly, without worry, and without effort, is given in some detail by Edwin W. Hirsch in *The Power to Love*, London, John Lane, 1936 (and reprints). See also Hirsch's *Modern Sex Life*, New York, Permabooks, 1949. This volume contains some interesting case histories, as well as sound and simple advice for the layman—*The Power to Love* is directed mainly to the professional reader, although it is intelligible to the educated layman.

[2] *Essays*, Book I, chap. XX. Cotton's translation. [D]

[3] Hippocrates, *de Aer*: aqua et loco, 210. [D]

[4] Mantegazza (*Igiene dell'amore*), Savarsi, and others, have held that loose garments and underclothes favour penile growth. See: Alan Hull Walton, *Love*

dress by keeping the parts too warm, affording them a constant support, and allowing the muscles but little freedom of motion, may, at least, relax them and cause them to become flaccid, if it does not totally incapacitate them for the due performance of their functions.

Equally disadvantageous, in this respect, is the practice of riding upon horseback, as the organs of generation are, of necessity, frequently compressed either against the saddle or the horse's back. Lalement, in his *Commentaries upon Hippocrates*, adduces the cases of bakers, upon whom, by their not wearing breeches, the contrary effect is produced. 'We have often heard', says he, 'that bakers and others whose parts of generation are not covered by clothing, but hang freely, have large, well-grown testicles.[1]

Another cause of impotence is the allowing of the parts of generation

Recipes Old and New, London, Torchstream Books, 1956, the long note on p. 73. See also Dr Jacobus X***, *The Ethnology of the Sixth Sense*, Paris, Carrington, 1899 (p. 93), and Rabelais, Book II, chap. 16, of which the recently published translation into modern English by J. M. Cohen is excellent: Penguin Books, Harmondsworth, Middlesex, 1955 (pp. 224–5). The impotence of the Scythians referred to above (and mentioned by Hippocrates) was much more than impotence. It is generally spoken of as 'the disease of the Scythians', and was believed due to excessive horseback riding. Virility was lost at an early age, the beard fell out, and the penis shrank. The voice became feeble, desire for women was lost, and these males soon became passive effeminate inverts, adopting feminine dress and pursuits. The modern equivalent is the Mujerados ('women-men') found in every tribe of the Pueblo Indians. See also Rosenbaum: *Geschichte der Lustseuche im Alterthume*, Halle, Verlag von H. W. Schmidt, 1882 (3rd edition. The 1st edition, Halle, Lippert, was printed in 1839.) A French translation is: *Histoire de la Syphilis dans l'Antiquité* . . . par le Dr Julius Rosenbaum . . . Bruxelles, N.-J. Gregoir, 1847. The only English translation is: *The Plague of Lust* . . . in Classical Antiquity, and including: Detailed investigations into the Cult of Venus, Brothels, The Feminine Disease of the Scythians, Paederastia, and other Sexual Perversions Amongst the Ancients, as contributions towards the exact interpretation of their writings, by Dr Julius Rosenbaum. Translated from the 6th (unabridged) German edition by an Oxford M.A., Paris, Charles Carrington, 1901. 2 vols. Edition limited to 500 copies only. The translator was actually Alfred Allinson, M.A., who produced much excellent work, including translations from Anatole France, Brantôme, etc. In quoting the title of the English edition of the above work I have slightly abbreviated the wording on the title-page. Copies are rare today, and there is a need for a reprint of the Allinson translation.

[1] *Treatise on the Venereal Disease.* [D]

to remain too long in a state of inaction.[1] Those parts of the body which are most exercised are always found to be better grown, stronger, and more fitted for the discharge of their natural functions, provided the exercise be neither too violent nor too frequent. The parts, on the contrary, which are condemned to rest and inactivity, wither, and gradually lose their tone, as well as the power of effecting the movements natural to them. Galen observes that the genital organs of the athletae, as well as those of all such whose profession or calling compelled them to remain chaste, were generally shrunken and wrinkled like those of old men, and that the contrary is the case with those who use them to excess. Says he:

All the athletae as well as those who for the sake of preserving or improving the voice, are, from their youth debarred the pleasures of love, have their natural parts shrunken and wrinkled like those of old men, while, in such as have from an early age indulged in those delights to an excess, the vessels of those parts, by the habit of being dilated, cause the blood to flow there in great abundance, and the desire of coition to be proportionately increased, all which is a natural consequence of those general laws which all our faculties obey. Thus it is that the breasts of women who have never had children remain always small, while those of females who have been mothers, and who suckle their children, acquire a considerable volume, that they continue to give milk as long as they suckle their infants, and that their milk does not fail until they cease to nourish them.[2]

So well, indeed, was this fact known to the ancients, that Aristophanes uses the expression, ωόσθην μικραν, *penem exiguum*, as an attribute of a youth who has preserved his innocence and κωλῆν μεγάλην, *penem magnum*, as the sign of a dissolute one.

It will easily be supposed that superstition, when brought to act upon weak and ignorant minds, is capable of producing temporary impotence.[3] The pretended charm or witchery common in France as late as the close of the seventeenth century, and known by the name of *nouer l'aiguillette* (point-tying), is a proof of this:

---

[1] Restated today by Hirsch (op. cit.). See also the erotic modern works of Henry Miller (Paris, Obelisk Press).

[2] *Comment. de Aer:* aqua et loco, 210. [D]

[3] i.e. True psychic impotence.

Ami lecteur, vous avez quelquefois
Oui conter qu'on *nouait l'aiguillette,*
C'est une étrange et terrible recette,
Et dont un Saint ne doit jamais user,
Que quand d'un autre il ne peut s'aviser.
D'un pauvre amant, le feu se tourne en glance;
Vif et perclus, sans rien faire, il se lasse;
Dans ses efforts étonné de languir,
Et consume sur le bord du plaisir.
Telle une fleur des feux du jour séchée,
La tête basse, et la tige penchée,
Demande en vain les humides vapeurs
Qui lui rendaient la vie et les couleurs.[1]

In olden times, prior to the invention of buttons, the femoral
habiliments of men, or hose, as they were called, were fastened up by
means of tags or points, (Gallice) *aiguillettes.* Thus, Falstaff says:
'Their points being cut, down fell their hose.' From this French word
aiguillette was derived the term *nouer les aiguillettes* (to tie up the
points), equivalent to our 'to button up the flap'[2]—to render a husband
—by enchantment—incapable of performing the conjugal rite. The
whole secret of this charm consisted in the impostor choosing for his
victim an individual whose youth, inexperience, or superstition
presented him with a fit subject for him to work upon.[3] The imagination
of the party being already predisposed for the trick, a look, a sign, a
menace—either of the voice or of the hand, accompanied by some
extraordinary gesture—was sufficient to produce the effect, and, as the
mere apprehension of an evil frequently occasions its occurrence, it
followed that, superstition having prepared the event, the latter, in his
turn, fortified the superstition; a vicious circle which may justly be
considered an opprobrium to a man's intelligence.[4]

[1] Voltaire, *La Pucelle d'Orléans,* Chant. xii. A good reprint was included in the
Maîtres de l'Amour series, Paris, Bibliothèque des Curieux: *L'Œuvre de Voltaire.*
[2] Or, as we should say, to find the zipper of his fly 'jammed at the top'.
[3] The casting of spells—and the lifting of them—are dealt with at extreme
length by Frederick Thomas Elworthy, *The Evil Eye,* London, John Murray,
1895; reprinted in facsimile by the Julian Press, New York, 1958 (additional Introduction by Louis S. Barron). In this connection, Elworthy quotes (p. 58) Petronius, and the freeing of Encolpius from this kind of enchantment (*Satyricon,* 131).
[4] In view of the work of Rhine at Duke University—not to mention many other

That such was the opinion entertained of it by sensible men when it was in vogue, will be seen by a curious passage in *Bigarrures du Seigneur des Accords*.

As to the mode of conjuration, Bodin, a writer upon these subjects, asserts that there are not less than fifty different ways of performing it:[1] of which the most efficacious one is to take a small strip or thong of leather, or silken, or worsted thread, or some cotton cord, and to make on it three knots successively—each of these, when made, being accompanied by the sign of the cross; the word *Ribald* being pronounced upon making the first knot, *Nobal* upon making the second one and *Vanarbi* upon making the third and last one; all which must be done during the celebration of the marriage ceremony. For the sake of change, one of the verses of the *Miserere mei, Deus!* may be repeated backwards, the names of the bride and groom being thrice pronounced. The first time the knot must be drawn rather tight; the second time still more so, and the third time quite close. Vulgar operators content themselves with pronouncing some cabalistic words during the marriage rite, tracing, at the same time, some mysterious figures or diagrams on the earth with the left foot, and affixing to the dress of the bride or bridegroom small slips of paper having magical characters inscribed upon them. Further details may be found in the works of Sprenger, an inquisitor, Crespet of Sens, Debris, a Jesuit, Bodin, Wier, De Lancre, and other learned demonologists.

This species of enchantment was not unknown to the ancients. According to Herodotus,[2] Amasis was prevented from enjoying his wife, Ladice, by a sorcery of this description, nor was it till after the

eminent scientists, and the undoubted miracles performed by genuine Hindu and Tibetan yogins—it may be doubted if such conditions are infallibly the result of superstition. Though it may be safe to say that in most cases they are.

[1] Bodin, one of the great authorities on witchcraft and demonology. Chiefly a French political philosopher, he was born in 1530, and lived until 1596, studying at Toulouse. In spite of his Protestantism he managed to escape the massacre of St Bartholomew. It is obvious from his *Démonomanie* that he believed in the superstitions of his age (1580), and his *Heptaplomeres* (first published in 1587) is a plea for religious tolerance.

[2] Herodotus, *The History, Euterpe*, clxxxii. [D] A good translation is published in the Penguin Classics series, edited by Dr E. V. Rieu, and Rawlinson's 2 vol. edition is available in Dent's Everyman's Library.

queen had vowed a statue to Venus, *'si secum coiret Amasis'*, that the king's wishes and her own were gratified.

Plato warns married persons against such sorceries.[1] And Virgil also speaks of impotence effected by ligature:

> Terna tibi haec primum, duplici diversa colore
> Licia circumdo.[2]

Ovid admits the power of such charms in the following lines:

> Carmine laesa, Ceres sterilem vanescit in herbam
> Deficiunt laesi carmine fontis aquae:
> Ilicibus glandes, cantataque vitibus uva
> Decedit, et nulla forma movente, flexunt.
> Quid vetat et nervos
> Et juveni et Cupido, carmine abesse viro.[3]

Of all the most detestable tyrants, it is said that Nero, finding he could not enjoy a female whom he passionately desired, complained of having been bewitched.

The fables of Apuleius are full of the enchantments of Pamphilus.[4]

Numantina, the first wife of Plautius Sylvanus, was accused of having rendered her husband impotent by means of sorcery 'injecisse carminibus et veneficiis vecordium marito'.[5]

Paulus 'Julius' of Tyr states that the law of the Twelve Tables

---

[1] Plato, *De Legibus* (The Laws), Lib. II. [D]

[2] Virgil, *Eclogue* viii. [D]

[3] Ovid, *Amores*, Lib. III, eleg. 6. [D] This is not given in the selection published in the Everyman series (London, Dent, 1939), but can be found in translation in *The Works of Marlowe* (edited) by the Rev. Alexander Dyce, London, 1850, 3 vols. Reprinted London, Routledge, Warne & Routledge, 1862, complete in 1 vol. (see pp. 342–4, where the poem appears as elegy 7—the numbers vary in the early original editions of Marlowe, but Dyce reprints them complete with many annotations and comments).

[4] One of the best modern translations of Apuleius (*The Golden Ass*) is that by Robert Graves, published by Penguin Books, Harmondsworth, 1950 (and many reprints). The editions published early in the present century by Carrington of Paris, and (the same translation as Carrington's) the Imperial Press of London, are complete and reliable enough.

[5] Tacitus, *Annals*, Lib. IV, 22. [D]. An excellent translation by Robert Graves is available in the Penguin Classics series, edited by Dr E. V. Rieu.

contained an express prohibition against the employment of ligatures: 'qui, sacra, impia nocturnave fecerint, ut quem incantarent', etc.[1]

Gregory de Tours relates[2] that Eulatius, having taken a young woman from a monastery and married her, his concubines, actuated by jealousy, put such a spell upon him that he could by no means consummate his nuptials. Paulus Aemilius, in his life of King Clovis, says that Theodoric sent back his wife, Herméberge, to her father, the King of Spain, as he had received her, a pure virgin, the force of witchcraft having incapacitated him from taking her maidenhead; which sorcery Aimonius Monachaus[3] asserts to have been effected by Queen Brunchante.

The practice of point-tying was formerly so general that princes and princesses made it one of their most amusing pastimes. Louis Sforza having seen the young Princess Isabella, daughter of Alphonso, King of Arragon, and who was betrothed to Galeas, Duke of Milan, was so enamoured of her beauty that he point-tied Galeas. Marie de Padille, concubine of Don Pedro King of Castille and Leon, point-tied him so effectually that he could not give the least marks of his fondness to his consort, Queen Blanche.

That the Church acknowledged the power of these 'point-tiers' is proved by the fact of their having been publicly anathematized by the provincial Councils of Milan and Tours, the Synods of Mont-Cassin and Ferriare, and by the clergy of France assembled at Melun in 1579. A great number of rituals specify the means to be employed as counter-charms to the sorceries of the point-tiers; and the Cardinal du Perron,[4] a very able and experienced prelate, has inserted in the ritual of Evreux very sage directions for this purpose. Similar precautions may be found in the synodal statutes of Lyons, Tours, Sens, Narbonne, Bourges, Troyes, Orléans, and many other celebrated churches. St Augustine, St Thomas and Peter Lombard positively recognize the power of point-tying and of disturbing, in this manner, married

---

[1] Lib. V, *Sentent*, tit. 23. [D]

[2] Gregory de Tours, *De Rebus Gestis Francorum*, Lib. IV, Cap. 94. [D]

[3] *Histoire des Français.* [D].—Davenport gives very few bibliographical details, always ignoring editions, and dates and places of publication.

[4] Nominated to the Bishopric of Evreux by Henri IV of France—that same Henri who married Marguerite de Navarre. Thus it is not surprising that the favourite authors of this Cardinal were Rabelais and Montaigne.

persons in the enjoyment of their dearest privilege. *'Certum est'*, says St Augustine, *'corporis vires incantationibus vinciri.'*

Our James I, who prided himself so much upon his skill in demonology, declares positively that witches and sorcerers possess the power of point-tying: 'Or else by staying married folkes, to have naturally adoe with each other, by *knitting knottes upon a point at the time of their marriage.'*[1]

The old Parliaments of France have generally admitted the power of these sorcerers. In 1582 the Parliament of Paris condemned one Abel de la Rue to be hanged and afterwards burnt for having wickedly and wilfully point-tied Jean Moreau de Coutommiers. A singular sentence was pronounced in 1597 against M. Chamouillard for having so bewitched a young lady about to be married that her husband could not consummate the marriage. But the most singular instance of the kind upon record is that of R. F. Vidal de la Porte, who was condemned by the Judges of Riom to make the *amende honorable*, and afterwards to be hanged, and his lady to be burnt until reduced to ashes, for having by sorceries and wicked and sacrilegious words point-tied, not only the young men of his town, but also all the dogs, cats, and other domestic animals, so that the propagation of these species so useful to man was upon the point of being stopped. In 1718 the Parliament of Bordeaux ordered a famous point-tier to be burnt. This pretended sorcerer had been accused and convicted of having point-tied a nobleman of high family, his wife, and all the men and women servants in his establishment.

It must not be supposed that no counter-charms or amulets existed. The curate Thiers, who has written at large upon this subject, enumerates twenty-two different ones, the most potent of which were the following:

1. To put salt in the pocket before proceeding to church; pennies marked with the cross and put into the shoes of the bride and bridegroom were equally efficacious.

2. To pass three times under the crucifix without bowing to it.

3. For the bridegroom to wear upon the wedding day, two shirts, one turned inside-out upon the other, and to hold, in the left hand, during the nuptial benediction, a small wooden cross.

[1] *Demonologie*, 1603, Book I, Chap. III, p. 12. [D]

4. To lay the new married couple naked upon the ground; to cause the bridegroom to kiss the great toe of the bride's left foot, and the bride the great toe of the bridegroom's right foot: after which they must make the sign of the cross with the left hand and repeat the same with the right or left hand.

5. To take the bridegroom's point-hose and pass it through the wedding ring: knot the said point, holding the fingers in the ring, and afterwards to cut the knot, saying: 'God loosens what the Devil fastens.'

6. When the newly married couple are about to retire for the night, to fasten upon the thigh of each a little slip of paper inscribed with the words: *Domine, quis similis tibi?*

7. To broach a cask of white wine from which none has yet been drawn, and pour the first of the liquor which flows, through the wedding ring.

8. To rub with wolf's grease the door posts through which the married couples pass on their way to the nuptial bed.

9. To write upon virgin parchment, before sunrise, and for nine days successively, the word *Arigaʒartor*.

10. To pronounce the word *Temon* three times successively at sunrise, provided the day promises to be fine.

But the mode of procedure in which the learned curate Thiers appears to place the greatest confidence is that employed by a priest of his acquaintance. This person's plan was to tie the bride and groom to a pillar and administer to them with his own hand the stimulus with which the pedagogue awakens the genius of idle and sluggish pupils; after this flagellation they are unbound and left together, amply provided with such restoratives and stimulants as are proper to maintain the condition so favourable to Venus in which he had placed them. The result seems to have been in the highest degree satisfactory.

Bodin informs us that he knew at Bordeaux a woman of middle age, but still lively and fresh, who professed to cure radically all enchantments of this description. Nothing could be more natural than her *modus operandi*. She got into bed with her patients, and once there, by the resources of her amatory powers, succeeded so well in arousing their flagged and sluggish desires, that their domestic peace was never afterwards disturbed by the reproaches of their disappointed spouses.

Upon her mother's death the daughter embraced the same interesting profession, and in addition to acquiring considerable reputation by her successful practice, realized a handsome fortune.

Ridiculous and contemptible as this quackery now appears, so great at one time was its power, that persons every way qualified for the generative act, have suddenly been reduced to a humiliating nullity, in consequence of an impudent charlatan, a village sorcerer, or a fortune-teller having threatened them with point-tying. St André, a French physician, gives an account of a poor weaver, who, having disappointed Madame André in not bringing home some work was threatened by that lady with being point-tied by her husband the doctor. The poor fellow was so alarmed that the charm had the same effect as a reality, nor was it until the work he had in hand was finished, and the lady had consented to restore him to his natural state, that he could resume the exercises of his conjugal duties.

Venette gives the case of one Pierre Buriel, and, to use Venette's own words:

This man was about thirty-five years of age, a cooper and brandy manu-facturer by trade. Being at work one day for my father in one of his country houses, he offended me by some impertinent observations, to punish which I told him the next day that I would point-tie him when he married. It so happened that he had the intention of uniting himself with a servant girl who lived in the neighbourhood, and although I had threatened him merely in a jesting manner, it made so strong an impression upon him that al-though, when married, he felt the most ardent desire to enjoy his connubial rights, he found himself totally incapacitated for the work of love. Some-times, when he flattered himself with being on the point of accomplishing his wishes, the idea of the witchcraft obtruded itself, and rendered him for the time being completely impotent. This incapacity alienated the affections of his wife, and produced on her part towards him the most repulsive coldness. I need not say what pain I felt on witnessing these effects, how greatly I regretted having, I may truly say, unintentionally caused so un-pleasant a state of things, and I did and said everything in my power to disabuse the man, and prove to him the folly of his impressions. But the more I did so, the more he testified his abhorrence of me, and his conviction that I had really bewitched him. At length the curate of Notre Dame, who had married them, interfered, and after some time succeeded, though with considerable difficulty, in freeing him from his imaginary bonds. They lived together for twenty-eight years, and several children, now citizens of Rochelle, were the issue of their union.[1]

Montaigne gives us a curious story upon this subject, which he introduces thus:

I am not satisfied and make a very great question whether those pleasant ligatures with which the age of ours is so fettered—and there is almost no other talk—are not mere voluntary impressions of apprehension and fear; for I know by experience, in the case of a particular friend of mine, one for whom I can be as responsible as for myself, and a man that cannot possibly fall under any suspicion of insufficiency, and as little of being enchanted, who having heard a companion of his make a relation of an unusual frigidity that surprised him at a very unseasonable time, being afterwards himself engaged upon the same account, the horror of the former story so strangely possessed his imagination that he ran the same fortune the other had done; he from that time forward (the scurvy remembrance of his disaster running in his mind and tyrannizing over him) was extremely subject to relapse into the same misfortune. He found some remedy, however, for this inconvenience by himself frankly confessing and declaring beforehand to the party with whom he was to have to do, the subjection he lay under, and the infirmity he was subject to; by which means the contention of his soul was, in some sort, appeased; and knowing that now some such misbehaviour was expected from him, the restraint upon those faculties grew less, and he less suffered by it, and afterwards, at such times as he could be in no such apprehension as not being about any such act (his thoughts being disengaged and free, and his body being in its true and natural state) by causing those parts to be handled and communicated to the knowledge of others, he was at last totally freed from that vexatious infirmity. After man has once done a woman right, he is never after in danger of misbehaving himself with that person, unless upon the account of a manifest and inexcusable weakness. Neither is this disaster to be feared but in adventures where the soul is over-extended with desire or respect, and especially where we meet with an unexpected opportunity that requires a sudden and quick despatch; and in these cases there is no possible means for a man always to defend himself from such a surprise as shall put him damnably out of countenance. And yet I have known some who have secured themselves for this misfortune by coming half-sated elsewhere, purposely to abate the ardour of their fury, and others who being grown old, find themselves less impotent

---

[1] Nicolas Venette, *Tableau de l' Amour.* The book is a serious early medical work, and of interest to psychologists, as well as to historians of medicine.

by being less able; and particularly one who found an advantage by being assured by a friend of his that had a countercharm against certain enchantments that would defend him from this disgrace. The story itself is not much amiss, and therefore you shall have it.—A count of a very great family, and with whom I had the honour to be familiarly intimate, being married to a very fair lady, who had formerly been pretended to and importunately courted by one who was invited to and present at the wedding. All his friends were in very great fear, but especially an old lady, his kinswoman, who had the ordering of the solemnity, and in whose house it was kept, suspecting his rival would, in revenge, offer foul play, and procure some of these kinds of sorceries, to put a trick upon him, which fear she also communicated to me, who, to comfort her, bade her not trouble herself, but rely upon my care to prevent or frustrate any such design. Now, I had, by chance, about me, a certain flat piece of gold, whereon were graven some celestial figures good to prevent frenzy occasioned by the heat of the sun, or for any pains of the head, being applied to the suture; where, that it might the better remain firm, it was sewed to a ribbon, to be tied under the chin. A foppery cousin-german to this of which I am speaking was Jacques Pelletier who lived in the house, presented to me for a singular rarity and a thing of sovereign virtue. I had a fancy to make use of this quack, and therefore privately told the count that he might probably run the same fortune other bridegrooms had sometimes done, especially some persons being in the house who, no doubt, would be glad to do him such a courtesy; but let him boldly go to rest, for I would do him the office of a friend, and if need were, would not spare a miracle that it was in my power to do, provided he could engage to me upon his honour, to keep it to himself, and only when they came to bring him his candle (a custom in France being to bring the bridegroom a candle in the middle of the night, on his wedding night) if matters had not gone well with him, to give such a sign, and leave the rest to me. Now, he had his ears so battered and his mind so prepossessed with the eternal tattle of this business, that when he came to it, he did really find himself tired with the trouble of his imagination, and accordingly, at the time appointed, he gave me the sign. Whereupon I whispered him in the ear, that he should rise under the pretence of putting us out of the room, and after a jesting manner, pull my nightgown from my shoulders, throw it over his own, and keep it there till he had performed what I appointed him to do, which was that when we were all gone out of the chamber, he should withdraw to make water, should three times repeat such and such words and as often do such and such actions; that every of the three times he should tie the ribbon I put into his hand about his middle, and be sure to place the medal that was fastened to it (the figures in such a posture) exactly upon his reins; which being done, and having the last of the three times so well girt and fastened the ribbon that it could neither untie nor slip from its place, let him confidently return to his business, and withal not to forget to spread my gown upon the bed so that it might be sure to cover them both. These ridiculous circumstances are the main of the effect, our fancy being so far seduced as to believe that so strange and uncouth formalities must of necessity proceed from some abstruse science. Their inanity gives them reverence and weight. However, certain it is that my figures proved themselves more *Veneran* than *Solar*, and the fair bride had no reason to complain.

Upon a due consideration of this singular superstition, it must be obvious to any person of sense that these pretended ligatures are, in fact, the consequence of an enfeebled constitution, weak intellects, and sometimes of an ardent imagination, an over-excited desire which carries the vitality to the head, and diverts it from its principal direction. Do away with these circumstances and imagine a man in full health, and gifted with a young and vigorous constitution, alike incapable of allowing himself to be acted upon by vain terrors, and of permitting his passions an uncontrollable course; and all the charms and incantation of these redoubted point-tyers would immediately cease. Who, for instance, could pretend to point-tie that hero of ancient Greece so famous for his twelve labours, of which by far the most brilliant was the transforming, in the course of one night, fifty young virgins into as many women![1]

The most singular circumstance, however, connected with impotence is, that for a long time there existed exclusively in France a particular kind of proof called—The Judicial Congress. In the old jurisprudence of that country but little value was attached to moral proof; all was made to depend on material ones, which were made by witnesses. The whole enquiry after truth was made to depend upon the establishment of the fact, and, too frequently, the administrators of the law were not over-scrupulous as to the nature of the testimony by which it was to be proved. Provided there was such testimony, no matter of whatever kind, no matter how contradictory to common sense, justice pronounced itself satisfied, for, relying upon this

---

[1] 'Hercules, puer, L Virgines, una nocte gravidus redit.' Coelius, Lib. XIV, Cap. 8. [D]

testimony, it was enabled to pronounce its decision, and this was all it required. Hence all those personal examinations of litigants, so often practised formerly, and hence the judge, whatever might be the nature of their complaint, ordered a report to be made by parties chosen to that effect, and who were called *experts* or *examiners*. This mode of procedure was employed in cases in which a woman applied for a divorce from her husband on the ground of impotence; hence arose the *Congrès*, in which the justice of the application was to be proved in the presence of examiners appointed to give to the court a report upon the case. Says a writer of the seventeenth century:

Ce qui est encore plus honteux, c'est que dans quelques procès, les hommes n'ont pas visité la femme, et au contraire, les femmes ont été admises à visiter l'homme, ce qui a été cause d'une grande irritation et moquerie, que de telles procédures, ont servi de contes joyeux et plaisants discours en beaucoup d'endroits.[1]

The whole was a most disgusting procedure, which, although greatly abused, was for a long time encouraged as offering a legal mode of dissolving a marriage which was incompatible with the happiness of both parties, but which the law declared to be indissoluble. The judges who introduced or maintained the Congress, who, in fact, protected it, only contemplated it, but certainly most erroneously, as a proper means of legalizing divorces.

All historians, and other writers, who have treated of this disgraceful institution, pretty generally agree in giving it an origin not further back than the commencement of the sixteenth century; it is, however, but the extension of a custom almost as obscene, which prevailed in the first ages of Christianity. This was nothing less than the subjecting of a young girl, whether nun or otherwise, accused of fornication, to a rigorous personal examination, whence was to result the proof of her innocence or guilt. Siagrius, Bishop of Verona, who lived towards the close of the fourth century, condemned a nun to undergo this disgusting and insulting examination. St Ambroise, his metropolitan, disapproved of the bishop's sentence, declared the examination as indecent, thus attesting its existence. The opinion, however, of this prelate,

---

[1] *Traité premier de la dissolution de Mariage pour l'impuissance et froideur de l'homme, ou de la femme,* par Antoine Hotman, p. 63. [D]

supported as it was by that of several others, did not prevent the continuance of this custom for a very long time. The ecclesiastical and civil tribunals frequently directed this proof to be made; and Venette[1] cites the procès-verbal of a similar examination made by order of the Mayor of Paris in 1672, in the case of a woman who complained of violence committed on her by a man of dissolute habits.

The first judicial sentence which ordered a Congress is said to have been caused by the shameless effrontery of a young man who, being accused of impotence, demanded permission to exhibit proof of his powers before witnesses, which demand being complied with, the practice was introduced into the jurisprudence of the country. But, as we have already shown, the custom of the Judicial Congress may be referred to a far earlier period, in fact to the remotest times of the middle ages, and that it originated with the Church, when the public morals were far from being well ascertained, as is proved by many well-known privileges belonging to the Seigneur or Lord of the Manor. Pope Gregory the Great, who was raised to the Pontificate in 590, appears to have been the first who conferred upon bishops the right of deciding this description of questions. It was, doubtless, from considerations of tender regard for female modesty that the Church took upon itself the painful duty of investigating and deciding upon questions of this nature. Numerous instances prove this, especially the dissolution of the marriage of Alphonso VI of Portugal and his Consort, pronounced in 1688, and mentioned by Bayle.[2] The great antiquity of this custom is proved by the 17th Art. of the Capitulars of Pepin, in the year 752, which bears a direct allusion to it: inasmuch as that article established as a principle that the impotence of a husband should be considered as lawful cause for divorce, and that the proof of

---

[1] *Tableau de l'Amour considéré dans l'état du Mariage*, Part II, Chap. II, art. 3. Originally published at Amsterdam, 1687, there have been many reprints in one or more volumes. An English translation was published at Paris, 1898, by Charles Carrington, in an edition limited to 250 copies, under the title of: *The Mysteries of Conjugal Love Reveal'd, or The Pleasures of the Marriage Bed.*

[2] Art.: Portugal. [D].—Davenport is obviously referring to Bayle's *Dictionnaire historique*. This learned work, with its free and critical spirit, anticipated to some extent the later work of Voltaire, Diderot, and the Encyclopaedists. Bayle was born in 1647, and died in 1706.

such impotence should be given, and the fact verified at the foot of the Cross—*exeant ad crucem, et si verum fuerit, separantur.*

That the Congress originated with the Church, who considered it as an efficacious means for deciding questions of impotence, is still further proved by President Boutrier and by other writers, who assert that the ecclesiastical judges of other times were alone empowered (to the exclusion of all secular ones) to take cognizance of cases of impotence.

It is well attested that during the sixteenth and seventeenth centuries all the courts of law in France held the opinion that a marriage be annulled on the demand of a wife who claimed the Congress.

The fatal blow to this disgusting custom was given by decree of the Parliament of Paris, under the presidency of the celebrated Lamoignon, dated February 18th, 1677, which decree forbids the practice by any other court whatsoever, ecclesiastical or civil. It is supposed that the ridicule cast upon it by the following lines of Boileau had no small share in causing its suppression:

> Jamais la biche en rut, n'a pour fait d'impuissance
> Trainé du fond des bois, un cerf à l'audience;
> Et jamais juge, entre eux ordonnant le congrès,
> De ce burlesque mot n'a sali ses arrêts.

Three causes were alleged for the abolition of the Congress—its obscenity, its inutility, and its inconveniences. Its obscenity; for what could be more infamous, more contrary to public decency and to the reverence due to an oath than the impurity of the proof, both in its preparation and execution? Its inutility; for what could be less certain and more defective? Can it be, for one moment, imagined that a conjunction ordered by judges between two persons embittered by a lawsuit, agitated with hate and fury against each other, can operate in them? Experience has shown that, of ten men the most vigorous and powerful, hardly one was found that came out of this shameful combat with success; it is equally certain that he who had unjustly suffered dissolution of his marriage, for not having given a proof of his capacity in the infamous Congress, had given real and authentic evidences of it in his subsequent marriage. This degrading mode of proof, in short, far from discovering the truth, was but the cause and foundation for impotence and falsehood. Its inconveniences; these are—the declared nullity of legitimate marriage, the dishonour cast upon the husband, and the unjust damages, oftentimes exorbitant, which he is condemned to pay—two marriages contracted upon the dissolution of the first—both of which, according to purity and strictness, are equally unlawful—the error or the malice discovered, *ex post facto*, and, nevertheless, by the authority of the law, become irreparable.

It was in the power of the magistrate, upon a complaint of impotence being alleged by a wife against her husband, to order examiners to make an inspection of the husband's parts of generation, and upon their report to decide whether there was just cause for a divorce; and this without proceeding to order the Congress. The following are a few cases of this description, and are extracted from the reports and judgements of the Officiality at Paris, in cases of impotence.

Case I. Jean de But, master fringe-maker, was, in 1675, charged with impotence by Genevieve Helena Marcault, his wife; he being inspected by Renaulot, a physician, and Le Bel, a surgeon, by order of the official; they declared that, after a due and thorough examination of all the members and parts of the said de But, as well genital as others which might throw a light upon the case and likewise his condition of body, his age, the just conformation and proportion of his limbs, but especially his penis, which was found to be of as proper a thickness, length, and colour as could be wished;[1] and likewise his testicles, which exhibited no perceptible viciousness or malformation, they are of opinion that from all these outward marks, which are the only ones they consider themselves justified in judging from, the said de But is capacitated to perform the matrimonial act. Signed by them at Paris, July 18th, 1675, and attested by the Sieur de Combes. And on August 23rd, 1675, by the sentence of M. Benjamin, official, the said Marcault was non-suited and ordered to return to her husband and cohabit with him.[2]

[1] Feelings of inferiority still abound today with regard to the length of the penis, etc. Anything within the range of five and a half inches to seven inches may be considered normal in length—the average being just over six inches. In thickness one and a half inches is about the average, some being a fraction more, and some a fraction less.

[2] If de But was impotent with his wife, then it must have been what today we would term a case of psychic impotence—but, of course, his wife may have been lying from sheer malice in an attempt to obtain a divorce. Or he may have been impotent *only with her*, for one reason or another.

Case II. Inspection having been ordered by the official of Paris, of the body of Joseph Le Page, who is taxed with impotence by Nicola de Loris, his wife, the said inspection was made by Deuxivoi and de Farci, physicians, and Paris and du Fertre, surgeons; and their report is as follows:

'We have found the exterior of this person to be like that of other men, the penis of a good conformation and naturally situated, with the nut or glans bare, its adjoining parts fringed with soft, fine hair, the scrotum of an unexceptional thickness and extent, and in it vessels of good conformation and size, but terminating unequally; on the right side they end in a small flabby substance instead of a true testicle; and on the left side we observed the testicle fixed to the extremity of one of the vessels, as usual, invested in its tunicle, which left testicle we do not find to be at all flabby, but of a middling size; upon the whole, we are of opinion that the said le Page is capable of the conjugal act, but in a feeble manner.' Signed and dated March 5th, 1684. By the sentence of M. Cheron, the official, the said de Loris's petition is rejected and she is enjoined to return to her husband.

Case III. Peter Damour being accused of impotence by his wife, Louisa Tillot, an inspection was ordered to be made by Rainset and Afforti, physicians, and Franchet and Colignon, surgeons. They report as follows: —'We have proceeded to inspect Peter Damour, master saddler at Paris, and having attentively examined his parts of generation, we have found them well constituted and in good condition as to their size, conformation, and situation for the conjugal act; according, however, to the statement of the said Damour himself, the erection is imperfect, the penis not being sufficiently rigid for perforating the vagina; admitting this, however, to be the case, we are of opinion that the imperfection may be remedied, repaired, and rectified, in time, by proper remedies.' Signed, January 16th, 1703. In consequence the official, M. Vivant, refused Tillot's demand, and ordered her to go home to her husband, and cohabit with him as her lawful spouse.

Case IV. In the suit of Demoiselle Marie Louise Buchères accusing of impotence Antoine de Bret, an inspection was ordered and performed by Venage and Lita, physicians, Lombard and Delon, surgeons. They reported as follows:—'We find the string of the foreskin shorter than it should be for giving the nut free scope to extend itself when turgid—that the body of the left testicle is very diminutive and decayed, its tunicle separated, the spermatic vessels very much disordered by crooked swollen veins—that the right testicle is not of a due thickness, though thicker than the other: that it is somewhat withered and the spermatic vessels disordered by crooked, swollen veins. On all which accounts we do not think that the natural parts of the said Sieur de Bret have all the disposition requisite for the well performing the functions they were designed for; yet we cannot

MAKING A LOVE-CHARM

Girl dropping sparks on a wax heart, symbol of the man whose
affections she is trying to arouse

From an old engraving

Pl. 2

AFTER THE MASKED BALL

From a nineteenth-century lithograph

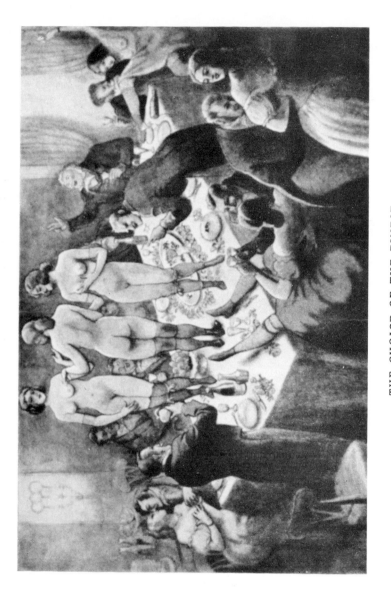

THE CHOICE OF THE FINEST
From a nineteenth-century drawing

AN OLD
PERUVIAN
PHALLIC
POT
*Gaffron
collection*

CHASTITY
BELT
Sixteenth century
*Wellcome
Historical
Medical
Museum*

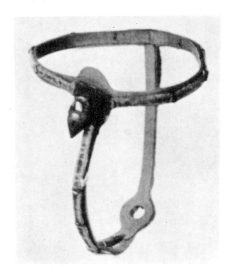

THE BEATING
OF LOUIS

*From a French
Anti-monarchist
caricature*

JOHN
GRAHAM'S
CELESTIAL
BED

THE RIGHT OF THE FIRST NIGHT
From the painting by Jules Garnier

Pl. 7

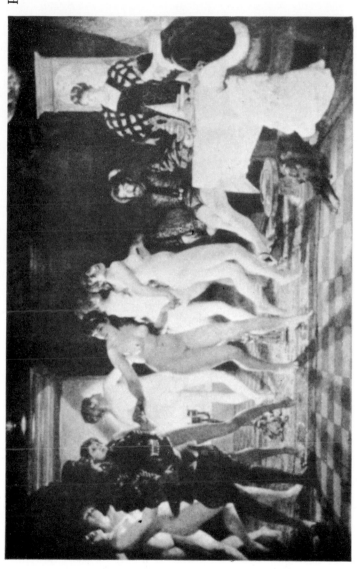

BORGIA AMUSES HIMSELF
From the painting by Jules Garnier

YOUNG GIRL CONFIDING HER
FIRST SECRET TO VENUS
From the sculpture by François Jouffroy in the Louvre

say that he is impotent until we have inspected the wife. Paris, July 11th, 1703, Signed. On the 22nd of July, 1703, the wife was inspected by the said physicians and surgeons, and by two matrons; the result of which was that they observed no viciousness of conformation in her womb; the vulva was circular and the carunclae myrtiformes, placed in the neck of the vagina, were soft, supple, flexible, entire, and did not seem to have suffered any violence or displacing, and the cavity of the womb-pipe was free and without any obstacle. Therefore they are of opinion that she is not incapable of the conjugal act, and that there has been no intromission, consequently that she is a virgin, and that if the marriage had not been consummated, it is her husband's fault, because of his great debility, and defective conformation of his parts of generation.' Another inspection of the same parties was ordered Aug. 1st, 1703, Bourges and Thuillier being the physicians, and Tranchet and Neri, the surgeons, who declared that after due and careful examination they found no defect which could hinder generation. Their report is dated Paris, Aug. 13th, 1703. M. Chapelier ordered, in consequence, both parties, —viz., the Sieur de Bret, and the said Buchères, to acknowledge each other for man and wife.

Case V. On the 2nd April, 1653, the Chevalier René de Cordovan, Marquis de Langey, aged 25 years, married Maria de Saint Simon de Courtomer, between 13 and 14 years of age. The parties lived very happily for the first four years, that is to say, up to 1657, when the lady accused her husband of impotence. The complaint was heard before the *Lieutenant Civil* of the *Châtelet*, who appointed a jury to examine the parties. The examination was made, and the report declared that both parties were duly and fully qualified for performing the conjugal act. In order to invalidate this report the lady affirmed that if she was not a virgin it was the consequence of the brutal efforts of one whose impotence rendered him callous as to the means he employed to satisfy himself. The Chevalier de Langey, much incensed at this imputation, demanded the *Congress*; the judge granted the petition, the wife appealed from the sentence, but it was confirmed by the superior court.

For carrying this sentence into effect, the house of a person named Turpin, who kept baths, was chosen. Four physicians, five surgeons, and five matrons were present. It is impossible to enter into the details of this disgusting prequisition; they are given in full detail in the *procès verbal*. Suffice it to say that the event being unfavourable to the Chevalier, his marriage was declared void by a decree of the 8th of February, 1659.

By this decree the Chevalier was not only condemned to pay back the dowry which he had had with his wife, but was prohibited from contracting another marriage—the lady, on the contrary, was allowed to enter into any other engagement she might think fit, as being considered entirely freed from her former bonds.

The next day after this decree the Chevalier made his protest against it before two notaries, declaring that he did not acknowledge himself to be impotent, and that he would, in defiance of the prohibition imposed upon him, enter into wedlock again whenever he pleased.

The lady Saint Simon contracted a marriage with Peter de Caumont, Marquis de Boèsle, and from this marriage were born three daughters. At the same time the Chevalier de Langey married Diana de Montault de Navaille, and their marriage was followed by the birth of seven children. In 1670 the Marchioness de Boèsle, the ci-devant Countess de Langey, died.

It was in consequence of the ulterior proceedings in the law courts respecting the real paternity of the children of the Marchioness that the government availed itself of the opportunity of abolishing, as we have seen, the useless and obscene ordeal of the Congress.

We shall conclude the present Essay by transcribing Dr Willick's judicious observations upon sexual intercourse:

> *Of the* SEXUAL INTERCOURSE *in particular; its physical consequences with respect to the Constitution of the Individual; under what circumstances it may be either conducive or detrimental to Health.*

A subject of such extensive importance, both to our physical and moral welfare, as the consequences resulting from either a too limited or extravagant intercourse between the sexes deserves the strictest enquiry, and the most serious attention of the philosopher. The inclination to this intercourse, and the evacuation connected with it, are no less inherent in human nature than other bodily functions. Yet, as the semen is the most subtle and spirituous part of the human frame, and as it contributes to the support of the nerves, this evacuation is by no means absolutely necessary; and it is besides attended with circumstances not common to any other. The emission of semen enfeebles the body more than the loss of twenty times the same quantity of blood; more than violent cathartics, emetics, &c.; hence excesses of this nature produce a debilitating effect on the whole of the nervous system, on body and mind.[1]

It is founded on the observations of the ablest physiologists, that the greatest part of this refined fluid is re-absorbed and mixed with the blood,

---

[1] These remarks are contrary to the opinion of contemporary medical science, and such remarks as that regarding the supposed weakening effects of ejaculation are superstitious, to say the least.

of which it constitutes the most rarefied and volatile part; and that it imparts to the body singular sprightliness, vivacity, and vigour. These beneficial effects cannot be expected if the semen be wantonly and improvidently wasted. Besides, the emission of it is accompanied with a peculiar species of tension and convulsion of the whole frame, which is always succeeded by relaxation. For the same reason, even libidinous thoughts, without any loss of semen, are debilitating, though in a less degree, by occasioning a propulsion of blood to the genitals.[1]

If this evacuation, however, took place only in a state of superfluity, and within proper bounds, it is not detrimental to health. Nature, indeed, spontaneously effects it in the most healthy individuals during sleep; and as long as we observe no difference in bodily and mental energy after such losses, there is no danger to be apprehended from them. It is well established and attested by the experience of eminent physicians, that certain indispositions, especially those of hypochondriasis and complete melancholy, and incurable by any other means, have been happily removed in persons of both sexes, by exchanging a single state for wedlock.[2]

There are a variety of circumstances by which the physical propriety of sexual intercourse is in general to be determined. It is conducive to the well-being of the individual, if the laws of nature and society (not an extravagant or disordered imagination) induce man to satisfy this inclination, especially under the following conditions:

1. In young persons, that is, adults, or those of middle age; as from the flexibility of their vessels, the strength of their muscles, and the abundance of their vital spirits, they can more easily sustain the loss thence occasioned.

2. In robust persons, who lose no more than is speedily replaced.

3. In sprightly individuals, and such as are particularly addicted to pleasure; for the stronger the natural and legal desire, the less hurtful is its gratification.

4. In married persons who are accustomed to it; for nature pursues a different path, according as she is habituated to the reabsorption or the evacuation of this fluid.

[1] As has been suggested, it is doubtful if the re-absorption of semen has any beneficial effect on the body in health. On the other hand, the Yogins and Guras of northern India and Tibet believe that chastity in the male Guru (or teacher of yoga) is essential (i.e. retention of semen), as, for reasons too detailed for mention here, such retention better enables the teacher telepathically to impart knowledge to his pupil. The subject is involved.

[2] These remarks are, of course, eminently sensible, and in line with modern opinion.

5. With a beloved object; as the power animating the nerves and muscular fibres is in proportion to the pleasure received.

6. After a sound sleep, because then the body is more energetic; it is provided with a new stock of vital spirit, and the fluids are duly prepared; —hence the early morning appears to be designed by nature for the exercise of this function; as the body is then most vigorous, and being unemployed in any other pursuit, its natural propensity to this is the greater; besides, at this time, a few hours' sleep will, in a considerable degree restore the expended powers.

7. With an empty stomach; for the office of digestion, so material to the attainment of bodily vigour, is then uninterrupted.[1] Lastly,

8. In the vernal months; as nature at this season in particular, incites all the lower animals to sexual intercourse, as we are then most energetic and sprightly; and as the spring is not only the safest, but likewise the most proper time to the consequences resulting from that intercourse. It is well ascertained by experience that children begotten in spring are of more solid fibres, and consequently more vigorous and robust, than those generated in the heat of summer or cold of winter.

It may be collected from the following circumstances, whether or not the gratification of sexual intercourse has been conducive to the well-being of the body; namely, if it be not succeeded by a peculiar lassitude; if the body does not feel heavy, and the mind averse to reflection, these are favourable symptoms, indicating that the various powers have sustained no essential loss, and that superfluous matter only has been evacuated.

Further, the healthy appearance of the urine in this case, as well as cheerfulness and vivacity of mind, also prove a proper action of the fluids, and sufficiently evince an unimpaired state of the animal functions, a due perspiration, and a free circulation of the blood.

There are times, however, in which the gratification is the more pernicious to health, when it has been immoderate, and without the impulse of nature, but particularly in the following situations.

1. In all debilitated persons; as they do not possess sufficient vital spirits, and their strength after this venerating emission is consequently much exhausted. Their digestion necessarily suffers, perspiration is checked, and the body becomes languid and heavy.

2. In the aged; whose vital heat is diminished, whose frame is enfeebled by the most moderate enjoyment, and whose vigour, already reduced,

---

[1] Classic Oriental love-manuals make the statement that coitus is healthier before eating.

suffers a still greater diminution from every loss that is accompanied with a violent convulsion of the whole body.[1]

3. In persons not arrived at the age of maturity; by an easy intercourse with the other sex, they become enervated and emaciated, and inevitably shorten their lives.

4. In dry, choleric and thin persons; these, even at a mature age, should seldom indulge in this passion, as their bodies are already in want of moisture and pliability, both of which are much diminished by sexual intercourse, while the bile is violently agitated, to the great injury of the whole animal frame. Lean persons generally are of a hot temperament,[2] and the more heat there is in the body the greater will be the subsequent dryness. Hence, likewise, to persons in a state of intoxication, this intercourse is extremely pernicious; because in such a state the increased circulation of the blood towards the head may be attended with dangerous consequences, such as bursting of blood-vessels, apoplexy, etc. The plethoric are particularly exposed to these dangers.

5. Immediately after meals; as the powers requisite to the digestion of food are thus diverted, consequently the aliment remains too long unassimilated, and becomes burdensome to the stomach.

6. After violent exercise; in which case it is still more hurtful than in the preceding, where muscular strength was not consumed, but only required to the aid of another function. After bodily fatigue, on the contrary, the necessary energy is in a manner exhausted, so that every additional exertion of the body must be peculiarly injurious.

7. In the heat of summer it is less to be indulged in than in spring and autumn; because the process on concoction and assimilation is effected less

---

[1] Wilhelm Stekel would by no means agree with this except in special cases. In his *Impotence in the Male*, Liveright, New York, 1939 (2 vols.), Vol. 1, p. 46, he says: 'A man only becomes old when he feels old. And only he becomes impotent who gives up his potency.... In men, the capacity for erection begins on the day of birth and extinguishes with death.' He points out that in many cases sexual activity practised sensibly throughout life (according to natural, and not artificially induced, demands) may well increase health and longevity. On p. 49 of the volume indicated above, he says: 'The acme of masculine potency does not depend on age, but on the sexual object placed at its disposal.' Likewise, one might add, the intensity of orgasm achieved depends on mood and the sexual object placed at one's disposal.

[2] See W. H. Sheldon, *The Varieties of Human Physique*, PH.D., M.D., Harper & Brothers, New York, and London, 1940. Also, *The Varieties of Human Temperament*, by the same author, Harper & Brothers, 1942. Sheldon has pointed out how the slender male is often much more erotic and sexually satisfying than the heavier male, and is often much in demand by women.

vigorously in summer than in the other seasons, and consequently the losses sustained are not so easily recovered. For a similar reason sexual commerce is more debilitating, and the capacity for it sooner extinguished in hot than in temperate climates. The same remark is applicable to very warm temperatures combined with moisture, which is extremely apt to debilitate the solid parts. Hence hatters, dyers, bakers, brewers, and all those exposed to steam, generally have relaxed fibres.

It is an unfavourable symptom if the rest after this intercourse be uneasy, which plainly indicates that more has been lost than could be repaired by sleep; but if, at the same time, it be productive of relaxation, so as to affect the insensible perspiration, it is a still stronger proof that it has been detrimental to the constitution.[1]

[1] Willick's *Lectures on Diet and Regimen*, p. 538 et seq. [D]

See also Alan Hull Walton, *Love Recipes Old and New*, London, Torchstream Books, 1956—published in America under the title: *Aphrodisiacs: from Legend to Prescription.*

PART TWO

*

ESSAY 4

On Virginity and Chastity

NUMEROUS authors[1] attest the high value which the Eastern nations, in general, attached to virginity; but by no people was it held in greater esteem than by the Jews, as may be inferred from the laws enacted by Moses respecting it, and which will be found in Deuteronomy as follows:[2]

If any man take a wife, and go in unto her, and hate her, and give occasion of speech against her, and bring up an evil upon her, and say, 'I took this woman, and when I came to her, I found her not a maid':

Then shall the father of the damsel and her mother take and bring forth the tokens of the girl's virginity unto the elders of the city in the gate:

And the damsel's father shall say unto the elders. 'I gave my daughter unto this man for wife and he hateth her: and, lo! he hath given occasion of speech against her, saying, I found not thy daughter a maid, and yet these are the *tokens* of my daughter's virginity'—and they shall spread the cloth before the elders of the city:

And the elders of the city shall take that man and chastise him:

And they shall amerce him in one hundred shekels of silver and give them unto the father of the damsel, because he hath brought up an evil name upon a virgin of Israel: and she shall be his wife, he may not put her away all his days.

But if this thing be true, and the *tokens* of virginity be not found for the damsel:

Then they shall bring out the damsel to the door of her father's house, and the men of the city shall stone her with stones, because she hath wrought

---

[1] Prosper, Alpin's *Egypt*, Beloes's *Observations*, Perry's *Travels*, Chardin, Tavernier, Thèvenot, Le Muire *Voyages*, Leon *Afric*, Savary, Niepbur, Volney, Sonnerat, etc. [D]

[2] *Deuteronomy*, XXII, 13–21. [D]

folly in Israel to play the whore in her father's house. So shalt thou put evil away from among you.

The reverence which the ancient Romans had for virginity, and, consequently, for virgins themselves, is well known. The highest citizens of the state gave way to them in the streets; they never went abroad without being veiled, and never showed themselves to strangers in the house of their parents. These latter scrupulously abstained from indulging in mutual endearments in their presence, and it is even asserted that a law expressly forbade a virgin's being punished with death. Hence, no doubt, originated the story of Sejanu's daughter, a girl only eight years of age, having been violated by the executioner previously to his strangling her.

'The Lombards', says Gibbon, 'allowed the *morgingcap* immediately after the wedding night, and this famous gift, the reward of virginity, might equal the fourth part of her husband's substance. Some cautious maidens indeed, were wise enough to stipulate, beforehand, for a present which they were not too sure of deserving.'[1]

Chastity was held in no less repute, the act of generation being, for the most part, associated with the idea of a brutish and purely animal function which appears to degrade our nature and lower us to the level of the brutes. In fact, ancient and modern religions have, with few exceptions, exacted the sacrifice of corporeal pleasures from their votaries, and, more especially, imposed upon their ministers the vow of chastity, and the obligation of immolating at the altar the most endearing affections of our nature. This effort of continence and virtue, which manifests the empire of the mind over the body, is always admired by man, because it seems to announce a superior nature and a sublimity of character which approaches him, in some degree, to the Divinity.[2]

Chastity, by preserving the vigour of the vital powers, and by returning into all the organs that superabundance of life which is

---

[1] Gibbon, *Decline and Fall of the Roman Empire*, Chap. 31 (note). [D]. The Dent *Everyman* edition in six volumes is the most easily available.

[2] A view still held by the religious psychologists of the East. See, for example, *How to Know God*, a translation (with extensive commentaries by the translators) of the Yoga Aphorisms of Patanjali, London, Allen & Unwin, 1953 (the translators are Christopher Isherwood and Swami Prabhavananda, and they have made an excellent job of their work).

concentrated in the genital parts, must, necessarily, increase the energy of all our functions.[1]

This physiological effect was known to the ancients,[2] who represented the muses as virgins to show the little disposition which the learned and the intellectual have for physical love, because they have too acute a sensibility.

With literary persons indeed the encephalon frequently absorbs all the activity at the genital organs, which are often prematurely emaciated and withered.[3]

From what has been advanced, it will be easily understood that in proportion as the morals of a nation become more depraved, the fewer it produces of celebrated characters.

Corporeal strength follows the same law as mental vigour; thus the athletes lived in celibacy in order to preserve their strength; and Moses interdicted the Jews from having connubial intercourse when they were summoned to arms. Whether this esteem in which virginity is held results from its effects upon the human body, or whether it emanates from religious opinion, even in climates where the propagation of the species is a religious injunction, it is found throughout the civilized world.

[1] Modern medical opinion would not agree with this statement. Yet there may well be some profound truth in it, for strict chastity is recommended in Buddhist and Hindu yogic practices, and also seems to increase the psychic faculty. There is also a popular saying that saints have appeared to reach great longevity—apart from those who were martyred.

[2] The ancient poets bear testimony, in their verses, to the esteem in which virginity was generally held; thus Ovid tells us that Daphne, changing into a laurel tree, cannot endure the action of fire without complaining, as in ancient times, she could not bear the flames of impudicity. [D]

[3] This may have applied to some great literary figures, but very many of them have led active—and very active—sexual lives. Byron is one example, Goethe, in his younger days, another.—And what of the Elizabethans, Hugo, Gautier, and the French Romantics?

Regarding emaciation and withering of the genital organs, Sulpicius tells us that in St Martin, famous for his austerities, 'the penis was found after death to be so much shrunken "that the organ would never have been detected, had not the observers known where to look for it" '. (See Réné Guyon, *Sexual Freedom*, translated from the French of *La Liberté Sexuelle*, by E. and C. Paul, London, John Lane, 1939 (there have been later reprints). The quotation made appears on p. 140 of the 1939 edition.)

Among the savage nations, such as the negroes, the native Americans, the South Sea Islanders, who possess no other religious system than Fetichism, virginity is not much, if at all esteemed. Lapeyrère asserts that the Icelanders compel their daughters to prostitute themselves to strangers. The northern Mongol tribes are reported by Steller to offer their wives to their guests, and the following is an amusing instance of this *liberality* among the South Sea islanders:

When the missionary ship *Duff* reached Christiana, or Ohittahoo where Harris and Crook were to be left, the first visitors who came off to them were seven beautiful young women, who swam to the ship, perfectly naked, except that a few green leaves were fastened round their waists, and no sooner had they got on board, than the hungry goats attacked ravenously their Eve aprons. Harris's eyes and delicacy had to undergo further shocks in the islands. Tenae, the king, invited them to go with him to another valley; Crook readily agreed, but Harris would not go, and the chief, to accommodate him in the most obliging manner he could, left him his wife, to be treated by him as if she were his own, till he came back. It was in vain that poor missionary Harris protested that he did not want the woman. She was left with him, and finding herself neglected, called some of her female friends to satisfy themselves concerning his sex, while he was asleep. This inquest was not made without awakening him. His fear at being so awakened, and his horror at the thought of remaining among a people so given to wickedness, completely overcame him, and he quitted the island, leaving brother Crook only to the labour of love.[1]

The abuse of the venereal act, and the too great loss of the seminal fluid, soon produces upon men effects very analogous with those of castration, such as weakness, dejection of mind, debility, and pusillani-

---

[1] See *Wilson's Voyage* and *Quarterly Review*, No. 3; also *Ulloa*, Tom. I, 343; Lignat, *Voyage*, Tom. III, Laperyrère, *Voyage*, p. 176; *Lettres sur l'Island*, etc.[D]

For further details regarding sexuality in Oceania (and Tahiti in particular), see William Ellis, *Polynesian Researches*, 1832—especially Vol. I, chaps. VI and IX. The work is now rare, and is in four volumes. See also Havelock Ellis, *Studies in the Psychology of Sex*, New York, Random House, 1936, 4 vols.—The cumulative index of subjects at the end of Vol. IV will supply the references. The volume containing the study on *Sexual Inversion* gives information regarding homosexuality amongst the Tahitians. Hawkesworth, in his *Voyages* (3 vols.), London, 1775, also gives details.

mity, together with all that mental timidity which exaggerates the least dangers and succumbs under the most trivial apprehensions. On the contrary, men most celebrated for their moral and intellectual faculties, and who have rendered themselves illustrious by their talents or their virtues, have, for the most part, been but little given to sexual delight; and some, indeed, such as Julian the Apostate, Newton, Kent, and William Pitt, have abstained from venery altogether.

Alegcombe gives some remarkable instances of chastity among the Jesuits. He says that Father Gill, who died in 1622, at the age of seventy-three, did not know any woman by sight, so careful was he that his senses should not dwell upon these objects—he was afraid of himself—it struck him almost with horror to touch his own flesh, and he thanked God, who had made him short-sighted, because that defect supplied him with a powerful guard against carnal concupiscence.

Father Casteras declared that his chastity was never overcome by any irregular emotions arising from the least unrestrained imagination.

Father Coton, who had been confessor to a very licentious prince, died a virgin, and so strictly preserved his internal purity, that whatever shocked his virtue, inspired him with horror.

Father Spiza, who died in the year 1594, passed for a virgin, he never looked upon a woman; he could not distinguish his two nieces, one from the other, though he was their confessor, and he would not go into the house where they lived, on any account, when he knew they were alone.

Father Poissevin's chastity went so far as possible, for Menage says, that, as he was going to read Tibullus, for the sake of his elegant Latin, he fell down on his knees and prayed God that the amorous ideas of that poet might not inspire him with love.

Louis VIII, of France, in the midst of his conquests, was seized with a disorder for which his physicians could prescribe no other remedy than that of breaking the seventh commandment, his Queen being then, of necessity, at Paris, as Regent, during his absence. It is imagined that his bigotry would not allow him to have recourse to this prescription, for, when he was asleep, his courtiers introduced into his bed a lady of exquisite beauty, who, on his awaking, confessed for what object she was there. 'No, my child,' said the king, 'I had rather die, than commit a deadly sin.' And then ordering the girl to be married off, made his will, and died.

What a contrast is the conduct of this king to that of 'the monarch after God's own heart'!

And it came to pass, in an evening tide, that David arose from off his bed and walked upon the roof of the king's house, and from the roof he saw a woman washing herself; and the woman was very beautiful to look upon.

And David sent and enquired after the woman. And one said, Is not this Bathsheba, the daughter of Eliam, the wife of Uriah, the Hittite?

And when David had called him (Uriah), he did eat and drink before him; and he made him drunk: and at even he went out to lie on his bed with the servants of his lord, but he went not down to his house.

And it came to pass in the morning, that David wrote a letter to Joab, and sent it by the hand of Uriah.

And he wrote in the letter, saying, Set ye Uriah in the fore-front of the hottest battle, and retire ye from him, that he may be smitten, and die.

And it came to pass, that when Joab observed the city, that he assigned Uriah unto a place where he knew that valiant men were.

And the men of the city went out and fought with Joab: and there fell some of the people of the servants of David; and Uriah the Hittite died also.[1]

Malcolm IV, King of Scotland, who died in 1166, was not only devout, but had made a vow of chastity, which all the raillery and schemes of temptation contrived by his mother Ada could not induce him to break.

Luther, according to his own account, led the most spotless life during all the time of his celibacy, until he was forty-five years of age.

Gulielmus Nubrigiensis relates that the physicians of Thomas the Second, Archbishop of York, having prescribed for him in his last illness, the use of a woman as the only effectual remedy, the worthy prelate, to oblige his friends, pretended to comply, but did not, and died.

Among innumerable instances of the exercise of this virtue, among women, the following are too remarkable not to be noticed.

Queen Zenobia's[2] chastity was so great that she never availed herself

---

[1] II *Samuel*, XI, v. 3–17. [D]

[2] A Queen of Palmyra, who was conquered and taken prisoner by the Roman Emperor Aurelian, A.D. 272. [D]

of those liberties which the wedded state allows, except for the procreation of children.

Francisca Frances, a devout lady, who was canonized in 1608, ate nothing but herbs and pulse, and drank nothing but water; and, in addition to other severities which she exercised upon herself, used to check the solicitations of the flesh by dropping scalding bacon upon her *pudenda*; a fact which is recorded in the Bull of Canonization.[1]

Maria[2] Caronel, wife of Juan de la Cerda, not being able to bear the absence of her husband, preferred committing suicide to yielding to the temptations of the flesh.

The abbey church of Chester was founded about the year 660 by Welpherus, king of the Mercians, as a nunnery, in favour of his daughter's indisposition to married life. This was the celebrated Saint Werburgh, who took the veil after living *immaculate* with her husband Ceolzedus, imitating the example of her aunt, the great Ethelreda, who cohabited for three years, with no less purity, with her spouse Tomberctus, and for twelve years with her second husband, the pious Prince Egfrid.[3]

Isabella Gonzaga, the wife of the Duke of Urbino, passed two years with her husband, still remaining a virgin, and so great was her ignorance of the matrimonial duty, that she imagined all married women lived in the like manner. 'At length, however,' said her historian, 'the mist before her eyes vanished away, whether it was that age taught her, or the free conversation, she had as a married woman, with the ladies, her friends, who were also in the connubial state, enlightened her.'

In proportion, as the heat of the climate augments the depravity of the morals, religious and civil institutions unite to curb the violence of the passions and keep them in check. The civil law of Asia exacts the proofs of virginity in marriages. The Jews, Egyptians, Persians, Turks, and Tartars, require, as an essential condition of the conjugal union, some proof of defloration, such as the effusion of a few drops of blood. It is the custom in the East, on the day after the consummation of the marriage, to produce the bride's linen, as an infallible token of her virginity. This custom still exists in some parts of Spain, where it was

---

[1] Tallement, *Histoire des Empires.* [D]

[2] Mariana, *Historia della España.* [D]

[3] Pennant, Coste, *Eloge des Dames Illustres.* [D]

introduced by the Moors; in some of the German states, and especially in Russia.

Now, notwithstanding that so great a physiologist as Hatter has countenanced this prejudice by his dictum 'the bridal bed, however, should be an ensanguined one'[1] it may be confidently asserted that nothing is less to be depended upon than such a reputed proof of defloration. The relaxed state of the parts of generation from the great quantity of mucus in a woman subject to the whites, or from the blood of the menstrual discharge, may make the hymen yield and not rupture, so that a woman might seem a virgin, without being such; while, on the other hand, the chastest and most moral of her sex might have her hymen destroyed by preceding illness, and thus be incapacitated from giving the husband of her choice the proof of her purity. It should also be remembered that there are persons, in whom the hymen is so indistinct, that several anatomists have doubted its existence altogether. With what eloquence does Buffon, who shared this incredility, inveigh against the absurd importance attached to this membrane by us lords of creation:

Les hommes, des primautés en tout genre, ont toujours fait grand cas, de tout ce qu'ils ont cru pouvoir posséder exclusivement et les premiers; c'est cette espèce de folie qui a fait un être réel de la virginité des filles. La virginité qui est un être moral, qui ne consiste que dans la pureté du cœur, est devenue un objet physique dont tous les hommes se sont occupés. Ils ont établi sur cela des opinions, des usages, des cérémonies, des superstitions et mêmes des jugements et des peines les plus illicites, les coutumes les plus déshonnêtes ont été autorisées ou soumises à l'examen des matrones ignorantes et exposées aux yeux de médecins prévenus les parties les plus secrètes de la nature sans songer qu'une pareille indécence est un attentat contre la virginité, que c'est la violer que de chercher de la reconnaître, que toute situation honteuse, tout état indécent dont une fille est obligée de rougir intérieurement est une vraie défloration.

It has been thought by some that the signs of defloration are not exclusively confined to the sexual parts: thus it was a popular belief at Rome that the volume of the bosom increased after defloration, for which reason that part was very accurately measured before the

[1] Prima Venus, attamen, cruenta esse debet. *Elem. Physiol,* Lib. **XXVIII**, et **XXVI**, 27. [D]

consummation of marriage, and if, the day after that event, the measure was found to be too short, the delight of the husband was indescribable; the fact of virginity being, from this circumstance, deemed incontestable. It is to this usage, doubtless, that Catullus alludes in the following verse

Non illam nutrix, oriente luce revisens
Hesterno collum poteret circumdare filo.

Serverin Pineau also considered it as an indubitable proof of virginity if the length of a thread extending from the tip of the nose to the junction of the sagittal and lamloidal suture sufficed to go round the neck, an opinion in which he is followed by many respectable writers.

Mr Mawman records a singular mode of testing chastity:

In ancient times, there was a narrow hole in a close-vaulted room, under ground, called *Winifred's needle* (at Ripon, in Yorkshire), in which female chastity was tried. The conceit was, that those women only were chaste who could pass through the needle.

The virginity of the body supposed that of the soul among the greater part of the ancients; thus we find that the primitiae of young girls were consecrated to the gods.

Strabo informs us that the Armenians immolated their virginity to the God Amiatis; and, according to St Augustine, the Romans dedicated a temple to Priapus, where virgins were compelled to sacrifice their virginity. But of all opinions, the most extraordinary is that which prevails at Madagas, in various parts of Africa, in Upper Asia, and even among some of the savages of Peru. In these countries so little value is set upon virginity and upon the virginity of the membrane called the hymen, that the culling of this first flower is considered as a servile trouble; that girls who have already lost it are preferred as being more accomplished. At Goa, the primitiae of virgins were offered up to the idol of the Lingam or Phallus, or to its priests; and the people believed that a woman betrayed her want of merit by remaining a virgin.

Virginity having only an imaginary, or rather, conventional value, which becomes greater in proportion to the rarity of it, the inhabitants of warm climates, where women are so complying, have sought for every means by which to secure the chastity of their females. They shut them up in their harems, and even provide them with girdles which forbid all approach to enjoyment.

If chastity be a virtue, its abuse may occasion serious inconveniences, especially when a warm temperament demands compliance with the dictates of nature.

Women who cohabit with men are more healthy, those who do not are less so.[1]

And this aphorism is so true, that women devoted to celibacy, either from religion or choice, are exposed to attacks of cancer, either in the breast or in the womb. Such was the case with the Vestals of Rome and the Virgins of the Sun in the temple of Cusco; and such it is, in the present day, with those pious females in Catholic countries, who devote themselves to the service of religion.

Amongst the Babylonians, the Egyptians, Arabians, Greeks, and Romans all intercourse even with their wives was forbidden on the eve of the sacrifices; and it was an established opinion among the Jews that nothing was more calculated to deprive the party of the gift of prophecy than sexual indulgence. It is principally among single women that various maladies of the breast and womb abound; more of them die between the ages of forty and fifty years than any other, and their life is shorter than that of married persons, for celibacy is generally less favourable to longevity than marriage.

That celibacy is in opposition to the laws of nature, and the desire which all creatures manifest of reproducing themselves is clear from the state of nullity to which it condemns each separate sex. The inferior animals never subject themselves to this abstinence from the functions to which nature has attached the most powerful charms; and if among the human species some individuals are found who make a merit and even a duty of it, it is because they are urged to it by motives either of policy or religion, unless, indeed, this sacrifice be the result of a vicious conformation of the generative organs.

The effect of celibacy and chastity is to throw back upon the animal economy a superabundance of vigour, which stimulates the nervous system, and gives an inflammatory appearance to the complexion.

---

[1] Mulieres si cum viris coeunt, magis sanae sunt, si non, minus.—Hippocrates: *De Generat.* [D]

Hence monks were obliged to be frequently bled, not only because the want of exercise, in spite of fasting and abstinence, amassed an excess of blood, but also, in order, that by this means, the erotic passion might be diminished.

The most cruel nervous disorders such as the *furor uterinus*, hysteria, spasms, etc., chiefly attack such as have, throughout life, refused the pleasure of love. Many fatal affections such as mania, epilepsy, etc., prey upon those who have imposed upon themselves too severe a continence. But the dangers resulting from the abuse of this pleasure are much more formidable. Besides, nature knows how to rid herself of too abundant a seminal fluid by the illusion of dreams in both sexes, an evacuation which is entirely confined to the human species; whether it depends upon the activity of our imagination, or arises from the abundance of food, and from a more acute sensibility than is found in other living beings.

Ere we quit the subject of virginity as regards women, we cannot refrain from saying a few words about the 'Virgin Mary of the Romanists'.

In Roman Catholic countries the Virgin is still addressed by her devotees under the following titles:

Empress of Heaven! Queen of Heaven! Empress of Angels! Queen of Angels! Empress of the Earth! Queen of the Earth! Lady of the Universe! Lady of the Earth! Patroness of Men! Advocate for Sinners! Mediatrix! Gate of Paradise! Mother of Mercies! Goddess, and THE ONLY HOPE OF SINNERS! under which two latter they profanely implore her to afford them salvation by the power which, as a mother, she is inferred to possess of *commanding* HER SON!

The following questions and answers are extracted from a Catechism for the churches in France, p. 171:

Q. Why does the Church render a particular honour to the most Holy Virgin?

A. Because the most Holy Virgin surpasses all others in Holiness, and because she has an incommunicable title.

Q. What is that title?

A. Mother of God.

Q. What does the Church more particularly honour in the most Holy Virgin?

A. Her immaculate conception, her holy nativity, her divine maternity, the perfect obedience and profound humility which she manifested on the day of the Purification and the presenting of Jesus in the temple, and, lastly, her glorious assembly.

The impropriety of this title (Mother of God) is exceedingly great. How would the compilers of the Catechism be pleased if any one were to call Anna, whose daughter Mary was, *the Grandmother of God?* The impudence of foisting these titles upon her is the greater because there is not a passage in the writings of the Evangelists (all of whom must have known Mary), to show that, when living, she was the object even of reverence, by the command of Christ. No divine honours were paid to her by the Disciples or Apostles; none were paid to her in the first three centuries of the Christian Church; nor was it till the general Synod, held at Ephesus in the year 431 (when she was declared to be the Mother of God), that she was deemed an object of invocation. Another appellation given to her, that of *Virgo et semper Virgo,* cannot but be considered as an absurd and ludicrous compliment, when we see it recorded by Matthew (Chap. 1, v. 25) that Joseph knew not Mary until she had brought forth her first-born son; a declaration which clearly implies that the same delicacy was not observed after that event. And when we see it stated by Mark (VI, 3) and by Luke (VIII, 19) that Jesus had brothers and sisters.

It is a singular fact that the Romish Church had no idea of the immaculate conception till the compliment had been paid her in the Koran, which was completed in the seventh century. It was however, condemned by St Bernard, the Oracle of Europe in his day, as a presumptuous novelty.

This species of conception being of a nature beyond all human comprehension, whetted the prurient curiosity of the audacious, and gave rise to the most profane opinions. Take, for instance, that of St Ambrose:

Non enim coitus valvae virginalis secreta reservavit, sed immaculatum semen inviolabile utero Spiritus infudit.

For the male organ penetrated not the recesses of the virgin vagina, but the Holy Ghost poured the immaculate semen into the inviolable womb.

St Austin, with less obscenity, but greater absurdity, says that

God spake by his angel, and the Virgin was impregnated by the ear.
Deus loquebatur per Angelum et Virgo per aurem pregnabatur.

We have no laws affecting celibacy: the bachelor enjoying equally with the married man all the rights and privileges of citizenship, which is a manifest injustice, for the husband and the father render the State services which the man disengaged from conjugal ties cannot afford.

On the contrary, the bachelor, stimulated by natural sexual wants, is obliged, in order to satisfy them, to trample upon the moral law, when he does not go to the length of violating the connubial bond. For him, in fact, there are no other resources than fornication or adultery; and if society is constantly disturbed by evils resulting from the frequent indulgence in those immoralities, bachelors are certainly most in fault. Thus, all ages, and in all states, bachelors have been considered as the natural enemies of society.

'It is not,' said Augustus, addressing them in a memorable speech, 'it is not the love of a single life which captivates you when you do not marry; if you deny yourself a companion for your table, and a partner for your bed, it is that you may, without restraint, abandon yourself to lasciviousness and debauchery.'

Augustus was in the right. The bachelor, whom no attachment fixes in his fickle desires, is often obliged to wait in order to satisfy them, and when he does obtain the present object of his passion, he abandons himself, without restraint, to the pleasure of the moment, uncertain, as he is, of again meeting, for a long time, with so favourable an opportunity; so that, with him, there is a constant alternation of irritation and exhaustion.

If he is worn out by preceding enjoyments, and chance presents him with new ones, he is compelled to be libidinous and to employ all the means likely to insure an instantaneous vigour. On the contrary, if he be not provided with a liaison, his irritated organs will make him little nice in the choice of his fair one. He will, then, address himself to *Venus Vaga*, or, in other words, he will imbibe in the obscene and disgusting brothel the most fatal poison which ever issued from Pandora's box, and will disseminate it in society by communicating it to the victims whom he has seduced from innocence or from their conjugal fidelity.

There is not the least doubt that concubinage is adverse to the progress of the species, since it seeks after pleasure, but avoids the expense it involves. Considering, therefore, the bachelor as a perfect egoist, legislators of every age and country have decreed penalties against this opposition to the laws of society.

With respect to the comparative longevity of single and married persons, the former would soon renounce the state of single blessedness, and contract marriage, did they consult the bills of mortality. Buffon and De Parcieux were the first to show that single men live a much shorter time than married ones. According to Hoffland and Sinclair, almost all individuals who have arrived at a very advanced age were married; and married women, even notwithstanding the dangers of childbirth, generally live a longer time than single ones.

Fodéré, who had accumulated a vast number of facts from an extensive medical practice, refers the comparative longevity of married persons to four circumstances:

I. To the assistance and consolations afforded to each other by married persons: in the attentions they mutually bestow and receive during illness, the commencements of which are usually neglected by those who live by themselves.

II. In the greater degree of activity which a person is found to observe when forced to maintain a family; now labour and exercise are as necessary for the preservation of health as food, for they undoubtedly keep off disease and prevent us from attaching to slight indispositions that importance which is so done by those whose care is wholly confined to themselves.

III. In the security from those diseases which are, almost always, the handmaids of the Venus Vaga, and which are not avoided even by those who confine their attachment to one person, for, in fact, if a woman is sufficiently debased to sacrifice her honour to one, there is scarcely any doubt of her allowing others to partake of her favours, a fact borne out by experience.

IV. The economy of the prolific fluid which is necessarily observed when both convenience and habit cause the desires to be rarely provoked. Bachelors, on the contrary, always led astray by new objects, impatient for enjoyment, often times forcing nature, one sex having no reason for sparing the other, have their sensitive and motive systems shaken by the frequent repetition of venereal delights; or else, men and women, who, from a regard to public opinion, live in apparent chastity, give themselves up to solidary indulgences, and, in those habits which are much more exhausting than the sexual union, contract severe maladies, the cause of which is most commonly kept secret from their medical advisers.

Remarked Galen, and after him Sanctorius and Cowper:

The pleasures of love, when they are moderate, and not indulged in until the body has had time to repair, in both sexes, but more especially in the male, the generative faculty, are salutary for the physical organization; they promote gaiety, contentment, and a sense of freedom in the female. But, as in the man, the secretion of the prolific juice is only made very slowly, as it appears to be the very quintessence of life, and to be destined, not only to fecundation, but also to being absorbed into the system for recruiting the strength of the individual; and as it is necessary that a certain quantity of it should be accumulated in the vessels, in order to procure the natural stimulus and the exhilarating emissions, it follows that too frequent enjoyments on the part of the male enervates the body and causes premature old age, and this the more rapidly, in proportion, as endeavours are made to renew them, in spite of the dictates of nature and the injunctions of morality and religion.

In conclusion it may be observed that chastity is a virtue which constitutes the essential portion of the education of females, it being for them what strength is for man. In the present day, when civilization is constantly enlarging the sphere of woman's activity and liberty, the number of her relations with our sex are almost infinitely increased, and the dangers to which she is exposed are, in consequence, proportionately multiplied, dangers against which her only safeguard is— *Chastity*.

Chastity is often confounded with continence, but there is this difference between them: that while the latter is understood as an abstinence from, or moderation in, the act of generation, the former, regarding the object more with respect to moral purity, is applicable not to the gross act alone, but to the thoughts and feelings of the individual.

ESSAY 5

On Marriage

BY THE word *marriage* is to be understood the union of a man and woman, formed by virtue of a mutual contract, and sanctioned by religion.[1,2] This union is a fact by which man is most distinguished from brutes.

It is not to indulge a gross appetite that such a union is contracted, but to unite two destinies liable to be severed by death alone, and to give birth to a family destined itself to produce others; thus adding new births to the chain of existence.[3]

Considered politically, marriage is a solemn union, having for its object the providing of the State with legitimate citizens, and the arresting of disorders and avoiding the disgrace consequent upon an illegal union.

'The greatest legislators,' observes Edmund Burke, 'knowing that marriage is the source of all relations, and consequently the first element of all duties, have endeavoured by every means to make it sacred. The Christian religion, by confining it to the pairs, and by rendering that relation indissoluble, have by these two things, done

---

[1] *Genesis*, I, 27–8. [D]

[2] See Westermarck, *A History of Human Marriage*, 3 vols., London, Macmillan & Co., 1921 (New York, Allerton Book Co., 1922).—The earlier editions of 1891, 1894, and 1901 are in a single volume, and differ considerably in text, although the general structure, method, and ideas remain similar in all editions. An abridged edition was published by Macmillan & Co., London, 1926, under the title of *A Short History of Human Marriage*—although it is an epitome rather than an abridgement in the usual sense.

[3] Such being the express object of marriage, some writers maintained that the generative act should cease to be performed, when from age, infirmities, or other causes there is no longer any hope of offspring. [D]

more towards the peace, happiness, settlement, and civilization of the world than any other part in this whole system of divine wisdom.'[1]

The Jews, as well as the Christians, esteemed matrimony far before virginity, and the latter never appointed unmarried men to any public office of trust or confidence. Even the Pagans made laws in its favour, and for its encouragement; while the Spartans established a public festival at which, if any unmarried men were found to be present, they were flogged by the women, as being unworthy of serving the Republic and contributing to its glory and advancement.

The laws enacted by Augustus, the Roman Emperor, are well known.

Patey made the following observations:

The greatest use of marriage institutions consists in their promoting the following beneficial effects:

1. The private comfort of individuals.

2. The production of the greatest number of healthy children, their better education, and the making of due provision for their settlement in life.

3. The peace of human society in cutting off a principal source of contention, by assigning one or more women to one man and protecting his exclusive right by sanctions of morality and law.

4. The better government of society by distributing the community into separate families, and appropriating over each the authority of a master of a family, which has more actual influence than all civil authority put together.

5. The additional security which the State receives from the good behaviour of its citizens, from the solicitude they feel for the welfare of their children, and from their being confined to permanent habitations.

6. The encouragement of industry.[2]

It must not be imagined that the indissolubleness of the marriage tie has not met with able and resolute opponents; on the contrary—against the perpetuity of marriage the authority of some of the most enlightened minds may be quoted. Milton says:

Indisposition, unfitness, or contrary humours proceeding from any unchangeable cause in nature, hindering and always likely to hinder the main

---

[1] *On the Sublime and Beautiful.* [D]
[2] *Philosophy*, Vol. I. [D]

ends and benefits of conjugal society, peace, and delights, are greater reasons for divorce than adultery or natural frigidity.

Toland, Grotius, Erasmus, Swift, Leibnitz, Hume, the good and the great philanthropist, Robert Owen, and Byron, have all openly avowed similar opinions, in which they are justified by innate principles and universal analogy throughout the animal creation.

On the same subject the sublime poet, Shelley, raised his powerful voice:

The present system of constraint does no more, in the majority of instances, than make hypocrites or open enemies. Persons of delicacy and virtue, unhappily united to those whom they find it impossible to love, spend the loveliest season of their lives in unproductive efforts to appear otherwise than they are for the sake of the feelings of their partners, or the welfare of their mutual offspring; those of less generosity and refinement openly avow their disappointment, and linger out the remnant of that union, which only death can dissolve, in a state of incurable bickering and hostility. The early education of their children takes its colour from the squabbles of the parents; they are nursed in a systematic school of ill-humour, violence, and falsehood. . . . The conviction that wedlock is indissoluble holds out the strongest of all temptations to the perverse; they indulge, without restraint, in acrimony, and all the little tyrannies of domestic life, when they know that their victim is without appeal. If this connection were put on a rational basis, each would be assured that habitual ill-temper would terminate in separation, and would check this vicious and dangerous propensity. . . . Prostitution is the legitimate offspring of marriage and its accompanying errors. Women, for no other crime than having followed the dictates of a natural appetite, are driven, with fury, from the comforts and sympathies of society. It is less venial than murder, and the punishment which is inflicted on her who destroys her child, to escape reproach, is lighter than the life and agony and disease to which the prostitute is irrevocably doomed. Has a woman obeyed the impulse of unerring nature, society declares war against her; pitiless and eternal war; she must be the tame slave, she must make no reprisal; theirs is the right of persecution, hers the duty of endurance. She lives a life of infamy; the loud and bitter laugh of scorn scares her from all return. She dies of long and lingering disease. Yet she is in fault; she is the criminal; she, the forward and untameable child—and society, forsooth, the pure and virtuous matron who casts her as an abortion from her undefiled bosom! Society avenges herself on the criminal of her own creation; she is employed in anathematizing the vice today which yesterday she was the most zealous to teach.[1]

With respect to the most important function of animal life—the generative act—it is curious to remark how differently it is designated according to the relative position of the parties performing it. Observed Voltaire:

The consummation of marriage, and of all connected with the great work of generation, will be differently expressed by the husband, and medical man, and the lover. The words employed by the last will awaken nought but the image of delight and satisfaction; those used by the doctor will be thickly interladen with anatomical terms; the husband will endeavour to express with decency and propriety what the young man had boldly uttered without regard to decency and propriety; while the priest will do what he can to give to what he says a religious tinge.

Whether the view taken by the Canonists, viz., *ad usum prolis suscipiendae* (for the purpose of obtaining an offspring), be correct or not, it certainly accords with the Roman law upon the same subject, which required that those who wished to marry should appear before the Censors and declare their object to be that of procreation: but independently of this it would be easy to show in how eminent a degree the matrimonial tie conduces to the duration and felicity of human society, and how soon celibacy and the violation of this bond of families draw after them the fall of states. It is, perhaps, the most general of all the institutions of man; no nation, however barbarous, having been found to whom it was unknown. Hence marriage has been, as truly as forcibly, designated 'generation regulated by law', as the key-stone of the social edifice, and hence the reason that the ancients entrusted *coitus* or the union of the sexes to so many Divinities.[2]

History proves what has been already observed—that the decadence of empires is precisely in relation with the increase of single men. In proportion as the Roman republic relaxed its rigid virtues, and relinquished its austere manners, the number of bachelors constantly

[1] *The Christian Mythology unveiled,* p. 262. [D]
[2] For the names of these divinities and the offices relative to generation which they performed, see Meursin's *Antiqit.,* Tom. V, *de puerperio.* [D]

increased. In vain the Senate enacted laws to compel them to marry: public immorality and the difficulty of supporting a family, on account of the increase of luxury, continually bade defiance to their wishes.

In feudal times, the barons, as will be seen, paid but little respect to the matrimonial rights of their vassals. They could force them to marry any person of their choosing; they could sell the fruit of such marriage, or compel the parents to redeem them. Some idea may be formed of the situation of serfs in France from a charter reprinted, at length, in the *Essais sur Paris* by Saint Foix.

The consent of one *William Bishop*, of Paris, is therein given to the union of a young man with a young woman, provided that the children proceeding from the said marriage should be shared between the said *William* and the Abbey of St Germain des Prez. Nor was this the only discouragement to matrimony in those times, for these feudal lords (ecclesiastical as well as secular), claimed the obscene and tyrannical right of passing the wedding night with the wives of their serfs and of thus contaminating the purity of the nuptial couch.[1]

The above author gives us an amusing anecdote on this subject. A nobleman, who possessed a large estate in Normandy, would, in the month of June, assemble round him all his serfs, including those who were awaiting his consent to consummating their marriage. After regaling them at a feast, and making merry with them, this facetious baron declared he was ready to give the wished-for sanction, but only upon certain conditions; thus, to one couple the condition was, that they should consummate their marriage up a lofty tree in his park; to another pair, that they should consummate theirs in the river Ardelle, where they should remain for two hours with nothing on but shirt and smock.

This right, which was almost general throughout Europe, was

---

[1] This custom is usually known by the name of the *Jus Primae Noctis*, and in medieval France was termed the *Droit du Seigneur*. See Ernest Crawley, *The Mystic Rose*, London, Watts & Co., 1932 (pp. 311, 445, and 448). This, the fourth edition, is considerably enlarged and revised by Theodore Besterman. The first edition was published by Macmillan, London, 1902; and the second edition by Methuen, London, 1927. Reference can also be made to Ch. Letourneau, *The Evolution of Marriage*, London, Walter Scott, 1891 (a volume in the famous 'Contemporary Science Series' edited by Havelock Ellis). See pp. 45, 47, 48, 50. The subject is touched on in many works relative to the history of marriage and sexual customs.

gradually changed into more moderate pretensions; a commutation in money being substituted for it, which commutation was known in England during the Saxon rule by the name of *Marcheta Saxonica*; during the Norman dynasty by that of *Marcheta*:[1] and in Scotland by that of *Marcheta mulierum*.

The *Marcheta mulierum* was ordained by Eugenius, king of Scotland, who enacted that the Lord or Master should have the first night with every woman married to his tenant or bondsman, which ordinance was, afterwards, abrogated by Malcolm III, who ordained that the bridegroom should have the sole use of his wife, and for that privilege should pay to the lord a piece of money called *marca*. In the time of our Henry III thirty-two pence were given to the lord by way of commutation. In France the lord of the soil, and the canons of the cathedral of Lyons, claimed a right to lie, the first night of the nuptials,[2] with their bondsmen's wives. The Bishop of Amiens, and the monks of St Etienne de Nevers, had, themselves, the same right, which they exercised with unblushing effrontery. The priests of Picardy asserted that no married couple could, without their permission, sleep together for the first three nights; the monks of St Theodard enjoyed the same privilege over the inhabitants of Mont Auréel, a town situated in the neighbourhood of their monastery.

Several German lords enjoyed the like privilege, but, much to their credit, restricted it to introducing a leg or a thigh into the bride's bed, and even this might be commuted into a fine called *cuissabe* or *droit de cuisse*.

It is not surprising that such disgusting and tyrannical pretensions should frequently excite indignation and resistance. In Scotland, it was the cause of several insurrections, and in Piedmont the lords of Persanni and of Presti, having refused to commute the pretended right into a fine, their subjects threw off the yoke, and placed themselves under the dominion and protection of Amadeus IV, Count of Savoy.

As before observed, in proportion as a nation proceeds to its decline, the number of marriages decreases, while that of single men becomes greater. Look at Rome when under wise government, and at the same

---

[1] Ducange, *Gloss.*, in voce Marchetta. [D].—An edition of Ducange's *Glossaire Erotique* was published by Isidore Liseux of Paris during the 1880's.

[2] Camillus Borelli: *Bibliotheca Germ.*, Vol. II. [D]

Rome crouching beneath the despotism of the Emperors. Despotic states are filled with monasteries and mendicant monks. It was at the fall of the Roman Empire that thousands of monasteries were founded in the East and in Europe. Compare Spain, Portugal, and Italy peopled with monks and persons devoted to celibacy, with the northern states of Europe, as England, Switzerland, Holland, Sweden, etc., where the population daily increases, and where it would become too abundant were it not kept down by continual emigrations.

Thus men are induced to marry in poor but free countries where morality is respected; but, on the contrary, are led to celibacy in those where the morals are corrupted, and where reign luxury and all the superfluities of life. Marriage protects and supports morality, society, and the laws; celibacy necessarily produces adultery and prostitution, which vices dissuade men more and more from marriage. Disgust, the usual consequence of the facility of the enjoyment, seeks after variety, till, at length, satiated with delight, the desire after irregular and unnatural pleasure is awakened.

It has, indeed, been remarked, that the most abandoned vices are nowhere more common than in countries where women are most accommodating and in greatest numbers; that is, in warm climates and under despotic governments.

'No one is ignorant', observes Bossu,[1] 'how ancient is the vice of pederasty[2] throughout the East: among the Mohammedan polygamists the women shut up in harems tribadize one another, and when discovered are severely punished by the Turks, for so indulging themselves. Pederasty is also practised among some savage tribes; for instance, among the Chactas of North America who keep young catamites dressed in female attire.'[3]

---

[1] *Nouveau Voyage aux Indes Occident.*, Tom. III, p. 108. [D]. Pederasty is not a term applied to women, but to men. Literally it means a 'lover of boys', but in common parlance it is used to denote the act of buggery (or sodomy) upon another male (or the submitting to such by a male).

[2] According to Ovid, Orpheus was the first who introduced this disgusting vice. [D]

[3] See also Edward Carpenter, *Intermediate Types Among Primitive Folk*, London, George Allen & Unwin, 1919 (second edition). Chapters one and two are important in this connection: *The Intermediate as Prophet or Priest*, and *The Intermediate as Wizard or Witch*. The book is well deserving of a reprint.

It is obvious how much such causes must undermine governments, enfeeble nations, and enervate mankind; it is under such circumstances that the greatest political changes and the most disastrous revolutions take place. So true is this that the French Revolution of 1789 may be attributed quite as much, if not more, to the licentious manners of the two preceding reigns, than to the writings of the philosophers, or to any other cause which has been assigned.[1] Were not the following description given by Bussy Rabutin of the horrible and disgusting depravity of the Court of Louis XIV, confirmed by contemporaneous writers, it would be scarcely credible:

The very *accommodating* disposition of every lady at court had rendered their charms so worthless to the young men, that even to look at them was almost unknown. In no other place in the world was *debauchery* (sodomy) in such vogue;[2] and although the king had several times manifested and expressed the greatest horror at these kinds of pleasure, it was in this alone, that he was neither followed nor obeyed. Wine, and what I shall refrain from naming, were so much the fashion, that scarcely any respect or consideration was paid to those who preferred a more decent mode of passing their time; and however great their inclination to live agreeably to the dictates of nature, yet, as the number of those who preferred indulging in the prevailing vice was greater, the bad example of these latter perverted the better-inclined, who accordingly soon renounced their feeling for decency.

Among the votaries of this Socratic vice were no less personages than Monsieur (the king's brother) Condé, Conti, Permandais, Villars, Prince Eugène, and so on, and as a proof how this detestable taste

[1] *Histoires Amoureuses des Gaules*. [D].—Davenport is probably also referring to *La France devenue Italienne*, a work which is generally printed together with Bussy Rabutin's *Histoires Amoureuses des Gaules*, and which concerns itself much with homosexual activity. There have been many reprints of this book, though perhaps not all contain the additional treatise.

[2] The prevalence of homosexuality has altered little throughout the centuries, but is sometimes more obvious, sometimes less; sometimes fairly open, sometimes very secret. Rabutin's statement therefore is an exaggeration, for such practices were equally common at the courts of the Valois and the Medici in France, as also in earlier times at the court of Heliogabalus, and other emperors. Verlaine, in one of his privately printed poems, has exclaimed that 'The Valois were mad for the male!', and Kinsey has shown us that about a third of the population have homosexual tendencies. Such proclivities are equally widespread in the animal kingdom.

prevailed it will be sufficient to say that Morel, a gentleman of Provence, *sold boys as if they were horses,* driving his bargains in the pit at the opera.[1]

It will scarcely be credited that a regular society or college of the *Cinoedi* was actually instituted; that three competitors for the grand mastership presented themselves, viz. the Count de Maricamp, the Duc de Grammont, and the Chevalier Tilladet. That all these three being deemed equally worthy (that is equally distinguished for obscenity and filthiness), three grand masters were, in consequence, established (in imitation of the religious society of St Lazare). That a fourth grand master was afterwards added, in the person of the Marquis de Biron, and that to this society of disgusting and depraved iniquity was entrusted the duty of drawing up a set of canons, for the regulation of the fraternity, and which were as follows:

[1] The names of homosexuals amongst the great and celebrated in the worlds of literature, music, poetry—and even the sciences—are legion. It may be that such a sexual constitution tends to be associated with great intellectual or artistic gifts. To mention but a few, we have Marlowe (see: *The Man Who was Shakespeare,* by Calbin Hoffman, London, Max Parrish, 1955—Sir Walter Raleigh and his circle are mentioned herein as being largely homosexual, and the preference was certainly common in Elizabethan times), possibly Shakespeare (bi-sexual), Richard Barnfield (the Elizabethan poet), King Edward II, Sir Francis Bacon, Edward Carpenter, Verlaine, Rimbaud, André Gide, Tschaikovsky, Debussy, and countless others in all countries and periods, including Lawrence of Arabia.

Davenport's attitude is, of course, unscientific and unenlightened. Apart from Havelock Ellis's study (*Sexual Inversion*) in *Studies in the Psychology of Sex,* New York, 1936 (and the edition of the *Studies* issued in England by Heinemann, London), the best, most thorough, and eminently sane studies of the same subject are: *Society and the Homosexual,* by Gordon Westwood, London, Gollancz, 1952; *The Homosexual Outlook,* by Donald Webster Cory (pseudonym), London, Peter Neville, 1953 (originally published in the U.S.A. by Greenberg, New York, 1951, under the title: *The Homosexual in America*); and *Homosexuality and the Western Christian Tradition,* by Derick Sherwin Bailey, London, Longmans, 1955.

The following three volumes by André Gide are also important: *Corydon,* London, Secker & Warburg, 1952, 1956, etc. (originally published in French by Gallimard, Paris, 1924—extremely limited privately printed editions had previously been done in 1911 and 1920 in France by Gide himself); *If it Die,* London, Secker & Warburg, 1951, Penguin Books, 1957 (originally published as *Si le Grain ne Meurt,* Paris, Gallimard, 1926—this is an autobiographical volume); *Et Nunc Manet in Te,* London, Secker & Warburg, 1952 (privately printed in an edition of 13 copies, in French, in France, 1947; first published by Ides et Calendes, Neuchâtel, 1951).

I. That, for the future, no person shall be admitted into the order but such as have been previously examined by the grand masters, in order to ascertain if every part of their bodies were sufficiently healthy, so that they might be able to bear the trials (*austérités*).

II. That they take an oath of obedience, and also of chastity, with regard to women; and that, if any one should contravene it, he should be immediately turned out of the company, never more to re-enter it, under any pretence whatever.

III. That every one should be admitted into the society, without any distinction as to quality.

IV. That if any one of the brethren should marry, he must declare that it was for no other cause than the benefit of his concerns, or because all his relations compelled him so to do; or because it was absolutely necessary that he should leave an heir; that, moreover, he must ask permission to have the said intercourse with his wife, which could be granted for one day only in the week.

V. That the brethren should be divided into four classes, in order that each grand prior might have an equal number of them. And that, with respect to those who should present themselves for the purpose of entering the order, the four grand priors should have them, turn by turn, on their list, so that no jealousy should injure their union.

VI. That the brethren should report to each other all that shall have taken place in private, so that if any office should be vacant, it might only be filled up by the most deserving, who should be discovered by this means.

VII. With respect to indifferent persons, or such as are not members, it is forbidden to reveal to them the mysteries, and that if any member should so do, he should be deprived of the enjoyment of them for one week, or even longer should the grand master, to whose list he belongs, consider it expedient.

VIII. Nevertheless, such communication may be made to persons who, it is hoped, may be induced to enter the order: this, however, must be done so discreetly, that success must be assured before making the attempt.

IX. That those who should introduce brethren into the convent, should enjoy, during two days, those to whom the grand masters were entitled, provided, however, that the former should have the precedence, and the latter be contented with their leavings.[1]

The king, who mortally hated this vice, having procured indisputable evidence of these excesses, banished some of the delinquents to towns remote from the court, had one of the princes horsewhipped in

[1] *Mémoires de la Duchesse d'Orléans* (mother of the Duke d'Orléans and Regent during the minority of Louis XV). Tom. II, p. 297 (notes), Brussels edition. [D]

his presence[1] and sent the other to Chantilly; and by these measures this detestable fraternity was broken up. As might be naturally expected the ladies were exceedingly rejoiced at this *dénouement*, and some of the crosses belonging to the chevaliers, whom they judged worthy of being committed to the flames, were, accordingly, made a bonfire of, which was, however, but a poor vengeance for the insult and wrong done them.

But to return from this digression, savages are not very amorously inclined, especially in cold climates; but in proportion as they become civilized, gallantry is more frequent, and more general. Aristotle has observed that the nations who are the best acquainted with the real passion of love are the most warlike.

In the polar and temperate regions, Nature allows only one woman to each man; in hot countries she instituted polygamy, by creating more females than males. The object of this is evident, for the inhabitants of the north are slower in their loves, their women are a long time fruitful and less exposed to abortions than those in the south. Besides which, cold countries should not be so thickly peopled as hot ones, since they produce less food for their inhabitants. Warm countries, on the contrary, stimulate the passion of love to an excess; women soon become barren, and are subject to frequent abortions. The riches and fertility of the soil of those regions moreover easily maintain a large population. In cold temperatures, love comes late, remains chaste and temperate, and lasts a longer time than in warm countries, where it is awakened very early, flames with violence, and becomes soon extinguished.

European women, who marry in India, are exposed, like all persons of hot countries, to frequent abortions, and from this cause perish by uterine hemorrhages.

As the activity of the uterus is diminished by the cold in northern countries, the state of pregnancy of women is more fortunate and less exposed to danger. They often produce twins, their accouchements are followed by fewer diseases, but become more painful and difficult on account of the natural contraction of the parts in consequence of the cold.

The great heat of southern climes is less favourable to the increase of the species than the chaste loves of the northern ones. Poor and

---

[1] There is a very scarce French edition of the above work, with a frontispiece representing the king witnessing this punishment. [D]

chaste people, such as those of cold and mountainous countries, follow the law of nature, without indulging it by excess, as do the corrupt and luxurious nations inhabiting warm countries.

Thus population constantly increases with the former, and diminishes with the latter, for nothing is more hostile to production than the abuse of sexual intercourse. Experience, however, proves that the coldness of climate is injurious to the population of the negroes, who are in better health and multiply more under the hottest sky; they there acquire that brilliant ebony black, the sign of their health, instead of those yellow, brownish hues which are the tokens of the diminution of their strength.[1]

It should appear, at first sight, that the most natural state of man is that of monogamy; the most perfect numerical equality of the sexes,[2] especially in our climates, the peace of families, the social happiness resulting from it, the mutual intercourse so necessary to ensure the rearing of the offspring, the example even of apes and other animals which approximate to us, and which have but one female at a time, as also that of many husbands who, in different countries, being allowed, both by the ecclesiastical and civil laws, to take several wives, prefer living with one alone, all these considerations appear to prove that man and woman should unite in pairs, to form and bring up their progeny. It is true that, according to the natural law alone, and independently of conventional and social ones, it is impossible to prove that the promiscuous intercourse of the sexes, and even any employment of the sexual organs for mere voluptuousness' sake, is absolutely illicit and criminal in the eye of Nature, as the writers upon jurisprudence assert; in corroboration of which may be quoted the saying of Cardinal de Medicis—

That there was no religion below the navel.

[1] See Nicholls, *Remarks Upon the Health and Life of the American Savages.* [D]
[2] This remark would appear to be doubtful, for it is by no means always the case that the sexes are numerically equal, and sometimes they are found to be very unequal; added to which there may be disparities in age which eliminate the possibility of union, thus increasing the actual inequality of numbers. Amongst the natural solutions of such difficulties might be listed: polygamy, polyandry, homosexual practices, and certain forms of prostitution—which might well be nature's way of maintaining balance.

'Reason alone', says Bayle, 'would suggest rather a community than a property of women'; and it is shown by ancient writers that this community existed in ancient times among many nations.

In many countries of the globe no marriage is contracted, but the two sexes mingle together as inclination prompts. This, according to Garcilas, was more particularly the case with the ancient Peruvians.[1] At Camboge, girls who have been debauched are the first to find husbands, for prostitution is not considered disreputable.[2]

This is similar to what Aelian relates of the Lydians, for whom, he says, it was the common practice for newly married women to prostitute themselves before cohabiting with their husbands; but, upon the marriage being once consummated, they owed the latter an inviolable fidelity.

At Nicaragua the girls select their husbands in the midst of public festivals, in the same manner as was anciently practised in the isle of Candia.

Amongst the Kubasches, a nation of the Caucasus, widows present themselves veiled to the first comer, and the children proceeding from such unions are considered legitimate. Several savage tribes of North and South America exchange their wives at pleasure, and practise incest without any sense of shame.

In short, this general confusion of individuals might bastardize the whole human race by incestuous unions, proofs of which are to be seen among the nations which have not prescribed bounds in this respect. Experiments made in Bohemia prove that the finest races of horses always degenerate when they copulate in a direct line with their parents.

---

[1] It is difficult to say which book Davenport is referring to here, but it is obviously one by Garcilaso Inca de la Vega, a historian of Peru who was born at Cuzco in 1540. In 1560 he went to Spain and served in the Spanish army, and later settled in Cordova, devoting himself to the writing of historical works, which included *El Florida del Inca* (1605), and *Historia General del Peru*. This later work was published between 1609 and 1616, and was translated into English in 1869. De la Vega died in 1616.

[2] See George Ryley Scott, *Phallic Worship*, London, Luxor Press, 1965. Also Havelock Ellis, *Studies*, etc. (the indices, under 'Prostitution', will supply the references, and information on the subject is abundant in the chapter on 'Prostitution' in the final volume of the *Studies*).

At Debrota, a small city near the mouths of the Cattaro, the inhabitants, not marrying out of their own community, become, in this manner, almost nearly related to each other, so much so as to require dispensations before they can marry. This consanguinity appears to be the cause of their having few children, three at most.[1]

Thus it seems that, independently of the feeling of modesty acknowledged by almost universal consent of mankind, and which prohibits unions being contracted between relations, nature herself reproves and condemns them.[2]

There is continually and universally a great loss of men, resulting either from war, shipwreck, unhealthy arts and occupations, accidents and excesses of every description, of which the last are the more frequent among the male sex; so that the number of women becomes equal, if not superior, to that of men, in our climates.

The loss of males occasioned by civil war, as well as the inconvenience resulting from it, appears from the following curious petition presented to Parliament in the year 1643:

THE MIDWIVES' JUST PETITION *or a complaint of divers gentlewomen of that faculty, showing to the whole Christian world their just cause of their sufferings in these distracted times, for their want of trading, which said complaint they tendered to the House on Monday last, being the 23rd January, 1643.*

YOUR PETITIONERS HUMBLY SHOW:

That whereas many miseries do attend upon a civill war, there is none greater than the breaking of that conjunction which matrimony hath once confirmed, so that women's husbands being at the wars, they cannot enjoy that necessary comfort and benevolence which they expect from them.

And whereas we are called Mid-wives by our profession, wee knowing the cases of women better than any other, being more experienced in what they sensibly suffer since the wars begun, living the religious lives of some cloystered nuns contrary to their own natural affections, if they could by

[1] Cattaro (sometimes called Kotor) is a seaport on the Dalmatian coast of Jugoslavia.

[2] Incest is very common amongst birds. If the mother dies, the male bird will mate with one of his female offspring, and vice versa. A fact which has been noted in cage birds especially. And it is not very difficult to find other examples in the animal world. Nor is it a fact that incest is always genetically disastrous, however much, from the moral point of view, we may genuinely deplore it.

any means help it, without wronging their husbands; and as women are helpers unto men, so are we unto women, in all their extremities, for which we were formerly well paid, and highly respected in our parishes for our great skill and mid-night industry, but now our art doth fail, and little getting have wee in this aye barren of all natural joyes and fruitful onely in bloody calamities, wee desire, therefore, that for the better propagating of our owne benefit and the general good of all women, wives may no longer spare their husbands to be devoured by the sword, but may keep them fast locked within their loving armes, day and night, perfecting their embraces in such a manner as is not to be expressed freely, but may easily be conceived by the strong fancy of any understanding women.

We desire, therefore, that a period may be set to these unhappy differences, and that the naturall standard may no longer lye couchant, but that women may be fruitful vines; that there may be no armes, but such as will lovingly embrace their dear spouses again.

Whereas all are not Penelopes that can withstand the siege of a long temptation, but must yield up the fort to the flattering enemie of her long preserved chastitie; it is better to keep than to make that fraile sexe honest; let, therefore, the drummer wound the ayre no more with false stroaks, nor the pike be bathed in the blood of guiltlesse men, let not the sword ravish from our bosomes the delight of our lives; this word—husbande—speaking benefit both to wives and midwives, since our felicitie cannot subsist without the others' fertilitie and fruitfulness, and, therefore, let us midwives, whome it most nearly concernes, desire that some order may be taken that the old song of England may not be againe revived, *Slow Men of London*; and that the celibate sexe of women may not lye in their beddes like cold marble images, cut out by some artificer's hand, but being fulle of warme spirit and life, they may obleege the world to them by repairing the losses of the warre, and have husbandes, as formerly, at their command, to maintaine them bravely, and bring them yearely under the delivering power of the midwife, which cannot be done unless the warres cease and men returne againe unto their wives.

Printed in London.

From what has been already said, it will appear that polygamy is, on several accounts, dependent upon the relative number of the sexes, especially in warm climates. It has been also practised among all the nations of the earth; it still exists among the Samoides, the Kamtschatkans, the Ostiacs, the Tongueses, and other Siberians, as well as among the North American savages, although in regions extremely cold.

Formerly, monogamy existed only among the polished nations of Greece and Rome, and among the Gauls and Germans, the two latter being the only monogamic nations among the barbarians of those times. Bigamy was allowed at Athens, and Socrates himself had two wives.

No nations have become so polished as those who have been monogamic; for polygamy has always kept people in the slavery of ignorance, or in the deplorable barbarity of the savage state.

Polygamy authorized by law supports and necessitates despotism, because the slavery of the female is the infallible consequence, and domestic slavery is naturally carried into the civil state.

It was, doubtless, the laxity of morals so prevalent which caused the remarks of an Ottoman ambassador at Paris:

We Turks are very foolish to spend so much money on our harems; you Christians spare yourselves all the expense and anxiety, for your seraglio is the houses of your friends.

The general deduction from all that has been said is first, that cold, poor, and rude countries, and republican states, are the most favourable for the multiplication of the human species, thus verifying the Chinese proverb:

The palaces of the rich abound with women; the cottages of the poor with children.

That monarchies, temperate climates, polished societies, and communities are less so. Lastly, that despotic empires, even when fertile, and nations where polygamy obtains, are hostile to it. In the first case, men became laborious, active, and simple in their manners; in the second, they are clever and industrious and of polished manners; and in the last, they become idle, debauched and corrupt.

That precocious marriages are unfavourable to population was remarked by Aristotle, for, throughout the entire animal kingdom, the first fruits of the premature exercise of the reproductive faculty are always found to be imperfect. It is precisely the case with humankind, and the proof is that whenever precocious marriages are allowed, men are found to be small, weak and ill-formed.

The extreme physical debility found in the Polish Jews and their offspring has, with justice, been attributed, by medical writers, to their premature marriages; and Montesquieu affirms that the fear of military service induced a great number of young French men to marry before they had arrived at puberty. It is true that these unions were productive; but that disease and weakness soon deprived France of the generation thus produced.

We shall now proceed to consider the effects of marriage upon the animal system.

There can be no doubt that abstinence and excess are equally foe to happiness: a truth which is applicable with peculiar propriety to sexual pleasure, which, when moderately enjoyed, is unquestionably conducive to the maintenance of health; for a too great abundance of the prolific fluid in a man full of vigour, and in the meridian of his vital powers, disturbs the animal functions, and even affects him mentally; and the best medical authorities are of the opinion that the retention of the seminal fluid is liable to very serious evils.

Salutary, however, as may be the generative act, when performed in moderation, its excessive indulgence entails the most lamentable consequences.

The important part which the seminal fluid takes in the maintenance of health shows that it is always indispensable that a portion of that fluid should be taken up into the mass of the blood after its complete elaboration; nothing can replace it; for the ablest physicians agree that the loss of one ounce of this humour is more debilitating than that of forty ounces of blood.[1] As long, therefore, as the semen remains in the body, it must be admitted to be an agent which communicates to every part fresh strength and vigour.

The changes which are operated in us at the age of puberty, and which are not found in eunuchs, is an incontestable proof of it.[2]

The writings of all medical men, ancient and modern, abound with

---

[1] This, of course, is utter nonsense.

[2] The changes taking place at puberty are not due to retention of semen, but to the functioning of the endocrine glands, and particularly to the secretion of the hormone, testosterone, by the testes. This hormone, now artificially manufactured, can be taken orally or by injection, and hastens delayed puberty, etc. See *The Male Hormone* by Paul de Kruif, New York, Harcourt Brace & Co., 1945. Also *Love Recipes Old and New*, by Alan Hull Walton, London, Torchstream Books, 1956, p. 217 et. seq. (Published in the U.S.A. under the title: *Aphrodisiacs: From Legend to Prescription*, Associated Booksellers, Westport, 1958.)

striking observations and examples calculated to alarm such as, by too frequent an emission of the prolific fluid, lay the foundation of numerous diseases, and thus sacrifice their health to their pleasure.

Hippocrates, the most ancient and exact of observers, was aware of the evils produced by the abuse of the pleasures of love. He describes them under the name of *Tabes dorsalis* (spinal consumption). This disease, he says, originates in the spinal marrow of the back. It attacks young married people, and those who are, unfortunately for themselves, of a libidinous temperament. These individuals have no fever, and, although their appetite is good they gradually lose flesh, and, at last, pine away. Every time they have to perform either of the two principal natural secretions, they lose a very thin seminal fluid in large quantities. They are incompetent to the act of generation, and have, frequently, voluptuous but exhausting dreams.

Aretaeus thus describes the evils produced by too great an evacuation of the semen:

> Young men have the appearance and all the infirmities of old ones; they become pale, emaciated, effeminate, idle, spiritless, stupid, and even, sometimes, idiotic: their body becomes bent, their legs refuse to support them, they are disgusted with everything, and are fit for nothing.

There are, also, circumstances under which this gratification will occasion immediate death. Individuals suffering from disease of any kind should wholly abstain from it, since it has proved fatal to many who had indulged in it before they had entirely recovered their strength.

Many instances may be found in Montaigne. Galen reports the case of a man who, not being completely cured of a violent disease with which he had been afflicted, died the same night that he paid the conjugal tribute to his wife.

Van Swieten knew an epileptic person who expired on his wedding night from the same cause. Fabrice Holden records the unfortunate history of a young man whose hand had been amputated, and whom when the cure was nearly, but not quite, effected, having wished to embrace his wife, and being forbidden by the surgeon, had recourse to masturbation, and died four days afterwards.

Similar cases are reported by Hoffman, Boerhaave, De Sauvages,

Bertholin, Chesnau, and others. Sir Alexander Crichton, in his work *On the Disorders of the Mind*, mentions the case of an attorney, who, being in his seventy-eighth year, married a young girl, and being of a very warm temperament, had also a mistress, whom he visited every evening, so that, by paying his devoirs to both these *Dulcineas*, he must have been in a high state of excitement. The consequence was that he was seized with vertigo and insensibility, followed by loss of memory, so that, instead of asking for bread he would order his boots to be brought, and upon his order being obeyed became very angry, as he wanted something to eat: but he still kept asking for boots in place of bread. Instead of calling for a tumbler, he would call for a chamber utensil, and when he wanted the latter, would order a tumbler or dish, and yet he was conscious he was wrong; and when the proper words were spoken by others, would recognize them.

The Marquis de la Chetardie, who was the French ambassador at the Russian court in the reign of Elizabeth, daughter of Peter the Great, was born under the following singular circumstances:—

His mother was Mademoiselle Monasterolles, who was taken from her convent at fifteen years of age, in order to be married to the old Comte de la Chetardie, aged eighty, whose *nécessité de se marier* was so imminent, that he expired in the arms of his young bride, on the wedding night, immediately after consummation. In nine months after, la Marquise gave birth to a son, but felt so mortified by the catastrophe that befell her husband, that she would never be called by her married name, and shortly afterwards retired to her convent, where she passed the remainder of her life.[1]

There are some individuals whose sensibility is so acute, and who are so disposed to epilepsy, that they have a real attack of it whenever they indulge in the venereal act.

Dedier knew a shopkeeper in Montpelier, who had this idiosyncrasy. Galen, Henri Van-Hers, Tissot, Hoffmann, Haller and many other medical writers report similar cases. Napoleon I is said to have been subject to such attacks: one of which is said to have caused a serious misunderstanding between him and the Empress Maria Louisa. The facts were these. At the head of the Emperor's bed were two bells one of which being rung, summoned his confidential valet, the other

[1] *Pièces intéressantes et peu connues*, Tom. IV. [D]

communicated with the Empress's bedroom. One night, when the Empress's place was filled by the celebrated actress Mademoiselle Mars, Napoleon finding, after the embrace, that the epilepsy was coming on, desired his fair companion to ring one of the bells, indicating the right one; but Mademoiselle Mars, alarmed at her bedfellow's situation, entirely lost her presence of mind, so that instead of pulling the bell which summoned the valet she, most unfortunately, rang that which was to call the Empress, who instantly ran into the room, when a scene ensued more easy to be imagined than described. Mademoiselle Mars was subsequently *invitée* to absent herself from Paris for some time.

This peculiar tendency to epilepsy has been observed even among animals. M. Alphonse Menard had a setting dog of a very large size and very strong, which was seized with epilepsy whenever he coupled with a bitch. These fits were characterized by convulsions and privation of sense; their duration was variable and always proportionate with the ardour of the animal; when no longer coupling, the animal never experienced any attack of the kind.

The influence of physical love appears to be less prejudicial among women than among men, which may be easily accounted for; the properties of the fluid which they emit being less vital than those of the male semen. In fact, such unfortunate females whom want or dissoluteness have forced to become prostitutes, would soon become the victims of the exhaustion necessarily consequent upon their wretched trade, if, when circumstances permitted them enjoyment, they did not refuse it; for if, on the contrary, they took their due part in the orgasm, all the diseases consequent upon excessive debility must necessarily follow.

M. Tissot says that, in the year 1746, 'une fille âgée de 23 ans, défia six dragons espagnols, et soutient leurs assauts pendant toute une nuit; elle expira bientôt après. Cette scène affreuse se passa à Montpellier.'

As to the long-vexed question, which of the two sexes receives the greatest pleasure in the conjugal embrace, a question upon which Jupiter and Juno differing was referred by them to Tiresias, that worthy, who had himself been a girl for seven years, and had been married as such, and who, in consequence, could speak with perfect *connaissance de chose*, gave his award in favour of Jupiter's opinion, declaring that the gratification received by the female was ten times greater than that experienced by the male.

If the subject be considered physiologically, the structure of the generative parts would lead to the supposition that men are most favoured in the act of love. Indeed, the length of the vessels in which the seminal fluid is obliged to traverse in its endeavour to escape, presents advantages not found in women; the quality of the seminal fluid, much more volatilized, must affect those vessels much more voluptuously, while the delicate structure of the organ necessary to transmit this liquor must still further increase the orgasm.

Such are the advantages of the male. But, although the woman certainly cannot boast of such, yet the delicacy of her constitution, her weakness even, procures her others, of which men are deprived.

The parts which concur in exciting voluptuous sensations are more numerous in women than in men, and the agitation of these suffices to excite the sensibility of others. One part (the clitoris) especially endowed with an exquisite sensitiveness, is the seat of pleasure in women.

The imagination also affects women more than men, both in joy and sorrow; their nervous system is more susceptible of impressions, and it may, therefore, be affirmed, with tolerable correctness, that if the enjoyment of women be not so acute as that of men, it is much more extensive than ours.

It, therefore, appears difficult, if not impossible, to decide satisfactorily which sex receives the greatest share of delight in the act of love.

Let each sex, then, enjoy its peculiar advantages and let not man, whose rapture is so ecstatic, think himself neglected by Nature if woman appears to retain for a longer time the voluptuous sensation he has shared with her.

MONOGAMY[1]

From all the researches and facts hitherto made and investigated, monogamy appears to be a law of human nature in cold and temperate countries, and the most proper condition for an advanced civilization.

On the other hand, polygamy appears to depend upon the number

[1] From *monos*, single, and *gamos*, marriage. [D]

of females as compared with that of men, especially in hot countries, where women are three times more numerous than males.

It has also been practised throughout all the countries of the East, so long back as the days of the Patriarch Abraham, as is proved by innumerable passages in the Bible. In former times, monogamy alone was practised among the polished nations of Greece and Rome, as well as among the Gauls and the Germans, the only monogamic nations among the barbarians.

Even bigamy was permitted at Athens, and even Socrates was a bigamist. Polygamy was permitted among the ancient Greeks. It was also defended by Euripides and Pluto. The ancient Romans were more severe in their morals, and never practised it, although it was not forbidden among them, and Marc Antony is mentioned as the first who took the liberty of having two wives.

From that time it became pretty general in the empire, until the reigns of Theodosius, Honorius, and Arcadius, who first prohibited it by an express law, A.D. 390.[1]

After this the Emperor Valentinian permitted, by an edict, all the subjects of the empire, if they chose, to marry several wives, nor does it appear from the ecclesiastical history of those times that the bishops made any objection to its introduction.

---

[1] P. 337 et seq. [D]

ESSAY 6

On Circumcision

CIRCUMCISION, or the practice of cutting off the prepuce or foreskin, is a usage of the remotest antiquity, widely diffused over Africa and the East, and founded almost exclusively upon either religious or political motives.[1]

Sanconiathon,[2] Herodotus, Diodorus Siculus, and Strabo, inform us that the Egyptians and Ethiopians practised this painful rite; Herodotus adds the Colchians. He says:

> The inhabitants of Colchis, Egypt, and Ethiopia are the only people who from time immemorial have used circumcision. The Phoenicians and the Syrians of Palestine acknowledge having borrowed this custom from Egypt. These Syrians, who lived near the rivers Thermedon and Parthenos, and their neighbours, the Macrones, confess that they learned it, and this recently, from the Colchians. These are the only peoples who use circumcision, and who use it precisely like the Egyptians.[3]

As this practice can be traced both in Egypt and Ethiopia to the remotest antiquity, it is impossible to say which first introduced it. The

[1] Eusebius, *Praep. Evangel.* [D]

Remondino's volume, *Circumcision*, Philadelphia, F. A. Davis Co., published early in the present century, is useful. A good reprint of Rawlinson's *Herodotus* (minus some of the translator's longer notes) is available in Dent's Everyman's Library, and another very commendable translation of the same author is available in the Penguin Classics.

[2] Davenport seems to mean Sanchuniathon, reputed to be a Phoenician writer and native of Berytus, who lived about 1220 B.C. His work on Phoenician history and theology was stated to be translated by Philo of Byblus (c. A.D. 50–100), but was obviously written by Philo himself. Only a small fragment of the whole survives, and it was edited by Orelli in 1826.

[3] Beloe's Herodotus, *Euterpe*, Chap. IV. [D]

Egyptians certainly communicated it to the other nations by means of their commercial intercourse. The Phoenicians, who were connected with Greece, did not any longer imitate the Egyptians in this particular, their male children not being circumcised. This practice, which among the Egyptians most likely arose from causes connected with health, as well as from those of religion or policy, soon became neglected by the common people, so that, in the time of Pythagoras, it was observed by priests and philosophers only; whether it was the national prejudices still held a place in the affections of the enlightened few, or that the rite was already made the distinctive mark of philosophical and religious sects; however this may be, the connection of the Jews and their legislator Moses, with the Egyptians, was too close for the former not to have derived from the latter the solemn rite of circumcision.

Although the Bible informs us for what reason the chosen people of God received circumcision, it is silent as to the causes which, long before, induced the Ethiopians, that is the Egyptians and the negroes, to adopt it.

It appears very probable that Upper Egypt was peopled by the Ethiopians, and that the Egyptian customs bore a considerable affinity to those of the former people, hence circumcision may have originated with the Ethiopians, who may have been compelled to adopt it on account of health. Gibbon is of this opinion:

I am aware how tender is the subject of circumcision, yet I affirm that the Ethiopians have a physical reason for the circumcision of males and even of females.[1]

That it was practised in Ethiopia long before the introduction of Judaism or of Christianity appears certain from the testimony of various ancient writers.

There cannot, therefore, exist a doubt in any unprejudiced mind, that the practice obtained in Egypt for a very great length of time previously to its being adopted by the Hebrews.

It is spoken of, for the first time, in the Book of Genesis, XVII, 10–13:

This is my covenant, which ye shall keep, between me and you . . . and it shall be a token of the covenant betwixt me and you.

---

[1] *Decline and Fall*, Chap. IV. (note). [D]

Abraham hastened to obey the precept, the non-compliance with which was to be punished with severe penalties, and, in one day, Ishmael, his son, all his slaves, and Abraham himself, underwent the operation, which was performed by the Patriarch's own hand. It is worthy of remark, as a curious circumstance, that it was not until his return from his first journey into Egypt, that Abraham, who had hitherto called himself Abram, added a syllable to his name, at the same time that he curtailed a portion of his skin, thus effecting a kind of compromise, or *quid pro quo*. A different reason is assigned by the old Scholiast, for Abraham having introduced this rite, and it is as follows:

The Jews were deprived of their foreskin, and were, therefore, called *curti*: the reason for which was that Moses, the king and legislator of the Jews, having, from want of cleanliness, a diseased prepuce, was compelled to cut it off, and fearing that this privation, if known to his subjects, might expose him to ridicule, ordered them all to undergo the like operation.[1]

Up to this period, the stock of the house of David was ignorant of a practice which was one day to distinguish them from among other nations.

None of the antediluvian patriarchs, neither Noah, nor any of his sons, were circumcised, while that operation had, on the contrary, been practised, from time immemorial, on the borders of the Nile. If, therefore, the assertion of Herodotus be entitled to credit, viz. that the inhabitants of Colchis, on the borders of the Pontus Euxinus (Black Sea), were an Egyptian colony, practising circumcision, and that they were settled there by Sesostris, the observance of this rite must have already been for many ages in Egypt when God commanded the Chief of the chosen people to adopt it. Since Abraham was born 2222 years before the common era, and Sesostris must have conquered Asia at about 3326, that is to say, more than eleven hundred years before, it is true that this calculation places the reign of the Egyptian conqueror before the epoch assigned by the different chronological systems, but the difficulty will cease, when it is considered that, without failing in the respect due to the sacred Scriptures, it may, for philosophical reasons, be denied that the deluge was universal which has, hitherto, been

[1] Bagster's *Horace. Sat.*, Lib. IX. (May not this be considered as the prototype of the fable of the Fox who had lost his tail?) See Aesop. [D]

supposed to have been the case, rather in accordance with the letter than with the spirit of the Book of Genesis.

Circumcision is found, not only among the nations who believe in God, but also among those who groan under the most degrading superstitions, and was, most probably, introduced into nascent civilization before men were acquainted with the use of iron; it must be dated from the obscure ages, when our progenitors were not far removed from the condition of mere mammiferae or brutes, being ignorant of the arts, the invention of which is attributed, in the Book of Genesis, to Tubal Cain, and made their rude cutting implements of stones or flints. Hatchets and knives were always found made of these materials among nations which are yet in their infancy; copper and brass come next, and iron, the last; hence it follows that for the ceremonies of primitive religion which, in the social order, were anterior to the working of mines, flints have been preserved from a respectful motive as connected with the origin of the worship when, for instance, the people of Adamic race practised embalming or circumcision, the bodies of the dead were opened, and the foreskin of the living was cut off with flints; and we read in Pliny, that the priests of Cybele mutilated themselves with a sharp flint or with the fragment of a broken jar.

Notwithstanding the command received by Abraham, circumcision was not so permanently established among the Jews but that they ceased to submit to it, so that Moses was obliged to restore the rite by causing the son he had by Zipporah to be circumcised, the instrument employed in the operation being a sharp flint. At a still later period, that is, nearly three hundred years after the treacherous and infamous massacre of Sheckem, Joshua received the command of God to make sharp knives and to circumcise the people, the majority of whom had neglected to undergo that rite in the desert.

At that time the Lord said unto Joshua, make thee sharp knives and circumcise the children of Israel a second time, and Joshua made him sharp knives, and circumcised the children of Israel at the 'hill of the foreskins'.[1]

Since Joshua's time, however, the people of God became more observant. Some apostates, notwithstanding, have been found among them, who, about the time of the Maccabees, endeavoured to efface

[1] *Joshua*, V, 3. [D]

from themselves this mark of distinction, but they were accursed in consequence; Jesus Christ was circumcised.

St Paul contended in favour of circumcision against St Peter, and caused his disciple Timothy to submit to the rite. The first bishops of Jerusalem were all circumcised, but the custom was afterwards abandoned by them. The Coptic and Abyssinian Christians retained the usage: the latter even considered it as advantageous to their women on the score of cleanliness, for those who had not undergone the operation were contemptuously called *cofa* (unopened), and were held in such abhorrence that the vessel out of which they had eaten was broken in pieces, as if polluted.[1]

The Jews and Mohammedans, as also some negro nations, who were unacquainted with Moses and Mohammed, are the only communities whose males are circumcised.

Although circumcision is not, as we have said, so much as mentioned in the Koran, it is nevertheless considered by the Mohammedans to be an ancient divine institution, confirmed by the religion of Islam; and, indeed, the Mohammedans have a tradition that their prophet declared circumcision an indispensable rite for men and an honourable one for women. The Arabs, who practised circumcision for many ages before Mohammed, had learnt it from Ishmael.

Many attempts have been made by modern writers to account satisfactorily, and upon physiological principles, for a practice so generally adopted throughout the East. Some travellers pretend to have discovered the cause in the intention of the primeval legislators to prevent libertinism by suppressing, to a certain degree, amorous propensities, but in this case the result of the prevention was diametrically opposite to that which was desired.[2]

[1] Voltaire, *Philosophie de l'Histoire.* [D]

[2] The conscious practice of retarding ejaculation of semen is known in Arabia as *Imsák.* See Burton, *Arabian Nights*, either the original Benares edition.(16 vols.), or any of the Burton Club facsimile reprints (some in 16 and some in 17 vols.). A long note is given in Vol. V, pp. 76-7 (which is quoted at length in: *Love Recipes Old and New* by Alan Hull Walton, London, Torchstream Books, 1956, pp. 81-2).

A modern scientific work devoted almost entirely to this subject is: *The Power to Love* by Edwin Hirsch, London, John Lane, The Bodley Head, 1937. There are a number of reprints, and the work has appeared in Canada and the U.S.A. under other imprints.

Other writers suggest that the idea of sacrificing to God a portion of the most important organ of man, of that member which enables him to enjoy the only immortality to which he has a right to aspire, may have been one reason, at least, for instituting so singular a custom. It appears, however, natural to suppose, from this rite having been adopted by so many nations, and those chiefly of warm countries, that it should possess some physical utility, although none has been assigned by Mohammedans and Eastern Christians.

Philo[1] is of opinion that circumcision was instituted for the prevention of a disorder of a very dangerous character and very difficult to cure, called *carbo*, and to which all those who retained the prepuce were peculiarly liable.

M. De Paw thinks that both the Egyptians and Abyssinians were compelled to be circumcised in order that they might be protected from a worm which in warm climates was apt to breed between the prepuce and the glans penis.

It is also affirmed that the generality of Orientals would have the prepuce naturally too long, and, consequently, very inconvenient for sexual union, if the prevention of shortening it were not adopted; and the reason of the inconvenience is that heat dilates the parts of the body; thus the breasts of women become elongated and flabby, in proportion as the climate they inhabit is hotter. The same thing occurs with their sexual parts, since the nymphae and the clitoris of Eastern women appear much more developed than in our climates. To such an extent is this the case, that nymphae of the length of one's finger are found among the Hottentot women. This enlargement is analogous with that of plants and flowers, in proportion as the temperature is higher and the soil more genial.

The elongation of the prepuce may also oppose the free egress of the seminal fluid, in the conjugal embrace, and it is to circumcision that the fecundity of the Jews and of other circumcised people is to be attributed.

'The pleasure of the sexual union is greatly increased by the prepuce,' says Bauer,[2] 'for which reason women prefer cohabiting with those who retain it than with the Turks or the Jews.'

---

[1] *De Circumcisione*, Vol. II, p. 211. [D]

[2] Bauer, *De causis fecunditatis gentis circumcisae.* Praeputium voluptutem in coitu auget, unde faeinae praepuptatis concubitum malunt agere quam cum Turcis et Judaeis. [D]

It must not, however, be supposed that this inconvenient length of the prepuce is common to all the Orientals, many individuals being met with among them having the prepuce naturally so short as scarcely to cover the glans penis, and native writers affirm that such is the case with those who are born during the wane of the moon. Blumenbach assigns a much more probable cause: he says that a literary man of great acuteness, when conversing with him on the subject of casual mutilations becoming, in process of time, hereditary marks of distinction, stated the following objection—if artificial mutilations have this effect, children born of circumcised parents must often be born without the foreskin, which does not appear to be the case. Continues Blumenbach:

At this time I was acquainted with only one instance of this kind as reported in Berbach's *Journal*, but one example only did not appear to me to be of sufficient weight to justify drawing a conclusion from it. I, however, one day happened to ask a Jew of this place, a man not destitute of learning, and well acquainted with the ritual of his nation, and was told by him that it frequently happened that Jewish children were brought into the world with so short a foreskin as to require an expert and careful hand to circumcise them. This innate deficiency is distinguished by a particular Hebrew appellation, viz., mould (*modl*), or born circumcised. This person's own father, who had circumcised above 700 boys, and who was celebrated on account of his expertness, often spoke of the great difficulty of performing the operation under such circumstances.

Another motive for the introduction of this usage may have been cleanliness, so important in warm climates, and which requires that there should not be allowed to accumulate around the base of the glans the white caseous matter which the glands are continually secreting there, more especially when their activity is increased by the heat of the climate. In fact, a negligence in this particular, in European travellers, in the East, often causes them painful inflammations and excoriations in that part of the body, while, on the contrary, the circumcised Orientals are in no way exposed thereto, as the removal of the prepuce renders it impossible for that humor to remain and accumulate under its folds.

An English physician, who had resided for a considerable time at Aleppo, was of opinion that in warm countries a greater degree of moisture was contracted under the glans penis than in cold ones; a circumcised person washes himself in that part of the body with greater facility than one who is not so, especially if, being a Mohammedan, he is forbidden to employ more than one hand. Circumcision must, in this case, be a great convenience, and might have been a cogent reason for the natives to retain this rite after having once adopted it.

The matter secreted from the neck of the glans, from behind the ears, and some other parts, is apt to become more acrid than it does in colder climates; the urine also which, in summer, is voided in small quantities, is sharp, high-coloured, and quickly putrefies. Hence, perhaps, it is that Christians are more subject to prurient efflorescences than circumcised persons. The glans of the circumcised is certainly more callous than that of Christians, who seem more liable to venereal affections than the Turks, who seldom have a gonorrhea accompanied with formidable symptoms.

Virey thinks that the only reason for the introduction of circumcision was that of preventing the detestable and fatal practice of masturbation, onanism or self-pollution, for he observes that as the heat of the climate rapidly develops the passions and promotes, in an excessive degree, the desire of sexual union, the Egyptian, Hebrew, and Arabian legislators were desirous of putting a restraint upon self-abuse, and, therefore, introduced the rite as an obstacle to a vice so frequent and so fatal in those warm climates, especially among young persons.[1]

The Romans considered circumcision as barbarous and disgraceful, but the account given of it by Tacitus, although imperfect, is, nevertheless, correct as far as it goes.

'They' (the Jews), says he, 'instituted circumcision of the parts of generation as a mark of distinction from among other nations.'

The sarcastic *Curtis Judaeis* and *Judaeus Appella* of Horace[2] and the illiberal misrepresentations of Juvenal are well known.[3]

---

[1] Circumcision was introduced for reasons of cleanliness, and also as a religious rite. It seems in many cases to eliminate the tendency to premature ejaculation by reducing the sensitivity of the glans penis. But it certainly does not reduce a tendency to masturbation, for its effect in this direction is neutral.

[2] Hor., *Sat.*, Lib. I, 9. [D]

[3] Juvenal, *Sat.*, X. [D]

The manner and time of performing this ancient rite varies according to the country. Among the Jews circumcision was to take place within eight days after the birth of the child. The ceremony, as observed by them, is thus described by Leo de Modena, a celebrated rabbi:

Two seats are prepared, in the morning, with silken cushions, one for the godfather, who holds the child, the other for the Prophet Esdras, who is supposed to be present invisibly. The person who is to circumcise, called in Hebrew *Mohel*, and who is distinguished by the length of his thumb-nail, brings the necessary utensils—the razor, styptic, linen fillet, and oil of roses, to which some add a shell-full of sand to put the prepuce in when abscinded. A psalm is sung until the child is brought into the room by the godmother attended by a crowd of women, and who delivers it to the godfather, none of the females entering the room. The godfather being seated places the child in his lap; then the circumciser takes the razor and, preparing the child for the operation, says: 'Blessed be Thou, O Lord, who has enjoined us circumcision!' And so saying, cuts off the thick skin of the prepuce, and, with his finger-nails, tears away the edges of the remaining skin in several places, sucking the blood two or three times as it jets forth, and putting it into a glass of wine; then he lays dragon's blood on the wound with powder of coral, and, lastly, a compress of oil of roses, and then binds up the whole. This done, he takes the glass of wine, and, blessing it, adds another benediction for the child, and names it.

The laceration of the remaining skin is the reason why the circumcised Jews are cured much sooner than the Turks. The Turks, before they commence to circumcise, squeeze the skin with small pincers, in order to numb the parts, and then cut the prepuce off with a razor. The wound is cured by the application of caustic, or an astringent powder, particularly burnt paper, which, according to Chardin, is the best remedy. They never circumcise till the seventh or eighth year, and sometimes, the eleventh or twelfth, as they do not consider the rite as necessary to salvation. The same author informs us that the operation when performed upon grown persons is attended with considerable pain; that they are obliged to confine themselves to the house for four or five weeks, and that even death is sometimes the consequence.

In Madagascar the operation is performed by cutting off the flesh at three several times, and the most zealous of the relations present catches hold of the prepuce and swallows it.

In the Maldive islands children are circumcised at the age of seven years, being previously bathed in the sea for six or seven hours, in order that, by the skin being thus made softer, it is better prepared for abscission.

Circumcision is practised among the Caffres and Maschappas, and it is performed on their young men at the age of fourteen and upwards. For this purpose they are seized, as they seldom submit willingly, and are forced into a house where the operation is performed, after which they are not permitted to sleep, until they are healed, while to keep them awake a man in each district is paid to keep beating them on the tips of their fingers. The circumcised are then painted white, and furnished with an apron of leaves. When thus painted and dressed, they dance together, at a little distance from the kray or village, but they are not permitted to enter it until they are perfectly recovered. Having washed off the paint in the river, the women present them with a garment, the house in which they were circumcised is burnt, and now, being considered as men, each is presented with a young woman.

Herrera informs us that a kind of circumcision existed, in his time, among the Mexicans, though they are very far from Judaism or Mohammedanism. They not only cut off the prepuce with great ceremony when the child was born, but the ears also.

Among the nations inhabiting the banks of the Maranon, circumcision is practised among the men and excision among the women.

The Otaheitans[1] are represented by Dr Hawkesworth[2] as performing circumcision by merely slitting the prepuce through the upper part, in order to prevent its contracting over the glans penis.

The Persians circumcise their children, sometimes within ten days after their birth, and at other times at ten years of age; that of girls, or excision, as Bruce calls it, is not known. The wound is healed with caustic, astringents, and burnt paper. Persian women of the lower class have a singular superstition: such as are barren swallow the part of the prepuce cut off in circumcision and having so done, feel fully convinced that it will prove an infallible and sovereign remedy for sterility.

Circumcision is by no means a dangerous operation for men, for we see in Genesis that Abraham was ninety-nine years old when he

[1] Otaheitans—an old form of spelling for the word 'Tahitians'.
[2] Hawkesworth's *Voyages*. [D]

performed the operation upon himself; but Hamor and Shechem, his son, with the Hivites, did not escape so easily, for the two princes having consented to become circumcised, with all their people, in order that Shechem might obtain the beautiful Dinah, were treacherously murdered.

And it came to pass on the third day, when they were sore, that two of the sons of Jacob, Simeon and Levi, Dinah's brethren, took each man his sword, and came upon the city boldly, and slew all the males.

And they slew Hamor and Shechem his son with the edge of the sword, and took Dinah out of Shechem's house, and went out.[1]

Circumcision was, with the exception of the Mohammedan population, unobserved either as a religious rite or a hygienic practice, for, as regards the first, the Hindoos, when they invaded that country, fourteen or fifteen centuries ago, or about 3000 years before our era, brought with them the worship of the Phallus, and ingrafted it, as it were, upon their own *Trimourti* or *Trinity*, a religion which thenceforth adopted as its emblem or symbol the *Linga* or Lingham, a single obelisk or pillar, the representative of the male organ of generation. Hence to mutilate, by circumcision, that sacred prototype of the Lingham, would have been deemed an act of the greatest and most unpardonable impiety.

As connected with considerations of health and cleanliness, although the heat, particularly in the Deccan or the south, was very great, its ill-effects as experienced in Africa, Egypt, and Ethiopia, were either prevented or counteracted by the facility afforded by bathing in the refreshing streams so abundant throughout that vast peninsula.

In modern times, renegades who embrace Mohammedanism suffer circumcision at all ages with little inconvenience. The Count of Bonneval, a French gentleman, and the Duke of Riperda, a Spanish minister of state, the celebrated Jew Spinoza, and the notorious Lord George Gordon, all underwent the operation without experiencing any ill-effects, although advanced beyond middle age.

It is not, however, the male sex only that is subjected, in some countries, to this cruel operation. The inhabitants of many Eastern nations are accustomed to make their female children undergo a kind

[1] *Genesis*, XXXIV, 25–6. [D]

of circumcision, which consists in cutting off the most obtruding parts of the *vulva*.

The circumcision of females consists of cutting off a portion of the clitoris, which part, in some, particularly southern climes, attains, in women, to such a size, as to render the use of the knife indispensable.

A contemporary medical writer also observes that the Egyptians judged it indispensable that the operation should be performed before the excrescence had increased much in volume, especially in marriageable girls. Herodotus is silent upon the custom. Strabo mentions it, but is mistaken in asserting that the Jews performed this operation upon girls.

In some countries of Arabia and Persia, as, for instance, near the Persian Gulf, and on the shores of the Red Sea, the operation is never performed upon young females until they have passed the age of puberty, because there is no elongation, or scarcely any, before that time. In other climates, the excessive increase of the nymphae takes place much earlier, and is so general among some tribes, such as those who dwell on the banks of the Benin, that it is the practice to circumcise all the girls as well as boys within a week, or at most a fortnight, after their birth, the object being, not only to remove an obstacle to coition, but to prevent women's abuse of each other.[1]

The following is Bruce's account of this singular custom:[2]

Strabo informs us that the Egyptians circumcised both men and women, like the Jews. I will not pretend to say that any such operation ever did obtain among the Jewish women, as Scripture is silent upon it, and indeed, it is nowhere pretended to have been a religious rite, but to be introduced from necessity in order to avoid a deformity which nature had subjected particular people to in particular climates and countries. We perceive, that among the brutes, nature who created the animal with the same limbs or

[1] See Tulpuis, and the *Philosophical Transactions*, No. 32, p. 624, Badham's Abridgement. [D]

[2] Bruce's *Travels in Abyssinia*, Vol. V, p. 52. [D]. Regarding male circumcision see Burton's *Arabian Nights* (Benares or Burton Club editions), Vol. V, p. 209 note 3. For female circumcision see the long note in Burton's *Nights*, Vol. V, p. 279, note 2. Amongst many other things he says: 'An uncircumcised woman has the venereal orgasm much sooner and oftener than a circumcised man. . . . The moral effect of female circumcision is peculiar. While it diminishes the heat of passion it increases licentiousness.'

members all the world over does yet indulge itself in a variety in the proportion of such limbs or members. Some are remarkable for the size of the heads, some for the breadth and bigness of their tails, some for the length of their legs, and some for the size of their horns. There is a district in Abyssinia, within the perpetual rains, where cows, of no greater size than ours, have horns, each of which would contain as much water as the ordinary pail used in England does; and I remember, near the frontiers of Sennaar, near the river Dendo, to have seen a herd of many hundred cows, every one of which had the apparent construction of their parts almost similar with that of the bull, so that, for a considerable time, I was persuaded that they were oxen, their udders being very small, until I had seen them milked. This particular appearance, or unnecessary appendage, at first made me believe that I had found the real cause of circumcision from analogy, but upon information they did not hold. It is, however, otherwise in the excision of women. From climate, or some other cause, a certain disproportion is found generally to prevail among them; and, as the population of a country has, in every age, been considered as an object worthy of attention, men have endeavoured to remedy this deformity by the amputation of that redundancy. All the Egyptians, the Arabians, and the nations to the south of Africa, the Abyssinians, Gallas, Agoids, Gafals, and Gorgas, make their children undergo this operation, at no fixed time indeed, but always before they are married.

When Roman Catholic priests first settled in Egypt, they did not neglect supporting their mission by temporal advantages and small presents given to the needy people, their proselytes; but, mistaking this excision of the Coptish women for a ceremony performed upon Judaical principles, they forbade, upon pain of excommunication, that excision should be performed upon the parents of children who had become Christians.

The converts obeyed, the children grew up, and arrived at puberty; but the consequences of having obeyed the interdict, were, that the man found, by choosing a wife among the Catholic Copts, he subjected himself to a very disagreeable inconveniency, to which he had conceived an unconquerable aversion, and, therefore, he married heretical women free from this objection, with whom he relapsed into heresy.

The missionaries, therefore, finding it impossible that their congregations could ever increase, and that this unforeseen obstacle frustrated their labours, laid their case before the college of cardinals *de propaganda fide* at Rome. They took it up as matter of moment, which it really was, and sent over visitors skilled in surgery, to make a fair report upon the case, as it stood.

They, on their return, declared that the heat of the climate, or some other natural cause, did, in that particular nation, invariably alter the formation, so as to make a difference from what was ordinary in the sex in other countries, and that this difference did occasion a disgust which must impede the consequences for which matrimony was instituted.

The college, upon this report, ordered that a declaration being first made by the patient or her parents that it was not done from Judaical motives, but because it disappointed the ends of marriage, the imperfection was, by all means, to be removed, so that the Catholics, as well as the Copts in Egypt, have undergone excision ever since.

The practice of circumcision is very general in Omar, at least, in the country of Sohâr, and among the greater part of the nations inhabiting both shores of the Persian Gulf; and it is equally so with the Mohammedans and Copts in Egypt. At Bagdad, the women of Arabian race cause their daughters to be circumcised.

The Turks have not the custom, and in proportion, as we remove from the frontiers of Arabia, less numbers of circumcised women are found in the Turkish towns. Certainly, one advantage gained by the women from this operation is the greater facility of washing themselves, but the chief object is to prevent the erection of the clitoris, which, in the Arabian language, is called *Sunbula*.

The women who circumcise the girls at Kaberé are as well known as midwives are in Europe, and it is even said that when their services are required, they are called from out the street; a clear proof that the operation is not much thought of. It is performed between the ages of seven and eight years, and a superstitious tradition has fixed the period for practising it as the commencement of the overflowing of the Nile.

'Who wants an expert circumciser?' is a common cry in the streets of Cairo. The razor and a pinch of fine cinders suffice for the cure.

Sonnini says, that previously to his visiting Egypt and having an opportunity of ascertaining the nature of the circumcision of Egyptian women, he had imagined that it consisted in the amputation of the nymphae or of the clitoris, according to circumstances, and according as those parts were more or less elongated.

This author, suspecting that there must be something more than an excess in those parts which, far from being met with in all women, could alone have given rise to an ancient and general practice, determined to submit the matter to the test of experience, and, accordingly, he witnessed an operation of this kind, which he describes in the following words:

I first examined a little girl about to undergo the operation. She was about eight years of age, and was an Egyptian by birth. I was much surprised at the appearance of a thick, flabby, flaccid, fleshy, excrescence covered with skin. This excrescence originated above the joining of the lips of the pudenda, and hung down about half an inch. A tolerably correct idea may be formed of it by comparing it, for size, and even for form, to the pendant carbuncle with which the beak of the Turkey cock is provided. The female about to operate seated herself upon the floor, and having also placed the little girl in front of her, she, without the least preparation, began to remove the singular excrescence in question, the only instrument she used on the occasion being a bad razor. The child did not give signs of feeling much pain. A pinch of fine cinders was the only topical remedy applied to the wound, notwithstanding that it bled very profusely. The female operator touched neither the nymphae nor the clitoris neither of which were externally visible in the child. Such is the nature of the circumcision of Egyptian girls, and it may well be supposed to be a necessary operation, for this species of elongated carbuncle increases with the age of the individual, and were it left to itself would, in time, cover the entire opening of the vulva. The woman who performed the operation assured me that, at the age of twenty-five years, the excrescence acquired the length of four inches. It is peculiar to women of Egyptian origin.

It has been remarked by Balon, Thévenot, and others, that all the Coptic women, even those who are free from this appendage, have the nymphae uncommonly and inconveniently large.

This abscision is of the remotest antiquity, and is practised by all the Arabian physicians; it exists not only in Egypt and Ethiopia but towards the Persian Gulf, at Benin, and in Central Africa. Cleanliness has rendered it necessary. In some climates the nymphae, from their great length, become inconvenient, for in the vicinity of the clitoris of women is collected an acrid and stimulating humour called *smegma* (from its resemblance to soap), and this secretion is partly covered by the nymphae. This white saponaceous and almost foetid substance is one of the most powerful stimuli of the sexual organ. Thus, such persons as observe great cleanliness are generally less given to venery than those who are negligent in this respect.[1]

In cold or even in temperate regions this secretion becomes less abundant and, as it is consequently less active in its effects, the sexual organs are more quiescent than in southern regions.

A few observations upon sterility and some of its causes may not be deemed irrelevant in this place. It is admitted by all medical writers that sterility depends more upon women than on men, and that natural heat is one of the principal instruments of all our actions, and that the defect, failure, or falling off of this heat is the principal cause of sterility in both sexes. If it be wanting to the otherwise complete state or condition of the genital apparatus of man, all action of those parts is interrupted, and, under such circumstances, generation is not to be expected.

As to the other sex, let a woman be in the flower of her age, in the enjoyment of perfect health, and married to a husband of a sound and vigorous constitution, with whom she freely enjoys all the delights of the connubial state, yet, notwithstanding all these advantages, if she be not, naturally, by her constitution, disposed to contribute to the making of a child, never can she expect to enjoy the pleasing satisfaction of being honoured with the name of mother; for if her *pudenda* or natural parts be contracted, and she abandons herself too much to the impulses of her love, if an excessive heat consumes or preys upon her internal parts, if her menstrual discharge be irregular or possesses not the red colour peculiar to it, there is but little chance of her conceiving. She burns and, as it were, dries up the semen received by her from the male, and if, by chance, a child be conceived, it is ill-formed and does not remain nine months in its mother's womb.

If, on the contrary, an excessive coldness and much humidity occupy the principal parts of the matrix, if her reins or loins be contracted, and the belly be narrow, and if the only part of her body on which the hair appears be her head, never will she be able to retain the

[1] See Sonnini, *Voyage en haute et basse Egypte.* Niehbuhr, *Beschriebung von Arabien.* Balon, Thévenot. [D]

semen which she has received, and, consequently, conception is impossible or should a child be conceived, it would be suffocated by the great humidity of its mother's parts of generation, and would be born prematurely. So much is this the case, that such a female could never bear a child unless these great defects were corrected, which is scarcely ever the case.[1]

It is the same with women who have an ill-formed womb, whether from some natural defect, or from accident. With respect, however, to the above circumstances, some only of them would be considered by the canon law such as to justify a divorce. It is only such inconveniences and such obstacles which are so great as to oppose the pleasures of love, and hinder a man from enjoying the conjugal embrace, that can be the legitimate cause of the dissolution of a marriage; for if the woman be very contracted, and if the vagina be almost closed, or by the excessive size of the clitoris,[2] or other irremediable causes, it justifies the belief that such a woman is absolutely sterile, since it is impossible for her to bear the caresses of her husband.

The excessive size of the clitoris has been mentioned as being an insuperable obstacle to sexual union, and a very extraordinary, but well-authenticated, instance of its so being is reported in the *Annales Médicales et Physiologiques*, published at Paris in the year 1789. It is as follows:

A man was greatly surprised on his wedding night, while fondly smoothing his hand over the naked person of his bride, at feeling a member as stiff as his own virile one flapping against him. In the utmost confusion, not to say, alarm, he got out of bed, imagining, at first, that he was bewitched, for in those days the power of sorcery was an article of almost universal and implicit belief, or if not, that it was a trick played upon him by substituting in the marriage bed a man instead of his beloved spouse.

---

[1] Davenport's conclusions are extremely doubtful in this case. The defects are probably in large measure glandular defects, but such a woman might produce quite a normal child.

[2] For details and life-size drawings of various forms and lengths of clitoris (some almost like very short male members) see *Human Sex Anatomy*, by R. L. Dickinson, M.D., F.A.C.S., 2nd edition, London, Baillière, Tindall & Cox, 1949. Also: *Sex Variants*, by George W. Henry, M.D., Paul B. Hoeber, Inc., New York, 1948 (reprinted in England by Cassell).

No sooner, however, had he procured a light, than he recognized the countenance of his wife, who fondly entreated him to return to bed, but all her entreaties failed to rouse him from the state of surprise, bewilderment, and disappointment in which he was plunged; and when, after some time, love vindicated its power over him, his genital organs refused to lend their assistance. Their disobedience was not, however, of long duration, and the man returned to his bed, and began, a second time, to renew his amorous attack; but, upon this second tentative, he was as much surprised as before, and his astonishment became still greater when he found that he could not disengage himself from the arms of his beloved, who, in proportion as her passion increased, clasped him still closer and closer to her breast. It was now that he no longer doubted of being the victim of witchcraft, for upon this occasion, by a strange metamorphosis, the man became, as it were, a woman, while the latter was playing the part of one of the male gender. At length the man having recovered himself somewhat, began to examine the cause of his embarrassment. He no sooner cast his eyes upon his wife's *pudenda* than a penis, as long and stiff as his own, presented itself to him. Questioning his wife upon the subject, she informed him as delicately as she could, that she had imagined all women to have been formed like herself in those parts. She told him, moreover, that during the excessive cold of winter, her clitoris almost entirely disappeared, being at that time neither longer nor thicker than the half of the little finger; but that, as the summer heat set in, it became excessively enlarged.

The husband, after maturely considering what was best to be done under such extraordinary and delicate circumstances, proposed that the case should be laid before an able and experienced surgeon, she cheerfully consented. The opinion was given that a portion of the clitoris must be amputated, but before the time fixed for the operation the nervous system of the patient became so highly excitable, that it was absolutely necessary to abandon altogether having recourse to excision.

ESSAY 7

On Eunuchism

THE unfortunate beings who, whether in ancient or modern times, have been condemned, either by jealousy, vengeance or unnatural lust, to the loss of their virility, have been distinguished by different appellations, according to the degree of privation suffered, the modus operandi or the offices sometimes filled by them, etc.; and hence the terms—*eunuch, castrato, spado, thlasias, thlibia, cremaster,* and *bagoas.*[1]

Of all these appellations, the one most common is that of *eunuch,* a word compounded of two Greek ones, signifying *bed* and *to have*; the occupation of eunuchs in the East being generally that of guarding the harem.

Another etymology has, however, been proposed by someone evidently well disposed towards the emasculated, viz. Greek words signifying *on account of having good intellects.* The term *castrato* comes from the Latin, *castrare,* to cut off, the testicles being removed by the knife.

Vossius gives two etymologies for *spado,* the first being the Gallic word *spata,* a razor, that being the instrument with which the operation is performed; the second from *Spada,* the name of a Persian village in which this cruel practice was first introduced.[2] The *Thlasiae* from a Greek word, signifying to crush—their testicles being destroyed by crushing. The *Thlibiae,* from another Greek word, meaning to *rub,* from the same effect being produced by strong frictions made with hemlock and various other herbs, in the same manner as the ancient

---

[1] Such modes and appellations have been discussed by Havelock Ellis in his *Studies.*

[2] This is a doubtful statement. But it may be that men especially expert in the practice were found there.

Romans arrested the signs of virility in their catamites, by rubbing their chin and sexual parts with an infusion of hyacinth root.

This mode of emasculation, if we may credit Zacchia,[1] was practised by wild boars, which animals, when tormented with a leperous itching of the scrotum, rub that part against the stump of trees, thereby obliterating their testicles and depriving themselves of the power of generation.

The *cremasters* were so called from the destruction of the muscle called in Greek *cremaster*, by which the testicle is suspended and drawn up, or compressed in the act of coition. As to the term *Bagoas*, it is a Babylonian one, signifying *eunuch*, and appears to have been generally applied to eunuchs of all the above descriptions, being also occasionally used to signify the office filled by them.

By the word *eunuchism*, therefore, must be understood the condition of an individual who has been partially or wholly deprived of his generative organs; of a being who is a nullity on the face of the earth, and who, in his ambiguous existence, is neither male nor female. This miserable creature, alike an object of contempt to men, on account of his emasculation, and of abhorrence to women, by reason of his impotence, unites himself with the strong against the weak, and is fated to carry within his breast passions, the gratification of which is utterly denied him.[2]

The cruel and detestable practice of castration has been performed from time immemorial by the Egyptians, Assyrians, Persians, etc. Frequent mention of it is also made in the Old Testament; nor was it unknown to the Greeks and Romans, as appears from the writings of certain of their medical and satyrical authors.[3]

---

[1] Zacchia, *Quaest., med. legal.* [D]

[2] Gratification is not always denied the eunuch, some of whom retain the ability to copulate (that is, if castration has taken place after full maturity is reached). There are Oriental tales of irate husbands finding potent (but sterile) eunuchs meeting the needs of women in their harems. And the possibility, though not common, remains a fact. The emotions which Davenport mentions, such as jealousy of other males, seems to have been not uncommon amongst eunuchs, judging from episodes in literature.

[3] This offence was regarded as so atrocious by the old laws of England as to amount to felony: 'et sequitur aliquando poena capitalis, aliquando perpetuum exilium, cum omnium bonorum ademptione'. Bracton, fol. 144. [D]

> Semiramis, Queen of Assyria, the widow of Ninus and mother of Ninyas, whom she put to death, was the first who introduced the custom into that country, in order, according to some authorities, that she might meet with less opposition to her female rule;[1] while others assert that she was actuated by jealousy, inasmuch as having enjoyed the handsomest men in her army, she ordered them to be castrated immediately afterwards to prevent them from affording the like pleasure to other females.

Andramytis, King of Lydia, is said to have been the first who invented the castration of females, an operation which consists in the extirpation of the ovaria, and is far more dangerous and more often fatal than that of the testicles. Women so castrated no longer menstruate. Paul Zacchia, Boerhave, and others assert that the object of this castration was to extinguish in them all appetite for the male sex. Diodorus Siculus says that the Egyptians made it the punishment for offences against modesty, and travellers state that the same custom existed, not only in Persia, but also in Hindoostan, where an adultress was condemned to lose her ovaria before being put to death, upon the same principle that, in some countries, parricides, before being beheaded, have their right hand cut off, in order that the criminal may be more particularly punished in that part which was the instrument of his guilt.

It is possible, however, that this castration was nothing more than nymphaeotomy, which is still in use in countries where the nymphae of women are inconveniently large. Paul Zacchia asserts that this operation was, at a very remote period, performed upon females in Germany, and Frankius reports the case of a daughter of a gelder of animals who, on account of her excessive lasciviousness, was deprived of her ovaria by her father.

The Greeks, for a considerable time, held eunuchs in abhorrence, nor were they introduced into Greece and Italy until the time of the Emperors. Observes the philosophic Gibbon:

These unhappy beings, the ancient production of Oriental jealousy and despotism, were introduced into Greece and Rome by the contagion of

---

[1] See Zacchia, *Quaest., med. leg.*, Lib. II., tit. III, quaest. VII, p. 9, and also Aristot. *Hist. Animal.*, Lib. V, i. [D]

Asiatic luxury. Their progress was rapid, and eunuchs, who in the time of Augustus had been abhorred as the monstrous retinue of an Egyptian queen, were gradually admitted into the families of matrons, of senators, and of the emperors themselves.[1]

The most general classification of eunuchs is into two kinds, viz., those who have been deprived of their testicles only, and those whose entire genital apparatus has been amputated; but the different questions which, at various times, arose concerning the marriage of persons accused of being eunuchs, and which frequently involved the restitution of the wife's dowry, induced jurisconsults to examine more particularly this description of persons, and to divide them into four classes.

The first consists of such as are born so, they being eunuchs, properly so-called. A singular instance of this kind was to be seen, in the year 1704, in the streets of Berlin: this was a cripple, entirely without posteriors, that is, having neither hips nor buttocks, on which account he was carried about in a box on a man's back. He had a well-shaped head, furnished with chestnut coloured hair, with a pleasing countenance. Although more than twenty years old, he had not the least signs of a beard. His hands and arms were well proportioned, and his body tolerably well shaped. His height was between two and three feet, and when out of his box, he supported himself on a block of wood, walking, as it were, upon his hands. He had two orifices, like other men, for the natural dejections; the one, in front, was very small and short and below it was a kind of scrotum very lank and flabby, in which not the least sign of a testicle was to be seen. Upon his parents being questioned they declared that he had always been in that condition from his birth.

The second class of the castrated include those who have been deprived of their virility, either with or without their consent, who are incapable of performing any of the functions of generation, and who are obliged to void their urine by means of an artificial pipe.

The third class consists of those whose cremaster muscles have, by means of continual friction, disappeared, and become altogether obliterated.

[1] *Decline and Fall*, Vol. II, p. 292. [D].—Available in Dent's Everyman's Library. There is no indication as to which edition Davenport used.

The fourth class includes those who, from natural malformation, frigidity of temperament, or accident, are incapacitated from performing the generative act.

To these four may be added a fifth class, embracing those who voluntarily eunuchized themselves in order to escape leprosy and gout, preferring exemption from these diseases to the pleasures of sexual intercourse. The classification made by Jesus Christ is somewhat similar:

> For there are eunuchs which were so born, from their mother's womb, and there are some eunuchs which were made eunuchs of men, and there be eunuchs which have made themselves eunuchs for the kingdom of Heaven's sake.[1]

With respect to the first of the above classes, namely, those who are born eunuchs, it must be observed that the absence of apparent testicles in the scrotum would not always be regarded as a mark of eunuchism, since they may have remained in the abdominal cavity: this has been proved by numerous anatomists, and is the case with birds, rabbits, and almost all young animals. It very rarely occurs that the testicles of adults are hidden; nature seems, at the period of puberty, to make an effort to cause them to appear, and their descent is often the effect of some violent movement, such as fall or a leap. But, even if the testicles do not descend, the party is not, on that account, the less fit for the generative act; on the contrary, it has been remarked that persons in that state may be more vigorous in the amorous conflict than others.

Such as have only one testicle (*monorchides*) are not, for that reason, disqualified from propagating their species—witness Sylla, the dictator, and the Tartar Tamerlane, both of whom had this conformation, the existing organ, in this case, being considerably larger and able to fulfil the duty of two.[2]

---

[1] *Matthew*, XIX, 12. [D]

[2] Pope Sextus V allowed the monorchides to marry. 'Ex dictis,' says Dens, 'patet spadones et eunochos utroque testicule carentes non posse matrimonio inire valide. *Unde Sextus V matrimonio ad hujus modi Eunuchis in Hispania contracta irrita esse, decrevit, secus enim si alterutro duntaxat careat.* [D]

From what has been said it is clear that geldings and eunuchs cannot validly enter into matrimony. For which reason Sextus decreed that the marriages contracted by such kind of eunuchs in Spain were null and void, though it were otherwise if they wanted but one testicle. [D]

The *Triorchides*, or such as have three testicles, are not always more lascivious and ardent than the biorchides.

Says the Marquis d'Argens in his edition of Cellus Lucanus:

Quand j'étais à Rome il y a trente-deux ans, un châtré, fils d'un domestique du Cardinal Octoboni, à qui l'on avait ôté les deux testicules, s'aperçut, un jour, d'un troisième qui, dans sa jeunesse avait été attaché à la racine des bourses, et qui, par la suite du temps s'était détaché et avait occupé la place d'un de ceux qu'on lui avait enlevé. Cette découverte fit perdre la voix à ce châtré qui pouvait avoir vingt-deux ans lorsque ce nouveau testicule parut.

Two curious instances may be cited of eunuchism produced by accident.

The first one, related by Paulus Jovianus, is that of one Simon Baschi, who, when very young, was emasculated by a sow which, while he was asleep, tore off and devoured his virile member.

The second is that of no less a person than Boileau, the celebrated French poet and critic, who, when an infant, had received a like injury from a Turkey cock. This anecdote, which was first published in the *Année Littéraire*, and repeated by Helvetius and others, is asserted by some to be a malicious falsehood, merely invented to explain the poet's aversion to the fair sex, so strikingly exhibited in his tenth satire.

With regard to the fifth class it is certain that leprosy never attacks eunuchs. Mezerai says, in his *Histoire de France*, 'J'ai lu qu'il y avait des hommes qui appréhendaient si fort la ladrerie,[1] cette vilaine et honteuse maladie, qu'ils se châtriaient pour s'en préserver.'

That eunuchs never become bald, and that they are exempt from gout, is affirmed both by Hippocrates and Pliny.

As before observed, the term eunuch has also been employed to signify officers holding high rank in the courts of Eastern princes. These persons were thus described merely because of their office, since they filled posts formerly held by eunuchs properly so-called, *ratione impotentiae et adempta virilitate*. Such was Potiphar, mentioned in the Old Testament,[2] who bought Joseph of the Ishmaelitish merchants, and who could not possibly have been a real eunuch, since he had a wife

---

[1] *Ladrerie* is an ancient French term for leprosy.
[2] *Genesis*, XXXVII, 36. [D]

and a daughter named Asenech, who is supposed to have been married to Joseph.

It is, indeed, clear from history both sacred and profane, that as before observed, the principal offices at court were entrusted to eunuchs, who enjoyed, in the highest degree, the confidence and favour of their princes. Thus we see in the Book of Esther, that seven eunuchs were the ordinary officers of King Ahasuerus, and that the eunuch Egeus, in particular, had the duty of guarding the king's concubines. There were two others named Bagathan and Thares, who kept the first entrance to the king's palace.

The history of Judith informs us that the ushers of the chamber of Holofernes were eunuchs, and that Bagoas was the chief of them.

The eunuch of Queen Caudaces, who was baptized by Philip, was one of the chief officers of that queen, and had the charge of all her treasure.

It was a eunuch who commanded the troops of Zedekiah, King of the Jews. Cyrus having vanquished his enemies, and taken Babylon, established his residence in the royal palace of the greatest city in the universe, but being apprehensive for his personal safety, determined upon forming a bodyguard all of whom were eunuchs; the reason for which as well as that for his appointing them to be officers in his palace are given in the Cyropedia.[1]

The remark made by Gibbon upon this fact is too judicious to be here omitted:

Cyrus had observed in animals that, although the practice of castration might tame their ungovernable fierceness, it did not diminish their strength or spirit, and he persuaded himself that those who were separated from the rest of humankind, would be more firmly attached to the person of their benefactor. But a long experience has contradicted the judgment of Cyrus. Some particular instances may occur of eunuchs distinguished by their valour and their fidelity; but if we examine the general history of Persia, India and China, we shall find that the power of the eunuchs has uniformly marked the decline and fall of every dynasty.[2]

As to the objects for which this cruel practice was first introduced, besides that already assigned, the most general one was that of obtaining safe and trusty guardians for women, whether wives, concubines

[1] *Cyropaedia*, Book VII. [D]
[2] *Decline and Fall*, Vol. II, p. 293, note. [D]

or daughters; individuals so operated upon being considered as in-capacitated from infringing the chastity of the one or the conjugal fidelity of the other.

From time immemorial, indeed, the eunuchs have been employed to guard the women in the harems of the East, and to fulfil near the sovereigns or wealthy princes of Asiatic countries the most intimate duties. Sometimes they acquired by the most shameful means and detestable compliances, a great ascendancy over their masters, as *Bagoas* (this word, in the Babylonian dialect, signifies eunuch) over Alexander the Great,[1] Sporus over Nero, etc.[2] And when the Roman emperors imitated the luxury and the effeminate and haughty etiquette of the Eastern despots they had also eunuchs in their palaces.

In consequence of this, eunuchs became an important article of commerce. Black eunuchs appear to have been preferred. Eunuchs are found in the catalogues of Eastern commodities, which, about the time of Alexander Severus, were made subject to the payment of duties.

Men have, likewise, been castrated for the purpose of being offered up as victims to false gods, an inhuman custom eloquently inveighed against by St Augustine in his work *De Civitate Dei*.[3] The priests also, in many kinds of worship, were required to be eunuchized, in order that the sacred office might be administered by persons who were pure and chaste.[4] This was always the custom of the Athenians, of the Galli, priests of Cybele, as well as those of Diana of Ephesus.

That castration was inflicted as a punishment in the remotest times we learn from Diodorus Siculus,[5] and that it was so employed by the

[1] See Curtius (Rufus Quintus), Lib. VI, cap. 5, and Lib. X, cap. 1. [D]

[2] See Suetonius, *The Lives of the Twelve Caesars*, translated by Robert Graves, Harmondsworth, Penguin Classics, 1957 (there is also the valuable Loeb edition, translated by J. C. Rolfe, with Latin text on opposite pages, London, Heinemann; New York, The Macmillan Co., 2 vols. complete, 1914).

[3] A complete English translation from St Augustine's *De Civitate Dei* is available in Dent's Everyman's Library: *The City of God* (2 vols.).

[4] See Sir J. G. Frazer, *The Golden Bough* (abridged edition), London, Macmillan & Co., 1932 (there are many reprints, both earlier and later), pp. 347 and 350.

[5] Diodorus Siculus can be obtained in twelve volumes, in the Loeb Series (London, Heinemann, and Harvard University Press, U.S.A.), translated by several hands, including Oldfather, Sherman, Geer, and Walton. The Greek text is given on opposite pages.

Romans might be shown by numerous quotations from their works—
two will here suffice:

> The eunuch Thelis, when begown'd he saw,
> Sage Numa cried: 'a punk condemned by law'.[1]
>
> *(Elphinston)*

> Audacious stripling, lost to shame!
> To tempt an armed tribune's dame!
> And dost thou, youngster, barely fear
> The chastisement all boys revere?
> No more be this, thy boldness propp'd:
> Thine *all of manly will be lopp'd,*
> The law, thou sayst will n'er allow,
> Does law, my lad, thy pranks avow?[2]
>
> *(Elphinston)*

[1] Davenport quotes the Latin:

> *Thelin, viderat in toga spadonem,*
> *Damnatam, Numa dixit, esse matronem.*

He gives the reference as Martial, *Epig.*, Lib. VII, ep. 51—it is actually ep. 52. The Latin, as given by Pott and Wright, in *Martial, Twelve Books of Epigrams*, London, Routledge, no date (New York, Dutton), is:

> Theylin uiderat in toga spadonem,
> Damnatum Numa dixit esse moecham. (p. 316)

Davenport's quotations from Elphinston differ in punctuation in some places from the same versions given in Bohn, *The Epigrams of Martial*, translated into English prose (each accompanied by one or more verse translations by Fletcher, Prior, Hay, Sedley, Elphinston and various anonymous hands), London, Henry G. Bohn, 1860. The Elphinston versions are generally unworthy of their originals, as even Bohn himself admits in his preface. As regards 'Thelis', the eunuch, Elphinston has: *Thelis*; Davenport: *Thelin*; Bohn's prose version: *Thelys*; and Pott and Wright: *Theylin*. It is, of course, probable that Davenport used an earlier edition of Elphinston.

Roman women convicted of adultery were compelled, when they went abroad, to wear the *toga*, in order that they might be distinguished from modest women who were habited in the *stola*. [D]

[2] Uxorem armati, futuis, puer Hylle, tribuni,
   Supplicium tantum, dum puerile times?
   Vae tibi! dum ludis, *castrabere*, jam mihi dices
   Non licet hoc: quid, tu quod facis, Hylle, licet?
   Martialis, *Epig.*, Lib. II., ep. 60. [D]

Even here, there are differences in the punctuation of Elphinston as given in

In later times Justinian made castration the punishment for sodomy.

The Gauls also awarded this penalty, in many cases, and a law of the Salii provided that if a slave committed fornication with a maid-servant, he should, when she was dead, be castrated.

A like penalty was found in the law of the Twelve Tables.

The emperor Domitian, at the commencement of his reign, forbade the castration of boys, a decree which elicited a fine epigram from Martial, in which he says:

> No longer cut by dealers void of pity,
> The youth shall mourn the loss of his virility.[1]

The emperor Adrian interdicted the castration of such men as desired to undergo the operation, and the emperor Justinian confirmed the law of his predecessor:

> We therefore decree that whosoever, in any part of this our Republic, dares to castrate any person, or even shall have already dared so to do, shall, if indeed, they who so dare, or have so dared, be men, suffer what they have so inflicted upon others.[2]

Davenport, and as given in Bohn. I have in most instances preferred Bohn. It might not be amiss to state that elsewhere, and with regard to other quotations, there are occasional slight differences, but I have preferred mostly to leave the author's work alone, as otherwise this volume would be cluttered with far too many additional notes and comments.

A better version of the above epigram is given in Pott and Wright, *Martial*, London, Routledge, n.d., p. 63:

> My lad, it's a captain's good lady you're meeting,
> Though you think if you're caught you'll get off with a beating.
> He's a sword and he'll use it. 'Not legal'—you say.
> Well, are they quite legal, your goings-on, pray?

> [1] 'Non puer avari sectus arte magonis
> Virilitatis damna maeret ereptae.'
> Mart., Lib. II, ep. 7. [D]

[2] Sancimus, igitur, ut qui, in quo cunque Reipublicae nostrae loco, quamcunque personam castrare presumunt aut etiam presumpserient, si quidem, viri sunt qui hoc facere presumunt aut presumpserint, idem quod aliis fecerunt, et ipsi patientur. —Just., *Novel.*, XLII, cap. i. [D]

Ovid, too, long before had maintained the justice of such a punishment:

> Whoe'er from youth does cut his manly part,
> Should, with the self-same wounds be made to smart.[1]

The Lex Talionis was abolished by the Emperor Leo as incompatible with the character of Christianity.

Boethius, in his history of Scotland, states that if any person were visited with madness, epilepsy, gout, leprosy, or any other such dangerous disease which was likely to be propagated from father to son, he was, according to the ancient law of Scotland, to be castrated; if a woman were so afflicted she was carefully secluded from all company of men, and if by chance, having some such disease, she was found pregnant, she, with her offspring, were to be buried.

Eunuchs were not allowed to make a will, some privileged ones about the persons of princes being excepted. At their death all their property devolved to the public treasury. They could not adopt children, nor appear as principals in any legal act.

By a decree of the Grand Chamber in Paris, in 1665, it is adjudged that a eunuch cannot marry, not even with the consent of the woman and of all the relations and friends on both sides.

The Council of Nice condemned such as from an indiscreet zeal, or from a wish to guard against sensual gratifications, should castrate themselves. Persons mutilating themselves were also excluded from entering into Holy Orders.

According to Luitprand, Merbonius, and other writers, it was a common practice to punish military crimes, such as desertion, mutiny,

---

[1] 'Qui primus pueris, genitalia membra recidit
Vulnera quae facit, debuit ipse pati.'
　　　　　Ovidius, *Amor.*, Lib. II, eleg. 3. [D]

Marlowe's translation runs:

> 'Who first depriv'd young boys of their best part,
> With self-same wounds he gave, he ought to smart.'

This version can be found in *The Works of Christopher Marlowe*, (edited and annotated) by the Rev. Alexander Dyce, London, 1850 (3 vols.). New edition, revised and corrected, complete in one volume, London, Routledge, Warne & Routledge, 1862. The elegy is entitled: *Ad eunuchum servantem dominam.*

etc. in this manner, and the following curious instance of its infliction as such is given by a French historian as having occurred in the reign of Henry I of France.

The Greeks who were at war with the Duke of Benevetum had carried it on with much cruelty. Theobald, Marquis of Spoleto, the Duke's ally, having come to his aid, and taken several prisoners, ordered them to be castrated, and sent back, so mutilated, to the Turkish general, together with a message to the effect that he had so done in order to oblige the Emperor whom he knew to be particularly fond of eunuchs, and that he (the Marquis) would do all in his power to provide his Imperial Majesty with many more such. The Marquis was about to keep his word, when one day, a woman whose husband had been taken prisoner, came all in tears to the camp, and entreated to be allowed to speak to Theobald. The Marquis having enquired the cause of her grief,

'My lord,' replied she, 'I am surprised that so great a hero as you are, can make war upon us poor women when men can no longer resist your arms.'

Theobald having replied that he had never heard of any war having been carried on against women since the time of the Amazons,

'My lord,' rejoined she, 'can a more cruel war be waged against us than that which deprives us of health, pleasure, and children? When you make eunuchs of our husbands it is not them only that you mutilate, but us also. Within these few days you carried off our cattle and baggage without my complaining of it, but the other loss which you have inflicted upon many of our fellow countrywomen, being an irreparable one, I have come to entreat the conqueror's compassion.'

The army was so pleased with the woman's simplicity and address, that they restored her husband to her, together with all she had been plundered of. As she was going away, Theobald asked her what he should do to her husband, were he again to be taken in arms.

'His eyes, his nose, his hands, and feet,' she replied, 'are all his own property; of them you may deprive him, should he deserve it, but leave him, I pray you, what belongs to me.'

A depraved and unnatural taste was another rife cause of castration, for in order to gratify the vilest and most detestable propensities, the most beautiful boys that could be found, from the age of fourteen to that of seventeen, were chosen for emasculation, a practice which St Gregory bitterly complains of in his 31st discourse.

Juvenal, likewise, stigmatizes it thus:

> No tyrant e'er within his dread abode
> A youth deformed depriv'd of his virility. (*Sat*, X, l. 306)

And Seneca in his *Controversiae* thus indignantly reprobates the practice:

> Wealthy men employ their riches in collecting around them, in violation of nature, crowds of emasculated minions, mutilated for the express purpose of being the better able to bear patiently the excess of impudicity; and this the wealthy do, because being ashamed that they are themselves men, they do all in their power to render men as scarce as possible.

Lastly, persons have been reduced to this miserable state from mere cruelty, an instance of which is thus given in Hume:[1]

> Geoffry, the father of our Henry II, being master of Normandy, the Chapter of Seez presumed, without his authority, to proceed to the election of a bishop; upon which he ordered the whole of them to be castrated, and caused all their testicles to be brought to him on a platter.

Hume's sarcastic remark on this fact is:

> Of the pain and danger they, the monks, might justly complain, yet since they had vowed chastity he deprived them of a superfluous treasure.[2]

The instance of Abelard is too well known to require repetition.

The outrage perpetrated by Pantaleon, as related by Heraclides, is certainly one of the most horrible on record:

> Over the Elei reigned Pantaleon, an oppressive and merciless tyrant, who upon certain envoys arriving at his court, ordered them to be castrated and then compelled to eat their own testicles.

Several instances occur in history of persons who, from various motives, have voluntarily castrated themselves. Lucian, in his dialogues, relates the following one:

> Combabus, a young lord at the court of Syria, was chosen by his sovereign to attend the Queen upon a journey she was about to undertake. Combabus, who was in the flower of youth and of great personal beauty,

---

[1] *Hist. of Eng.*, Vol. I, p. 348. [D]
[2] *Hist. of Eng.*, Vol. I, p. 258. [D]

being apprehensive that the king would conceive some jealousy against him, earnestly entreated that the honourable post might be conferred on some other nobleman, but being unable to obtain his request, he considered himself as a dead man, unless he could find some expedient to avert so great a danger. Seven days only were allowed him to prepare for the journey. After reaching home and lamenting the dreadful alternative which presented itself, either of losing his life or his sex, he, with a resolute hand, amputated the tokens of his virility, and having embalmed them, deposited them in a casket which he sealed. Upon his departure, he gave the box to the king, in the presence of many nobles, humbly desiring the majesty to keep it till his return, as it contained what he valued more than gold and silver, or the richest jewels, and was as dear to him as his life. The king having sealed the box with the royal signet, delivered it into the keeping of his head chamberlain.

The queen's journey lasted three years, and failed not to occasion what Combabus had foreseen. She became desperately enamoured of the young man, but exerted all her resolution to preserve her modesty and dignity. As in most cases of a similar kind, her attempt to extinguish did but add fuel to her amorous flame, and no longer able to vanquish her desires, she went to the bedchamber of Combabus, and discovering her love for him, implored him to return it.

After various excuses, all of which she refused to listen to, he had no other resource than to own his condition, and lest she should be incredulous, gave her ocular proof of his impotency. This revelation in some degree cooled her ardour for him, but she nevertheless, would be continually with him, endeavouring to console both herself and Combabus for the impossibility of gratifying her love.

In the meantime, the king, being informed of her conduct, recalled Combabus. This order by no means astonished the young man, and he boldly returned, well knowing that his justification lay deposited in the prince's closet. He was immediately committed to prison, and a short time after, the king sent for him into the royal apartment, and there accused him, in the presence of those who had seen the casket given, of adultery and treason.

Witnesses were produced who swore that they saw him enjoy the queen. He made no answer, till about to be led forth for execution, when he said that he did not die for having defiled the king's couch, but because his majesty would not return the casket he had put into the royal hands before starting upon his journey.

The king now commanded the casket to be brought to him, and upon its being opened, the contents fully proved the innocence of the accused.

Combabus then explained to the king the motives which had prompted him so to mutilate himself, and had the satisfaction of regaining the monarch's confidence, and of seeing his false accusers fall under condign punishment.

The voluntary castration of Heliogabulus is, perhaps, one of the most singular and disgusting examples of depravity to be found in a nation, itself the most corrupt and immoral. Says Gibbon:[1]

The master of the Roman world affected to copy the dress and manners of the female sex, preferred the distaff to the sceptre, and dishonoured the principal dignities of the empire by distributing them among his numerous lovers; one of whom was publicly invested with the title and authority of the emperor's, or as he more properly styled himself of the empress's husband; a dancer was made prefect of the city, a charioteer, prefect of the watch, a barber, prefect of the provisions. These three ministers with many inferior officers, were all recommended, *enormitate membrorum.*[2]

For this account Gibbon was much indebted to Lampridius, one of the *Historiae Augustae Scriptores*, who speaking of this disgrace to manhood, says:

Quis enim ferre posset principem, per cuncta cava corporis libidinem recipientem, cum ne belluam quidem, talem quis quamque ferat?
Agebat praeterea domi fabulam Paridis, ipse Veneris personam subiens; ita ut subito vestes ad pedes defluerent, nudusque una manu ad mammam, altera pudendis adhibita.[3]

Origen, one of the fathers of the Christian church, is a melancholy proof of how far the reason may be perverted by erroneous views of religious matters.

Origen was born at Alexandria in Egypt, in the year A.D. 185. He was educated for the church, and became profound in the science of theology. The testimony of St Jerome sufficiently proves this, for at the time of his greatest opposition to Origen, he owned him to have

----

[1] *Decl. and Fall*, Vol. I, p. 126 and note. Bohn's edit. [D]
[2] Homosexuals seem to have a preference for large members in their partners. This is often noted in case histories (see G. W. Henry, *Sex Variants*, New York, Hoeber, 1948). Homosexual slang also has a number of words indicative of penile dimensions.
[3] *Historiae Augustae.* Ant. Heliogab., p. 233. [D]

been 'magnus vir ab infantia'.[1] As his profession often obliged him to be in the company of women, as well as of men, in order to deprive the pagans of every pretext for suspicion as to immoral conduct resulting from his youthful years, he resolved to become a living commentary upon the Saviour's saying:

'There be some who have made themselves eunuchs for the Kingdom of Heaven's sake,' and, therefore, according to Fulgos, 'ut corpus ad omni venerea labe mundum servaret omnique suspicione careret, secis genitabilis membris, eunuchum se fecit'.[2]

He endeavoured to keep this act secret, but was unable to prevent its being discovered. He, however, lived long enough to condemn this his error. The passages in which he reprobates it are in his fifteenth sermon upon St Matthew, c. 19, v. 12, and in his work against Celsus, lib. 7.

Some of Origen's tenets were so extraordinary as to draw upon him the condemnation of the fifth General Council assembled at Constantinople in A.D. 533. Amongst these were the following:

That in the Trinity the Father is greater than the Son, and the Son greater than the Holy Ghost. That the sun, moon, and stars were animated and endowed with rational souls. That after the resurrection all bodies will be of a round figure. That the torments of the damned will have an end, and that as Christ had been crucified in this world to save mankind, he is to be crucified in the next to save the devils.

Valius, a disciple of Origen, was the founder of a sect called the Palesians or eunuchs, but this heresy did not last long.

1. Because it was condemned by the first General Council of Nice.

2. Because they who had undergone the operation had suffered such agonies and had so narrowly escaped death, that few persons were disposed to become proselytes.

3. Because castration was forbidden by the Roman laws and it was necessary to apply to a civil magistrate for permission to inflict it. The shame and ridicule consequent upon a refusal, which was almost always given, deterring the aspirants.

The following are a few well authenticated instances of voluntary self-castration similar to that of Origen:

---

[1] *Epistola* 5, ad Pammachuim de erroribus Originis. [D]
[2] Lib. IV, cap. 3. [D]

In 1750 at Fayence in Provence, a person having thought that by mutilating the organs of a lascivious temperament he should free himself from the prurient ideas which continually beset him, performed this dreadful operation upon himself, with his own hand, but a copious haemorrhage ensuing he would have bled to death but for the opportune arrival of a surgeon. After his cure, assuming the garb of a recluse, he retired to a hermitage near Baquole in Languedoc. It appears, however, that the painful sacrifice he had made was far from being followed by the desired impassibility, for upon being asked by a friend if he was free from all carnal desires, he frankly replied, 'Quant aux désirs, c'est à peu près la meme chose.'[1]

A young monk, who was incessantly tormented with the fires of concupiscence, resolved in consequence to destroy the source whence they proceeded. He first prepared himself for the emasculatory operation by experiments made upon different animals, and when he thought himself sufficiently au fait, he eunuchized himself with a razor, bearing the operation with unexampled firmness.[2]

The wife of a labouring man, being extremely jealous, rendered his life extremely unhappy by her unjust suspicions. Coming home one day from his work and being received by his spouse with her accustomed abuse and reviling, he became so infuriated thereat, that with one stroke of the sickle he held in his hand, he cut off all the parts she was so jealous of, and dashed them in her face.[3]

The last case of this kind which we shall mention is that of a young, handsome and amorous Spaniard. This gentleman having after a long siege, succeeded in inducing his fair one to comply with his desires, found himself when on the threshold of bliss, wholly deprived of the erectile power. Overcome with shame and disappointment, he rushed from the apartment and on reaching home, in a fit of rage and despair, amputated his treacherous member and sent it to his mistress as a bloody sacrifice for the expiation of his offence.

The wretched state of tantalization to which, notwithstanding their

---

[1] See the *Journal de Médecine* for the year 1758. [D]
[2] Ibid.
[3] Early during the present century an English housewife, drunk and jealous, castrated her husband while he lay in a drunken sleep.

deprivation, these unfortunates are often exposed, has been thus forcibly depicted by Montesqweu in his celebrated *Lettres Persanes*:

THE CHIEF EUNUCH TO IBBI AT ERZERON.

Thou followest thy ancient master in his travels. Thou passest through provinces and kingdoms. No chagrins can make any impression upon thee. Every moment presents thee with something new. Whatever thou seest diverts thee and makes thy time pass away imperceptibly.

'Tis not the same with me, who am shut up in a terrible prison, always surrounded with the same objects and tormented with the same cares, under the weight of which and of fifty years' annoyances, I am daily ready to sink. I can truly say that in the course of a long life I have not known one cheerful day, nor one moment's ease.

When my first master determined to entrust his women to me, and induced me by a thousand promises, supported by as many threats, to part with myself for ever, almost wearied out with painful service, I resolved to sacrifice my passions to my tranquillity and fortune.

Wretch that I was!

I foresaw what I should not suffer, but not what I should. I flattered myself with the gain, but did not consider the loss. I hoped to be delivered from the assaults of love, by the incapability of satisfying it. Alas! the effect of the passions was destroyed in me, without extinguishing the cause; and very far from being relieved, I found myself surrounded with objects by which those passions were more and more irritated. I entered the harem, where all I saw excited my regret for the loss I had sustained; every minute offered new excitements to desire. Numberless charms seemed to present themselves before me, only to rive my heart with despair. To complete my misfortune, I had ever before my eyes the happy possessor of all these charms.

Thus suffering, I have never conducted a lady to my master's bed and assisted in undressing her, than I returned to my chamber, with my heart bursting with rage, envy and despair. . . .

I remember that one day as I was helping one of the ladies into the bath, I was excited to such a degree that losing all command over myself, I dared to place my hand upon the most formidable spot about a woman. Upon recovering myself, I made sure of that day's being the last of my life. I was fortunate enough however, to escape with life, but the beauty who was at once the cause and witness of my weakness, made me pay dearly for her silence, for I entirely lost all authority over her, and the compliances she exacted from me continually exposed me to a dreadful death.[1]

[1] *Persian Letters*, translated from the French original of Baron Montesquieu, Letter IX. [D]

Eunuchs may be considered as either perfect or imperfect ones: the former are those whom the knife has deprived of every vestige of manhood, the penis itself as well as the testicles being amputated; the latter consist of such whose virile member is still left to them, but minus its appendages.

Eunuchs of this last kind are capable of coition, but owing to the absence of testicles, cannot emit semen, and consequently possess not the power of begetting children.

The powers of these emasculated are, therefore, limited to the gratification of sensuality, impurity and debauchery and their defect of the generative faculty causes them to be particularly desired by lascivious women, since they can indulge themselves without any risk.

Young eunuchs, if they still retain their penis, are very capable of abusing women; they preserve a freshness of complexion, a soft skin and an agreeable embonpoint, which cause them to be objects sought after, even by men, in those burning climes where the too great facility of connection with females diminishes the appetite for them.

By this sort of liaison, a liaison at once so criminal and so adverse to the great object of Nature, it was that so many eunuchs obtained the highest and most confidential posts in the Asiatic courts. Alexander the Great had his *Bagoas*; Nero, his *Sporus*; and thus *Photin* under Mithridates, and *Eutropius*[1] under Theodosius, governed the states of those princes.

---

[1] The poet Claudian is very severe against this favourite minister of Arcadius Emperor of the East; thus he says:

'Omnia ceserunt, Eunocho consule, monstra.' *Claudianus*, in *Eutropius*, Lib. I, v. 18. [D]

Claudius Claudianus was a celebrated Roman poet—in fact the last of the classic Roman poets. He was born, probably, at Alexandria, and flourished between the end of the fourth and the beginning of the fifth centuries A.D. He seems to have been almost the equal of Virgil, and Scaliger has observed that if his matter was poor it was redeemed by the purity of his language and his happy turns of phrase. *Eutropius* is one of his best compositions. An English translation appeared (by A. Hawkins) in 1817, and a translation by Platnauer (with Latin text) is available in the Loeb Series (Heinemann, London). Birt's Latin text appeared in 1892, and there have been others before and since. The above-quoted Latin may be rendered as:

'Let prodigies like these no more be told
Since Consul, now, a eunuch we behold.'

Martial, whose detestation of this *canaglia* was intense, omits no opportunity of lashing them with unsparing severity; witness his epigram upon Baeticus:

> Quid cum faemineo tibi, Baetice Galle, barathro?[1]
> Haec debet medios lambere lingua viros.
> Abscissa est quare Samia tibi mentula testa,
> Si tibi tam gratus, Baetice, cunnus erat?
> Castrandum caput est: nam sis licet inguine Gallus,
> Sacra tamen Cybeles decipis: ore vir es.[2]

The eunuchs who are made so by compression or by the distortion of the spermatic secretive organ are not always on that account deprived of the generative power. Some of the vessels may have escaped the operation; thus oxen have been found capable of impregnating their females.

Suidas informs us that Phythias, the chère amie of Aristotle, was the daughter of a eunuch by compression.

The eunuchs, therefore, who have been deprived of their testicles only by amputation are still susceptible of enjoyment in the part which is left them, and give symptoms of their irritability even more frequently than perfect men, although they cannot enjoy the pleasure of coition in its full perfection. They are also said to possess even an advantage over the uncastrated in being capable of a longer erection. Says Niebuhr:[3]

[1] Barathrum signifies a cave, but is here used as a euphemism for a woman's quim.

> [2]Thou Baeticus, of Cybele, the priest!
> And still art thou by female charms allured?
> Thy tongue should pleasure give to men at least.
> Was it for this the tortures you endured
> By Samian were inflicted, when you lost
> All that proclaimed the man; if still you seek
> That cave when on Lust's Ocean toss't,
> Thy tongue, Baeticus, thy lips, thy cheek,
> Thy head, must pay the penalty of Love.
>   (Martial, *Epig.*, Lib. III, ep. 81). [D]

The above translation is probably by Davenport. It is given in Latin only in Bohn's edition (London, 1860), and in the Pott and Wright translation published by Routledge, London (*Broadway Translations*), n.d.

[3] *Description de l'Arabie.* [D]

Les eunuques ne haïssent pas le sexe, comme bien des gens le croient, celui qui fit avec nous la route de Suez à Jambi avait plusieurs femmes esclaves destinées à ses plaisirs, l'une d'elles était traitée en grande dame. L'on me parla d'un riche Eunuque à Basra qui avait son Harem.

It must, however, be observed that the penis grows but little after the amputation of the testicles, it being nearly the same size as before the operation; thus, a person emasculated at seven years old has, upon reaching twenty, a genital organ not larger than that of a child seven years of age; those, on the contrary, who have not been castrated until the age of puberty, are as to size, similar to men of the same age.

Rainauld[1] relates many examples of an illicit connection between women and this mutilated gentry and he also ridicules the confidence which many husbands have in them.

Andrea de Verdier is of the same opinion, which he supports by the following anecdote:

Apollonius Tiamoeus had foretold to the King of Babylon that one of the eunuchs would abuse his bed, and while, the day after, he was in conversation with that prince, a screaming was heard from that quarter of the palace where the women and eunuchs resided. A eunuch had been caught in bed with one of the king's concubines. This eunuch they had seized and were dragging by the hair of his head round the women's apartments, treating him like one of the royal slaves. Whereupon, the chief of the eunuchs said, he had long perceived his attachment to this woman, and had given orders that he should not be suffered to dress her; and yet notwithstanding this prohibition, he had been found in bed with her.[2]

Limited and confined, as eunuchs, in general, are in commerce with women, to mere sensuality and lasciviousness, being incapable of procreating, except as has been shown, under peculiar circumstances, they become better fitted for such pleasures. During the orgasm they are known to emit a small quantity of mucous secretion, which probably proceeds from the prostate gland.

Amurath III is said to have been the first to introduce complete castration in Turkey, on the following occasion:

Having witnessed the perfect covering of a mare by a gelded horse,

---

[1] *De Eunuchis.* [D]

[2] Theophrastus, *de Apollinii vita*, Chap. XXXVII. Translated by Berwick. [D]

he was so alarmed at the risk he ran of his women being abused by his eunuchs (who had lost their testicles only), that he no sooner returned to the palace than he ordered them all to have the penis also amputated.

St Basil had like opinion of this description of eunuchs, for he assures us[1] that there is no trusting to the *completest* mutilation. He says that castration does not make him that was a male, become a female; he is still a male, just as an ox whose horns are cut off continues to be an ox, and does not become a horse.

He carries the comparison much further, observing that an ox, whose horns are cut off, does not cease, when irritated, to make all the postures that he made before, and even to strike with that part of his head where the horns are placed. St Basil continues:

Eunuchs stripped close to the body, are not free from loose desires, for though impotent in body, yet, in mind and inclinations, they wallow, like swine, eternally in the mire, and after abscission are more abandoned slaves to lust, who, free from discovery, glut their wild desires by wanton touches and loose embraces, not agreeably to their inclinations but their power.

In opposition to the above opinion may be adduced that of Cyrano de Bergerac, the old French dramatist, who, in some quaint lines in his play of *Le Pédant joué*, maintains that castration can effectually cure the amorous passion.

One of the greatest qualifications in eunuchs employed as guardians of the harem is their supreme and disgusting ugliness, for which reason black eunuchs were most esteemed. These came from Africa, chiefly from Ethiopia, and were required to have nose flat, the lips very large, and very thick, and above all, black and irregular teeth, widely apart from each other.

Complete eunuchs were extremely dear on account of the danger attending the operation and the numbers who died in consequence of it.

Tavernier and Thévenot, travellers worthy of credit, affirm that scarcely one-fourth of those subject to this kind of mutilation survive, the operation being performed upon negroes of from eight to ten years of age.

Besides these black eunuchs, there are others at Constantinople and Persia, who, for the most part, come from Golconda, Transgangetic

[1] *Lib. de vera virginitate.* [D]

India, Assam, Pegu, and Malabar, where the complexion is grey, and from the Gulf of Bengal where it is coloured.

There are also white eunuchs from Georgia and Circassia, these latter, however, are but few in number.

Tavernier says that when he was in the kingdom of Golconda, in the year 1675, not less than twenty-two thousand individuals were emasculated.

The complete amputation of the organs of generation is generally fatal if performed after fifteen years of age, and even at the most favourable period, viz. from seven to ten years of age, there is always considerable danger.

Chardin remarks that total amputation is always accompanied with the most excruciating pains; that it is performed with tolerable success on young children but that it is extremely dangerous after the age of fifteen years; that scarcely one-fourth of those operated upon survive; and that the wound is not healed under six weeks.[1]

Pietro delle Valle, on the contrary, asserts that those upon whom the operation has been performed in Persia as a punishment for theft and other crimes, are cured without difficulty, even when the parties are advanced in years, and that nothing is applied to the wound but cinders.

Castration is a law among some of the Hottentot tribes, the male individuals of which are deprived of one testicle, at the age of puberty, it being believed that this privation renders them swifter runners. The circumstances attending the operation are so singular as to justify a short digression for the purpose of describing them.

After having well rubbed the youth with grease from the entrails of a sheep just killed for the occasion, he is laid upon his back, his hands and feet are tied, and he is held down by three or four of his friends; then the priest, for the ceremony is a religious one, being provided with a very keen knife, makes an incision, removes the left testicle, replacing it by a ball of grease of the same size, which has been prepared with certain medicinal herbs; he afterwards sews up the wound with the bone of a small bird, which serves for a needle, his thread being the sinew of a sheep. The operation finished, the patient is untied, but ere the priest leaves him, he rubs him over with grease, still warm, of the

---

[1] Burton, in his *Arabian Nights*, describes in detail the Arab operation of castration, explaining that molten cheese was poured on the wound to close it.

killed sheep, or rather, pours it plentifully over his whole body, so that when it cools, it forms a kind of crust; he rubs him so violently at the same time, that the youth, who has already suffered so much, sweats profusely and smokes like a roasted capon.

After this, the operator, with his nails, forms in this crust of lard, furrows from one extremity to the other, and then urinates upon them as copiously as he can; he next recommences the rubbing process, covering the furrows, so filled with urine, with a fresh supply of grease.

Everyone now leaves the patient to himself, who is compelled to crawl, more dead than alive, into a small hut built for the purpose, in which he either perishes or recovers his strength, without receiving the least assistance and without any other refreshment or food than the grease with which he is so plentifully loaded, and which he may lick, without incurring any anathema; at the end of two days he is generally convalescent, and may then make his appearance in public, and usually proves his perfect cure by running a considerable distance as swiftly as he can.[1]

A state of eunuchism is not, however, produced only by such active means as above described; an excessive use of acids, the too frequent use of opium or narcotics in general, the habit of daily intoxication, and lastly, the repression of all inclination to venereal indulgence by a long and severe observance of chastity weaken and obliterate the sexual organs, render them impotent and effect the indirect castration of the individual. The exhaustion consequent upon excessive indulgence in the venereal act, a disease so common in warm climates where men marry young, and where the sexual pleasure is so much abused, renders the greater part of men little better than eunuchs, at the age of thirty. Leanness, marasmus, universal tremor of the limbs, loss of memory, derangement of the abdominal viscera, in short, the rapid decay of all the moral and physical faculties, are the fatal consequences of this excess of animal delight.

Nor are these effects to be wondered at, if it be true, as Warthon[2] observes, that every secretion of the seminal fluid is equivalent to

[1] *De Glandul*, p. 184. [D]
[2] *Mémoires de la Société Médicale de l'année 1779*. [D]. Such suggestions have already been dismissed in a footnote to Essay 6.

twenty times the same quantity of blood; but Buffon makes it forty times.

Although castration does not produce, universally, the same results as exhaustion, they are however, analogous. The first distinctive trait of the eunuch is softness, paleness, placidity, a relaxed state of his cellular tissue; while, as with women, his glandulous and lymphatic system is much developed and very moist. Observes Lory:

Le développement de la graisse suppose toujours plus ou moins de relâchement et de faiblesse dans la constitution du corps. Les animaux châtrés sont, en général, chargés de graisse et spécifiquement plus légers que les animaux de la même espèce qui, n'ayant pas le même volume, sont, cependant, et plus denses et plus forts. Ces animaux sont, aussi, moins actifs et moins vifs que les autres. On sait que les excès dans les plaisirs de l'amour engraissent ceux qui y sont adonnés, de même que les saignées multipliées ou les hémorrhagies qui viennent à la suite de grandes blessures.

The second trait is the absence of a beard and of the hair under the armpits and on the pubis, in persons who have been castrated before the age of puberty; the epoch at which these tokens of virility appear.

Animals, the males of which are distinguished by their horns, as the stag, or by combs, spurs, etc., as the cock, are always without these distinctive marks if they have been castrated before the production of them but if they undergo the operation after the age of puberty, they may preserve those masculine characteristics.

Thus man, when castrated after the growth of the beard, preserves it, although it is less thick and bushy than under other circumstances. It has also been remarked with respect to eunuchs, that there is scarcely any interval between their youth and their decrepit old age.[1]

It follows from this physical weakness, that eunuchs generally exhibit more plumpness and embonpoint than other individuals. The same is observed in oxen, sheep, and capons when compared with bulls, rams, cocks, etc.

Individuals who are too fat, especially females, become unfitted for generation on account of the weakness accompanying obesity.

Charlevoix informs us that the Caraib cannibals are always careful

[1] Gibbon, *Decline and Fall*, Chap. XXXII. (Note.) [D]

to castrate their prisoners of war before they eat them, in order that their flesh may be fatter and more delicate.

It has been further remarked that the belly of a eunuch is soft and flabby, his thighs thick, and his legs swollen by the superabundant humidity descending to them. As their organs are easily distended they are rarely subject to hernia or rupture, and to the affections dependent upon the *strictum* of the solids; thus it is that according to Hippocrates, they are scarcely ever subject to gout. For the same reason, instances have been known of maniacs being cured by castration and dogs subjected to this operation are never liable to hydrophobia.[1] In fact mad persons experience, by the venereal orgasm, redoubled violence, and they are sometimes given to coition distinguished by a fury truly horrible; hydrophobia, at times, excites the most violent priapisms followed by continual emissions.

With regard to the estimation in which eunuchs have been held at different times, it has already been seen that they were not tolerated in Greece until after the emperors; so greatly indeed were they detested, that a Greek proverb says

If you have a eunuch slay him, if not, buy one for that purpose.

Lucian informs us this hatred was so great that if a person accidentally met with one on his road, he instantly turned back, being sure that no good fortune would attend him that day.

Caesar expressly says that castration was considered by the Romans as a worse punishment than even death itself.

Ammianus Marcellinus declares that he would not credit even Numa, Pompilius and Socrates, if they spoke well of eunuchs.

St Basil gives their characters in these words:

Eunuchs are an abomination, void of every feeling of honour; they are creatures who being neither male nor female are infuriated by sexual desire. They are jealous, despicable, ferocious, suspicious and insatiable. They abandon themselves to womanly tears even for the privation of a meal. The knife has rendered them chaste, but this forced chastity avails them not, their lasciviousness renders them furious and yet produces them no fruit.

The opinion of Chardin, who resided a considerable time in Persia, is also by no means favourable; he observes that having no connection

[1] Columella, *De re rustica*. [D]

but with the master who purchased him, eunuchs are devoid of both tenderness and pity; but that for this very reason, they have a most devoted attachment to their owner, and would do for him what another would for his wife, his child, or his country, for their master is everything to them. Chardin does not, consequently, consider the fidelity of eunuchs, so highly praised by some writers, as deserving of so much commendation, but looks upon it merely as the natural consequence of their miserable condition.

Pliny asserts that animals have a similar aversion to such of their species as have been so mutilated, and observes that if a rat be castrated, all the others will prefer deserting their usual abode to suffering him to remain among them. Observes Virey:

By becoming a slave eunuchs contract all the vices of baseness. Their weakness renders them fearful, and consequently, gloomy and faithless; unable to effect anything by strength, they have recourse to intrigue and flattery; incapable of fruitful labours, they are sordidly avaricious; unable to obtain glory, they fall back upon vanity; entrusted with the care of women they become their rivals in stratagem and intrigue. Thus the generality of eunuchs, while they affect a mild and gentle character, are vicious and malignant. Nothing proves so effectually as this does, how much genuine virtue depends upon strength.

Nor is the opinion of Cabanis more favourable:

The ancients believed that castration deteriorated man, but on the contrary, improved the animal. The truth is that both are equally degraded, since their nature is changed. But by rendering the animal weaker, he is made more docile and better fitted for the purposes of man; by breaking the chain which unites him more closely to his species, there becomes developed in him the most lively sentiments of gratitude and affection for the hand that feeds him.

The effect is the same in man, mutilation separates him, as it were, from his species, and the divine flame of humanity is almost entirely extinguished in his heart, in consequence of the fatal act which rends asunder the dearest ties established by nature between beings of the same kind.

It is well known that eunuchs are, generally, the vilest class of human beings, cowardly and deceitful because they are weak, envious and malicious because they are unhappy. Their intellects also are sensibly affected by the absence of those impressions which impart so much activity to the brain, which animate it with an extraordinary vitality, and which, cherishing in the soul every expanded and generous feeling, elevate and direct its every thought.

The following striking portrait of one of these unfortunates is given by M. Bedor:

He was a eunuch from his birth, and had been drawn for a soldier by conscription. His manners were humble and effeminate; his eyes, either cast down or sunken in their sockets, seemed to fear supporting the look of others; far from being warlike, he was timid, pusillanimous, and was afraid to look upon the dead, but most of all, dreaded darkness. By his own confession, he had never felt any attachment for any person, even in his own family; on the other hand he was equally incapable of aversion or hatred. Music gave him no pleasure, and he had not the least idea of singing, in short, he was susceptible of no enjoyment whatever. He, however, never complained of his situation. His intelligence was very limited, his language confused and incorrect, and education took such little hold of him that although he had lived a year in barracks, he had contracted none of the habits of the soldier.

It cannot, however, be denied, notwithstanding the above unfavourable portraits, that history furnishes numerous instances of eunuchs who have been distinguished by high mental endowments, an ample list of whom may be found in Zuinger. Among others, he mentions the three youths represented by the Prophet Daniel as having been preserved by a miracle, when ordered to be burnt by King Nebuchadnazer.[1] Says our author:

To these may be added Bagoas, the eunuch of Holofernes, the same who introduced Judith into his sleeping tent; Hermias, a pupil of Aristotle,[2] and

---

[1] Nor should Peter Abelard be forgotten. His life has been brilliantly written in the form of a novel, *Peter Abelard*, by Helen Waddell, London, Constable, 1933 (and reprints). Also published as a paper-back by Pan Books, London, 1952.

[2] Aristotle himself must have had a favourable opinion of the emasculated, since he says, in his ninth book upon natural history: 'But all animals if castrated when young become larger and more elegant than those who are not so mutilated'; and Quintillian himself admits that castration improves the beauty of boys.—See *Inst. Orat.*, Lib. V, c. 12. [D]

who wrote upon the immortality of the soul; Origen, who castrated himself; and Narses, who obtained such celebrity as a general under the Emperor Justinian. But the most illustrious, and perhaps, the least known instance, is that of the Holy Evangelist St John.

Ecclesiastical writers declare that such (a eunuch) was the Holy Evangelist St John, whom Jesus loved beyond all his other disciples, who lay upon Jesus' bosom, who, while Peter tardily advanced, flew, borne on the wings of virginity, to the Lord, and who, penetrating into the secrets of the Divine Nativity, was emboldened to declare what preceding ages had been ignorant of.

In the beginning was the Word, and the Word was with God, and the Word was God.

As regards also the assertion that the operation in question affects the mind, so much as to deprive it of all fortitude in times of danger, there is great reason to doubt it, inasmuch as most of the generals of Eastern monarchs have been, at all times, of this class; and the bravest stand that ever was made against Alexander the Great was at Gaza, under the command of one of Darius's generals, who was a eunuch.

Eunuchs frequently held the highest dignities of the state at the Ottoman court. Two of the most celebrated pashas in the Turkish empire were such, the name of the one being Halis and that of the other Simon. Of the latter, De Thou relates the following anecdote:

A courier having brought him the unwelcome news of the town of Strigonia having been taken by the Christians in 1556, he only smiled and said that he himself had suffered a much severer loss when he had been deprived of the most important thing about him.

The theologians of the Romish church have discussed at considerable length the question of the validity of marriages contracted by eunuchs. Says Sanchez:

Castrated persons, who have the genital member sound and entire, are notwithstanding the absence of one testicle, competent to marry, inasmuch as they can emit a perfect semen.

A single testicle suffices for effectually exercising the generative faculty and for setting all the members in motion, precisely as a single eye suffices to enable a man to see; nay, sometimes, a single testicle serves, even better than two, for the seminal virtue which, in this case, would be divided is concentrated in one, acquiring, for that very reason, greater power, so much so indeed that a monorchide is generally found much more vigorous than biorchides. The difficulty, therefore, is to know if persons deficient in both testicles should be allowed to marry.

Many writers are of opinion that they may, provided their genital member be capable of erection, or they can introduce it into the generative receptacle, although they emit no semen therein, because the second object of marriage, that of gratifying the wife's desires, is accomplished; and as to the first object of marriage, that of the procreation of children, it is not indispensably necessary.

Aristotle tells us, in his history of animals, that testicles are not absolutely required for generation, but that they greatly contribute thereto, like the weight suspended to the weaver's loom, which prevents the run of the wool being interrupted or stopped. This great philosopher supported his opinion by the example of an ox, which notwithstanding its being castrated, if, shortly afterwards made to cover a cow, will impregnate her. Besides which, fishes and serpents engender without testicles. Hence, many learned theologians, relying upon these authorities, are of opinion, that provided the woman consent, eunuchs may marry.

But there are others who require something more than the woman's acquiescence for the validity of eunuchs' marriages, and this is, that they should be able to emit a kind of semen although it be not effective for generation, inasmuch as such an emission suffices in the matrimonial act, since barren persons never emit any kind of semen, and it may here be observed that almost all castrated persons have that kind of secretion. As to the different opinions of theologians favourable to the marriage of the emasculated, Sanchez, ever guided by reason, concludes notwithstanding the assertions of the above theologians, that all castrated persons deprived of both testicles can never contract a legitimate marriage, and for this reason because, in the conjugal act, it is necessary that the semen which is emitted into the vagina should be proper for generation.

Now, although some castrated persons have the power of erection and sometimes emit an aqueous semen, nevertheless that semen can never become effective, it causes no action or movement in the principal organs of the body in consequence of the absence of testicles, which act as blows, setting in movement every member. For the heart, the liver, and the brain, which are the three principal organs, send their vital spirits to the testicles, which have the virtue of retaining them; in consequence of which, the whole body receives a genial warmth. But these spirits are lost when testicles are wanting, and the necessary heat is not dispersed over the body; and this is the principal reason why eunuchs are incapable of generation, as is proved by Galen and several other celebrated writers. It must, therefore, be established as an incontestable fact, that eunuchs are not competent to marry.

Pope Sextus V expressly forbade the marriage of castrated persons. Writing to his Apostolic Nuncio, his Holiness says:

We charge and expressly order your apostolic brethren to forbid every kind of marriage to eunuchs deprived of the two testicles. You must, in obedience to our order, declare them incapable; forbid all priests to marry them; first causing to be separated those who may be already married, and declaring their marriage null and void.

The castration of males for musical purposes may be dated from the sixteenth century, for in 1569 the Elector of Bavaria's chapel, which was composed of ninety-two musicians and was very celebrated, under the direction of Orlando de Lasso, could reckon among its singers six castrati, who were most probably Italians, as were, also, all those who, fifty years later, were distributed among the chapels of the different courts, for Italy was, at the commencement, the very centre of this disgraceful and cruel operation, and an innumerable multitude of these falsetto singers left that country and dispersed themselves throughout Europe.

Some writers even assure us that the practice may be traced still further back, and that it originated neither in the Papal states nor any other part of Italy. In fact, Balsamon of Constantinople informs us in his commentary upon the Council of Trulles, that in his time, that is in the thirteenth century, castrati were employed as singers in the churches. Moreover, the history of the Russian church records the curious fact, never before quoted in any history of music, that in 1137 a castrato named Manuel, coming from Greece with two other singers, established himself at Smolensko as a musical teacher and director.

If to the above evidence be added that of Socrate, an ecclesiastical writer, who mentions a eunuch named Brison as being a teacher of hymn-singing, castrato-singing may with great probability be considered as having been introduced in the twelfth century.

From the church, the use of castrati passed to the theatre so soon as the opera began to be developed. The admission of females on the stage being, at that time, prohibited, the female *dramatis personae* were enacted by young boys; and this practice had many inconveniences. In the first place, such youths were incapable of giving the proper expression to the characters they represented, and secondly, the change of voice consequent upon their arriving at virility, soon rendered them unfitted for their employment. The opera, therefore, was compelled to have recourse to the castrati,[1] and the celebrated Pietro della Patte informs us that, in his time, castrati were distributed throughout the lyrical theatres of Italy.

Thus in request, both in the church and the theatre, castrati became all the fashion. No well-frequented chapel, no theatre of any importance, could dispense with employing voices which were the admiration of a people renowned as being the most musical in the world.[2]

But besides these enthusiastic admirers of *la bella voce dei castrati,* philanthropists were not wanting to reprove a practice so disgraceful to humanity, and in consequence of their laudable exertions, castration was frequently prohibited, under severe penalties, in the Papal states themselves. But the number of the castrati, nevertheless, continued on the increase, a circumstance which may fairly be attributed to the

---

[1] 'Pray, mama,' said a young lady who had been to the opera to hear the celebrated Veluti, 'what is the difference between an Italian soprano and a man?'

'The difference, my dear, is—is—is the same as between a bull and an ox.'

'And pray, mama, what is that?'

'Why, my love, the bull is the father of the calf and the ox is his uncle.'

'Oh!' [D]

[2] Casanova, in his *Mémoires,* mentions this, and once fell in love with a supposed *castrato,* only to find, upon embracing him, that he was in reality a woman in disguise. A new edition of Machen's translation of these *Mémoires* is published by Elek, London, in 6 vols.

inconsistency that while the operation was forbidden, the singers, who were the victims of it, were still admitted into the pontifical chapel. The prohibition also left a tolerably large *trou échappatoire* by excepting the cases in which surgeons considered the operation to be necessary, either on account of disease or accident.

The prospect of a brilliant career, and of amassing immense wealth, presented too many attractions for not taking advantage of so easy a pretext. Parents, void of all feeling, hesitated not themselves to deliver over their children to the knife of a mercenary operator, pleading poverty in excuse of their crime.

For a long time it had been erroneously supposed that Clement XIV (the liberal and philosophical Ganganelli), abolished this inhuman practice throughout the Papal dominions, a mistake which arose from the following curious circumstance:

Parini, a celebrated Italian writer, editor of the *Milan Gazette*, was accustomed to place the articles as they came from his pen into a small box, whence they were taken by the printer, as he wanted them. His tailor, passing by the box and being in want of paper for measures, perceived the manuscript, which he thought was thrown therein as waste paper. He therefore took and cut it up, heedless of its contents. Parini did not observe the circumstance until the *Gazette* was printing, and not recollecting the contents of the page had recourse to supplying its place by the following notice, entirely of his own invention, and which he dated from Rome:

The holy father [Ganganelli], in order to abolish, for ever, the crime of castration, unfortunately but too common in Italy, orders that, henceforth, no singer who has been subjected to this infamous mutilation, shall be allowed to sing, either in the churches or in the theatres of the Roman states.

This supposed intelligence was repeated in the *Leyden Gazette*, and by the French newspapers, so that the Pope received the compliments of the Protestants, Catholics and above all, of the Philosophers. This imaginary brief elicited two poetical epistles, of which the one ending thus:

> Aimez un peu moins la musique
> Et beaucoup plus l'humanité,

was written by Charles Bordes of Lyons, but attributed to Voltaire. The other one was entitled: *Epitre au Pope Clement XIV. Sur l'ordre de SS. qui défend la castration.*

It was not till the time of the occupation of Italy by the French that the severest measures were adopted and enforced against this evil: and since that time this disgraceful practice has been completely done away with. It must, however, be observed that, according to recent investigations, an attempt to resuscitate the practice has proved, to a certain degree, successful by the establishment of a school for singing called *Scuola degli Orfanelli,* where are to be found many children and youths of different countries who have been deprived of their virility, either by disease or accident, and the superintendence of the school is entrusted to a Roman castrato.

ESSAY 8

On Hermaphrodism

THE word *hermaphrodism* means the union of the two sexes personified by the names of *Hermes* (Mercury) and *Aphrodite* (Venus) in one and the same individual.

From the Mosaical account of the Creation, it would appear that the first hermaphrodite was Adam,[1] the *reputed* father of the human race, who as such received the Divine command:—

'Be fruitful, multiply, and replenish the earth.'

And that being thus created with two sexes, he only gave up the female one upon the creation of Eve, who was formed from one of his ribs.

Some learned rabbis asserted that Adam was created double, that is, with two bodies, one male and the other female, joined together by the shoulders; their heads, like those of Janus, looking in opposite directions; and that when God created Eve, he only divided such body into two.

Others maintained that Adam and Eve were, each of them separately, an hermaphrodite. Other Jewish authorities, among whom are Samuel, Manasseh, and Ben-Israel, are of the opinion that God did not form Adam an hermaphrodite, but that our great progenitor was created with two bodies joined together by their sides, and that He separated them afterwards, during Adam's sleep; an opinion founded by these writers upon the second chapter of Genesis, verse 21, the literal translation of the Hebrew text being:

He [God] *separated the woman from his side and substituted flesh in her place.*

This idea resembles that of Plato, as will be seen further on.

[1] *Genesis*, Chap. I, v. 27 and 28. [D]

There is yet another difficulty, upon which Catholic divines hold different opinions. In Genesis, I, 27, 28, it is said, 'male and female created he them, and God blessed them: and God said unto them, *Be fruitful, and multiply, and replenish the earth*'.

Whence it clearly appears, say those divines, that God created a woman with man *before* Adam was placed in the terrestrial paradise, and yet, in the following chapter, it is said that after God had so placed Adam in Paradise, He caused a deep sleep to fall upon him, and then, taking a rib out of his side, made it into a woman; an account which appears impossible to be in any way reconciled with the one given in the preceding chapter, inasmuch as in the former the woman is represented as having been made on the sixth day and the latter on the seventh.

Origen, St Chrysostom, and St Thomas, believed that the woman was not created till the seventh day; but the most generally received opinion is that Adam and Eve were created on the sixth.

In order to avoid the difficulty presented by these different readings, many rabbis assert that, in the beginning, God created two women, one of whom was named Lilas and the other Eve;[1] the first being created simultaneously with Adam, and like him, of the dust of the ground, while the other was fashioned from one of his ribs.

According, therefore, to this opinion, all the apparent contradictions arising from the different readings are removed; the first woman, Lilas, having been created on the sixth day and the second one, Eve, on the seventh.

Very little being known of this Lilas, some account of what the Jews think about her may not prove uninteresting. This we learn from the celebrated Baxtorf, in the following passage, which contains the whole history of this first wife of Adam, that she, having disobeyed him, divorced herself from him and endeavoured to destroy their son as soon as born. Says Baxtorf:

When a Jewess becomes pregnant and the time of her delivery is at hand, a decently furnished room is prepared for her, in which is placed whatever she may require. First of all, the father of the family, or as his substitute, some other Jew known for his piety and rectitude, having taken a piece of chalk, draws a circle with it round the room, and writes upon all the walls

[1] Lilas—another form of the name 'Lilith'.

of the room, both within and without, upon the door and the bed, in Hebrew characters, the following words, '*Adam, chava, chutz Lila*'; that is to say, 'Adam's Eve, avaunt thou Lilas'; the signification of these words being, if the woman is pregnant with a boy—'May God give him a wife like unto Eve and not resembling Lilas! if she is pregnant with a girl, may that girl serve as a help-mate to her husband as Eve was to her husband, and not disobediently to and quarrelsome with him, as Lilas was with Adam!'

As to the history of this Lilas, it was as follows:

In the beginning, God having created Adam in Paradise said: 'It is not good for man to be alone.' He, therefore, formed with the dust of the earth, a woman like unto himself, and to whom He gave the name of Lilas. But scarcely had she been so formed, than strife broke out between her and Adam and they began to quarrel.

·   ·   ·   ·   ·

According to the Greek mythologists, Mercury having rendered some services to Venus, the goddess fell in love with him and bore him an hermaphrodite, a child which united the talents of his father with the graces of his mother:

> From both the illustrious authors of his race
> The child was named; nor was it hard to trace
> Both the bright parents through the infant's face.

At the age of fifteen he began to travel, and bathing one day in a fountain in Cana, excited the passion of Salmacis, its tutelary nymph; but continuing deaf to all the offers and entreaties of the latter, she, throwing her arms around him, entreated the gods to render her inseparable from him whom she adored. The gods heard her prayer, and formed of the two a being of perfect beauty, preserving the characteristics of both sexes.

The Greek artists exercised their talents in the production of a kind of beauty mixed of that of the two sexes, and time has spared some of the masterpieces; such is the figure known under the name of the *hermaphrodite*. A cruel operation formed this beauty by depriving young men of the appendages of virility. That which art could only effect by a privation, nature executes by superaddition.[1]

---

[1] Davenport seems to confuse the issue here a little, for a genuine hermaphrodite is *not* a eunuch, although he (or she) may be sterile.

Plato's ideas upon the subject of *hermaphrodism* are too curious to be omitted:

In the beginning there were three kinds of men, not only the two which still exist, namely, the male and female, but a third, who was composed of the two first, and of whom nothing now remains but the name. The Androgynes, for so they were called, had not only both the male and female faces, but also the *pudenda* of both. Of these likewise, nothing now exists but the name which is considered *infamous*. All the males of these three different kinds were in a round form; they had four arms, four legs, two faces, turned one towards the other, placed upon only one neck, four ears, and two genital parts. They walked upright, but when wishing to move very fast, they rolled head over heels, like tumblers.

The reason for the different shape of these three kinds, was that the males were formed by the sun and the females by the earth, and the mixed race of Androgynes by the moon, which partakes both of the sun and the earth. They were of a spherical figure, because they resembled those whence they derived their origin, namely the sun, the earth and the moon.

Being robust, bold and enterprising, they resolved to make war upon the gods, and, like the giants mentioned by Homer, to scale heaven itself. On which account, Jupiter and the other Gods took counsel together as to what should be done, it being a matter of no little importance, for they knew not how to crush these rebels. If they destroyed them with thunderbolts, as they had done the giants, the worship of the gods would perish by the annihilation of the human race. On the other hand, it was impossible for the gods to suffer such audacity. After much reflection, Jupiter spake and said:

'I have discovered how to allow men to exist and at the same time abate their pride and presumption. They must be made weaker. I shall, therefore, divide them into two portions and thus they will lose half their strength, while by the increase of their numbers, that of our worshippers will be multiplied. Henceforward, therefore, they will go upon two legs; should they still continue to be rebellious, I shall divide them a second time, so that they will then go upon one leg only, as if lame, their onward motion being that of hopping.'

Having thus said, Jupiter divided men into two, as hard eggs or a hair are cut in twain; and having so done, ordered Apollo to turn the face round towards the part which had been cut off, in order that each man having been made sensible of the separation he had undergone, might become less audacious.

Jupiter, likewise, ordered that the wounds caused by the division should be healed. Apollo obeyed these directions, and after turning the face, he caused the skin to be drawn over the wound, fastening it in place where the navel is now situated.

Thus, then, Jupiter and all the celestials were secured against the assaults of our so punished ancestors, who were divided and reduced to the miserable state in which we their descendants now are. But as the best things have their inconveniences, so there arose from the separation a very great one wholly unforeseen by Jupiter. When two divided portions happened to meet each other, they embraced with such ardour that they could not again separate. Touched with pity at this new misfortune of men, Jupiter, with a sagacity exclusively his own, ordered that the parts of generation should, henceforth, be placed in front instead of as before, behind, and attached to the buttocks, whereby the act of generation was rendered impossible, the seed being let fall upon the earth, as is the case with storks. The genital parts, therefore, having been placed in front, it was Jupiter's will that generation should be effected by the junction of the male and female, in order that when a man united himself to a woman, the result might be the propagation of the human race.

Plato then proceeds to account for the love which some men have for some women, and vice versa, as also for the inclination which some women have for other women, and vice versa.

The males which are halves of an androgyne are much given to women, and the women which are the halves of an androgyne are passionately fond of men. As for the women who indulge an inclination for others of their own sex, they are the halves of the androgyne females who were doubled, and the men who exhibit a liking for other men are the halves of the males who were also doubled.

The opinion that Adam and Eve were, each of them, hermaphrodites, was revived in the thirteenth century by Amaury de Chartres, who also held that at the end of the world, both sexes shall be reunited in the same person; for which and other opinions he was condemned as heretical by Pope Innocent III.

Eugubinus was also of opinion that Adam was an hermaphrodite, and asserted that the two individuals adhered together by the sides, and that they resembled each other in every respect, save the sex. The male body was on the right, and embraced the other by the neck with his left hand, while the other did the like to him with the right, presenting (as it should seem) a similar appearance to that of the Siamese twins, who were exhibited publicly in London some years ago.

Antoinette Bourignon, a celebrated French visionary, who was born at Lille, January 13th, 1616, says, in her work called *The New Heaven and New Earth*:[1]

Men think to have been created by God as they are at present, although it is not true, seeing that sin has disfigured the work of God in them, and instead of men, as they ought to be, they are become monsters in nature, divided into two imperfect sexes, unable to produce their like alone, as trees and plants do, which, in that point, have more perfection than men and women who are incapable of producing by themselves, and need conjunction with each other, and whose parturition is accompanied with pain and misery.

The celebrated William Law, also, author of the *Call to a Holy Life*,[2] believed that the first human being was a creature containing both sexes in its own perfect nature.

Mirabeau took nearly the same view of the subject, maintaining that the first man must have been a perfect hermaphrodite, a most accomplished egoist, with ample powers for producing a posterity. In support of this paradox, this philosopher quoted the texts:

[1] Antoinette Bourignon was a truly good woman, and suffered much persecution by both Protestants and Catholics because she refused to take her religion at second-hand as formulated by the established Churches. It is written of her that: 'She spent whole nights in prayer, oft repeating: *Lord, what wilt thou have me to do?* And being one night in a most profound penitence, she said from the bottom of her heart: "O my Lord! What must I do to please thee? For I have nobody to teach me. Speak to my soul and it will hear thee." At that instant she heard, as if another had spoke within her: *Forsake all earthly things. Separate thyself from the love of the creatures. Deny thyself.* She was quite astonished ... and mused long on these three points, thinking how she could fulfil them. She thought she could not live without earthly things, nor without loving the creatures, nor without loving herself. Yet she said, "By the grace of God I will do it, Lord!" '—(*An Apology for M. Antonia Bourignon*, London, 1699, pp. 269–70). The passage is quoted at much greater length, with comments, by William James in his *Varieties of Religious Experience*, London and New York, Longmans, Green & Co., 1902, 1904, 1907, etc. (there are many reprints), pp. 321–3. Yet how different is this type of saintliness from that of St Francis with his love for 'all creatures great and small'.

[2] This important work is still available in the Everyman reprint published by Dent of London. It exerted a not inconsiderable influence over the celebrated Dr Johnson, and is mentioned in Boswell's *Life of Johnson*.

'God created man in his own image, male and female created he them.' 'Increase and multiply and replenish the earth.'

This command, he observes, was given on the sixth day, and Eve was not created until the seventh; hence Eve must have been born of Adam or separated from him. Admitting, moreover, that the term day, as used in Genesis, is employed to express an indefinite period of time.

Thus, in order to form woman, God deprived Adam of his androgyne character, and reduced him to a being having one sex only. Hence the irresistible inclination which draws one sex towards the other by the active tendency which the halves have to become united, and hence also that inconsistency and fickleness so common in human nature, each half encountering a thousand difficulties in finding its real counterpart.

Hermaphrodism considered physiologically is a disposition of parts, more or less real, more or less complete, and is found in a certain class of animals and still oftener in numerous plants.

In man and other classes of animals whose organization approaches the nearest to perfection, this disposition is always abnormal, never offering a character sufficiently decided for hermaphrodism, in the strict sense of the word, to be predicated of them. It is with hermaphrodism as with all other monstrosities; it being oftentimes nothing more than the persistence of one of the transitory phases of the foetal organization. As the genital apparatus is composed of a determinate number of parts, which is the same both in the male and female, and which correspond to each other, so there exists between those organs a relation, by virtue of which each of the sexual parts of the male possesses its analogy in one of the sexual parts of the female, a change, or a mere modification only, may be operated in the development of those parts; hence hermaphrodism *with* or *without* excess; *without excess*, if the development is only modified or different in the sex to which those parts belong; *with excess*, if there is an augmentation of the normal number of the parts, by the addition of male organs to the corresponding female ones, and vice versa, reciprocally.

A careful examination of the cases of hermaphrodism which have appeared in our days has constantly exhibited vices of conformation, the appearance of which might easily deceive superficial or prejudicial observers. The subjects in question belonged exclusively to one of the two sexes, some of them presented even nothing, as far as regarded the genital apparatus, than an imperfect organization.[1]

Formerly, the existence of true hermaphrodites was not doubted. In Winrick (*De Ortu Monst.*, c. 20), Riolan (*De Hermaphr.*, c. 8) and Shenkius (*Obs. Med.*, 373) we read of a maid-servant who, in 1461, was condemned to be buried alive for having got her master's daughter with child. Montems declares that he knew an hermaphrodite, supposed to be a female, who had brought her husband several children, and was in the habit also of intriguing with females.[2]

The existence of such a being as an hermaphrodite, either in the human species or indeed, in any of the superior classes of warm-blooded animals, has been not only questioned, but confidently denied by many medical men of the present age.[3]

Among others, M. Viery observes, that in the superior class of warm-blooded animal, in birds with one oviduct, and the mammifera, a real hermaphrodite has never been possible, for the co-existence of ovaria and testicles (the one being the representative of the other) implies contradiction; they cannot be simultaneous. Many instances have, indeed, been reported of females having the male attributes or of imperfect males preserving many of the exterior characteristics of females. But it is possible for masculine women (*viragines*) to present an extraordinary development of certain parts by which they acquire virile habits:[4] a gruff voice, a species of beard and masculine features, in the same way as some young boys of weak constitution, having no scrotum, nor the testicles descended clear of the inguinal ring, imitate, by their timid manners and effeminate features, the character of girls; they are without beard, and their breast becomes plump; they are, however, void of the real uterus, the penis is scarcely perceptible and their sexual desires either do not exist at all or are very feeble.

It is a curious fact that at an early period of existence, the sex of no

---

[1] A perfectly correct observation. Such types, though rare, are probably not quite so uncommon as one might believe.

[2] This must have been a case of a bisexual woman with a hypertrophied clitoris.

[3] And is still questioned by some; although 'sex-change' operations on partial hermaphrodites are changing such an attitude of unbelief.

[4] Viraginity in the female is due to a disturbance in the adrenal cortex.

living animal can be distinctly recognized. Some physiologists affirm that this evolution takes place during some period of gestation.

Sir Everard Home considers the ovum, previous to impregnation, to have no distinction of sex, but to be so formed as to be equally fitted to become a male or female foetus.

M. Ferrein observes, that if to constitute an hermaphrodite wherein the sexes are combined, it is necessary to have the distinctive characters of the male united to the female parts, there never was any woman who has not been a male during several months of her existence. In the earlier stages of pregnancy that distinctive organ is prominent and fashioned very nearly after the manner of males, so that the unskilful in anatomy may suppose the embryo a male though really a female.

To the above respectable opinions may be opposed three cases from which it would appear to prove that when a communication exists between the seminal vessels and the uterus, the individual can fecundate himself without the co-operation of another. Suppose, in fact, that a dream should excite the venereal orgasm during the night, and bring into play, on the one part, the testicles and on the other, the ovary, the spermatic fluid might, though the uterus, proceed to vivify the germ, and the latter would then go through, in the usual way, its series of developments.[1]

The cases above alluded to are the following:—

The *Bulletin de la Faculté de Médecine de Paris*, Tom. IV., p. 185, states that a man living at Lisbon in 1807, in addition to two testicles, with a penis capable of erection and perforated with a canal one-third of its length, had also the organs of the female sex like those of a well-formed woman. His features were masculine, and he had a slight beard, but his voice and inclinations were similar to those of a woman and he had, also, his menses regularly.

This hermaphrodite was twice pregnant, but miscarried on both occasions, the first time at the third month and the second at the fifth month.

---

[1] Nonsense in all probability. It is possible, nevertheless, that hermaphrodites almost completely female, but with an obvious viraginity, might attempt to cover a legitimate intercourse with the opposite sex, resulting in pregnancy, by claiming that they had fecundated themselves.

The portfolio of the ancient Academy of Surgery of Paris contains the drawing of a similar case, and one in which the examination was more complete. It was that of a person named Jean Dupin, who died at the Hôtel Dieu in 1734, aged eighteen years, and who had, on one side, a penis, a testicle, and a seminal vesicle, and on the other, a small oval matrix, an ovary, and a tube. The seminal vesicle communicated with the matrix.

Lastly, may be seen at the Musée de la Faculté de Paris, a model representing an analogous case to the preceding one, the passage of the fecundating fluid also bordering on the uterus.

The French anatomists who have more particularly investigated this subject have defined the several varieties of this *lusus naturae* that have hitherto been known to occur in the human subject.

According to them there is a vice in the formation of the parts intended by nature for the propagation of the species, when, besides those concealed parts which are necessary for the discharge of the prolific functions, the pudenda of the other sex also appear.

This monstrous production of nature is diversified in four different ways, of which three appear in males and one in females. In men, the female pudenda, clothed with hair, sometimes appear contiguous to the peritoneum; at others in the middle of the scrotum; while at others, and which constitutes the third diversity, through that part itself which, in the middle of the scrotum, exhibits the form of a male pudendum, urine is emitted, as it were, from female parts. Near that which is the test of puberty, and above the pudendum in females, the masculine genitals appear conspicuous, in all their three forms, one resembling the penis, the other like the two testicles, but, for the most part, it happens that of the two instruments of generation, one is feeble and inert, and it is extremely rare that both are found sufficiently vigorous for the feat of love; nay, even in a great many cases, both these members are deformed and impotent, so that they do not perform the functions either of a male or a female.

Among the medical writers of our own country, Dr Drake, in his work upon anatomy,[1] observes that the extraordinary size and laxness of the clitoris hanging out of the body, in some infants, had made the women mistake such children for hermaphrodites. On one occasion he

[1] Drake's *Treatise upon Anatomy*. [D]

had brought to him a child about three years of age, whose clitoris hung out of the body so far that it very much resembled a penis; but it wanted the perforation, instead of which the urine issued from a hole just behind it, which hole was nothing else than the corner of the *rima*, the clitoris filling all the rest of the orifice, so that the parents mistook the child for a boy, christened it as such, and esteemed it as such, when they exhibited it to the doctor.

It is certain that in some women, especially those who are very amorously inclined, the clitoris is so vastly extended that by hanging out of the passage it is mistaken for a penis, such have been called *fricatrices*, *tribades* and *subigutrices*,[1] and accounted hermaphrodites, because they are able to perform to a certain degree with other women the actions of men.

'In ogni età,' says an Italian physiologist, 'si sono trovate donne, fornite dalla natura di grossa o sproporzionata clitoride, o divenute tali per la detestabile vizio descritto dall' Appostolo Santo nella prima epistola *ad Romanos* abusandose elleno di tal membro diedero motivo agl' imperito di essere reputate ermafrodite.'[2]

Dr Parsons, the author of a work, the express object of which was to show that the notion of hermaphrodism was a vulgar error, coincides in opinion with Dr Drake, and considers all the subjects of this description as women whose clitoris, from some cause or other, exceeds the regular size.

If all that is reported of hermaphrodites were sufficiently attested, they might be divided into three classes, viz.:

1. Individuals having a perfect sex of which they can successfully avail themselves, together with the other sex imperfect.

2. Individuals possessing somewhat of both sexes, but who are imperfect as to both.

3. Individuals having both sexes sufficiently perfect as to produce, either as male or female, without, however, being able to produce of themselves alone, that is, independently of another male or female.[3]

1st Class of Hermaphrodites. There are many instances of human individuals, who, having one sex sufficiently decided and well formed

---

[1] These terms apply only to Lesbians.
[2] *Della regolata e viziosa generazione degli animali*, Napoli, 1755. [D]
[3] As has previously been stated, most hermaphrodites are sterile.

for them to employ it with effect in sexual congress, have the other only very imperfectly developed.[1]

This kind of hermaphrodite may be of two sorts, male or female; male when the masculine sex is predominant, and female when the feminine sex is perfect.

This is, perhaps, the first step of nature towards hermaphrodism; it commences by uniting to a perfect sex an imperfect development of the other one. Roman laws take cognizance of these imperfect hermaphrodites, and decide that they must be considered as belonging to the sex which predominates in them.[2] In the most ancient times they were treated as outcasts, or were even considered as unworthy to live.[3]

The naturalists who had an opportunity of observing several of these conformations have endeavoured to discover the cause, but have always failed, and ever will fail, for the origin of sex is involved in impenetrable mystery.

2nd Class of Hermaphrodites. The individuals belonging to this class, far from possessing the two sexes, have, in reality, neither the one nor the other. They have something of each, but in so imperfect a degree that they could not copulate, either as male or female. These barren beings, to whom nature has been too liberal, and yet not liberal enough, being incapable of the act of love, either actively or passively, are a mixture of the two sexes, in which the one mutually destroys the other. These, however, may be considered as necessary links in the universal chain of being, nor is it improbable that these attempts of nature will arrive at perfection after some generations.

'We have seen', says the celebrated French naturalist Robinet, 'that nature has produced a perfect hermaphrodite in some species of animals, and we observe her making continual efforts to produce the same phenomenon in the human race, and her essays to this end, although as yet imperfect, and falling short of her purpose, promise us something better in the future.'

In these hermaphrodites, the penis is, in general, imperforated at the extremity, so that although the individual may be capable of erection, no emission of semen can take place.

---

[1] *Considérations Philosophiques.* [D]
[2] Plin., *Hist. Nat.*, Lib. VII, Cap. III. [D]
[3] Lib. X, ad. Dorg—de statua hominum. [D]

Such was the hermaphrodite, an account of which is given in the *Mémoire de l'Académie des Sciences à Paris,* and who was examined by M. Moraud; such also, was the one seen at Amsterdam in 1764.

Of similar conformation was, likewise, the individual whose marriage was declared null by the Parliament of Paris on January 10th, 1760.

In all these subjects, the *vulva* was a small hole between the penis and the anus, and into which the little finger might be introduced with difficulty, and which had no exterior appearance of the organ except when the flesh was pressed up on both sides in order to form the *labia.* Their breasts were not larger than men's are in general; their skin was rather delicate, and their voice like that of a eunuch. Neither of them was subject to periodical evacuations, nor felt any emotions in the presence of women, their predominant inclination being for men.

Some hermaphrodites of this class have been seen with scarcely any hair even on the *pudenda,* and others, who had hairy legs and a beard, like a man, but all had a delicately formed neck and no hair on the breast.

3rd Class of Hermaphrodites. A celebrated physician relates the cause of a man who had married a female hermaphrodite by whom he had several children, male and female, and that the individual so considered a woman had frequent connection with the maid-servants, and had even gotten them with child.[1]

Here, then, was an hermaphrodite of the third class, who had both sexes and who could copulate either as a man or as a woman.

It is said that at Surat in India, there are many hermaphrodites of this description who, dressing, in all other respects like women, wear a turban in order to make known that they possess the two sexes.

Were this fact well authenticated the work of nature would be much more advanced than we dare to believe, in our present want of sufficient testimony.

Generally speaking, hermaphrodites unite the qualities of the male and female organization, but they possess them imperfectly, because

---

[1] Shenck, *Observ.* [D]. Extremely doubtful, as has been stated. This was probably a case of a bisexual woman with an unusually large clitoris. The maid-servants had also probably been enjoying themselves with young men.

they are themselves *imperfect* hermaphrodites. When nature shall have succeeded in uniting, in the same individual, the perfect organs of both sexes, these new beings will advantageously combine the beauty of Venus with that of Apollo, which is, perhaps, the highest degree of human beauty.

The following cases are subjoined in illustration of the preceding observations:

M. Veay, a physician who practised at Toulouse, thus describes an hermaphrodite in 1686.[1]

A very singular circumstance occurred to me a few days ago, in the female ward of the Hospital of St Jacques; a servant girl, who was an hermaphrodite, was brought to me as a patient. She is the native of a place named Pourdiac, about seven leagues from Toulouse, and was baptized as a girl under the name of Margaret. Her father is a poor working man of Pourdiac, named Melause. She is from 21 to 22 years of age, and to all outward appearance, is a girl, although possessing the real tokens of a vigorous man. Her face is feminine, and rather agreeable, her neck very pretty, and her breasts as well formed as can be desired in any girl; her hips and thighs as large as is the case with women; the pudenda precisely like those of a woman, but the slit is not longer than two fingersbreadth, and from the middle of it protrudes a virile member of a very considerable thickness, and which, when in a state of erection, comes out about eight inches. This member is well formed, except it has no prepuce, and is unaccompanied with apparent testicles. The urine and the semen issue from it as in men, and what is very extraordinary, the menstrual evacuation is also discharged from the same place. I should have had great difficulty in believing this had I not seen it myself, having examined the party very particularly at the time of the menses, which she had almost regularly every month, two months very seldom elapsing without their appearance, but they were almost always accompanied with great pains and tension of the abdomen, indicating a kind of inflammation in those parts. I showed my patient to several of my professional brethren, and after having consulted the Vicars General, we caused Margaret to assume a man's dress, and to take the name of Arnaud Melause, and he will shortly be taught some trade by which he may obtain a livelihood.

There was no room for hesitation, because our hermaphrodite could perform extremely well the functions of a man, and not at all those of a woman.

[1] *Phil. Trans.*, abridged. Vol. III, p. 356. [D]

Casper Bauchinus, a celebrated German physician, relates the following case of hermaphrodism:

A farmer, who had in his family a maid-servant, about 23 years of age, observed a very suspicious familiarity between her and his wife. Having at length determined to satisfy himself upon the subject, he applied to the judicial authorities, who committed the examination of the party to M. Baut and another physician of the name of Plat, whose description of the hermaphrodite was, that she was tall and thin, having a masculine voice, a head of long hair, but only a few soft hairs upon the chin (for he used to pluck his beard with tweezers as fast as it grew), had no breasts, but was hairy about the pubis, and had a long penis, the prepuce being drawn back and well worn; under this penis, in the peritoneum, where the operation of lithotomy is commonly performed, there was a kind of chink, about half a finger's joint deep, from all of which appearances we judged him to be a man rather than a woman.

Being asked respecting his amorous exploits, he confessed to having had connection with several women of the town, the act being accompanied by the usual emission of semen and great pleasure, and further, that whenever he had to do with any female, or even had an erection of the penis, his testicles swelled in his right groin, which he perceived to be there by the touch, but that on the left side nothing was perceptible, either during coition or otherwise, nor did anything flow from the aforesaid *rima* or chink.

The above mentioned physician also gives an account of a child who was baptized a male, and brought up as a tailor, but who, afterwards entering the army, served as a soldier in Hungary and Flanders, married a wife and lived seven years with her. At the end of that time he one night rose from his bed, complaining of a violent pain in the abdomen, and in half an hour afterwards was delivered of a daughter.

Upon this extraordinary circumstance becoming public, the magistrates instituted an enquiry; an examination of the individual took place, and the poor female soldier confessed herself to be of both sexes, and that a Spaniard had cohabited with her once only, in Flanders, by whom she proved with child; that she had never been able to perform the sexual act with her wife during the seven years they had lived together, but that the latter had concealed this her impotency.

Most nations have enacted laws against these unfortunates. The Jewish code is particularly explicit respecting them, as are, likewise, the civil and canon ones.

Eutropius informs us[1] that at an early period of Roman history children of this description were ordered to be shut up in a chest and thrown into the sea.

We are indebted to Casper Bauchinus for the following very curious account of the restriction imposed upon them by the Jewish as well as by the civil and canon law:[2]

Frequent mention is made of hermaphrodites in the Jewish law, although but little enquiry was made respecting the cause of this mixed conformation. The word androgyne[3] was very familiar with the Jews, who understood it to signify the having the parts of generation of both sexes, one of which, however, they allowed to be more fully developed and more vigorous than the other. Hence arose some disputes among them concerning the laws which such individuals should be subject to, and which are to be found in the *Talmud* as follows:

Androgynes are in their natures to be considered partly as men and partly as neither man or woman, but such as they appear in their proper persons.

I. They are like men in five respects, according to the law of the Book of Moses:

(*a*) By polluting whatsoever man or thing which they touch or which touches them, whensoever they have emitted their semen; as men pollute every thing in such cases, as declared by law;

(*b*) By being obliged to marry their brothers' widows, not having children, as men are;

(*c*) By being obliged to be dressed from head to foot, after the fashion of men, and to shave their heads as men;

(*d*) By being permitted to marry women, as other men do, and not to marry men;

---

[1] *Hist. Rom.*, Lib. II, Chap. 3. [D]
[2] *De Hermaphroditibus.* [D]
[3] Man-woman. [D]

(*e*) By being obliged to observe all the precepts of the Mosaic Law, as Jewish men are, but not as women, who are not subject to it all, because of those things which their different seasons require. (Secundum ea quae tempora requirunt.)

II. They are further likened to women in seven respects, according to the law of Moses:

(*a*) By polluting every man and all things which they shall touch, or are touched by at the time of their menstruation;

(*b*) Because it is not lawful for them to converse with man alone, or in any private place;

(*c*) Because they may shave their heads in a circular manner as women; and, besides, may spread out their beards, which the law of Moses forbids men to do.

(*d*) Because they are permitted to walk among the dead, as women, which is forbidden to men;

(*e*) Because they cannot bear witness, as women cannot;

(*f*) Because, as women, they are forbidden all unlawful copulation;

(*g*) Because, as women, it is unlawful for them to marry a priest of the seed of Aaron, whereby they are vitiated.

III. They are to be esteemed as men and women in six respects:

(*a*) Because, if assaulted by any person, compensation is to be made, as the law directs, for the injury so inflicted, provided it be fully attested;

(*b*) Because, if killed by chance merely, the person so killing them shall take refuge in one of the privileged places in sanctuaries ordered for security in such cases, there to remain until the death of the high priest, precisely in the same manner as if the said party had killed a man or a woman, but should the hermaphrodite be wilfully murdered, the murderer should die as if he had murdered a man or a woman;

(*c*) Because, whenever a woman brings forth an androgyne, she ought to be accounted *unclean* during seven days, as for a male child, that is, the days of uncleanliness and purification ought to be numbered as for the bringing forth of a son or a daughter according to the law of Moses;

(*d*) An androgyne, if of a sacerdotal race, is a partaker of sacrifices like other men that are so, according to the law of Moses;

(*e*) They have their share both of paternal and maternal inheritances, and also in such other inheritances as they may obtain by law as a man or a woman.

(*f*) When any androgyne has a desire to withdraw from all worldly affairs, such wish must be complied with.

The mode in which hermaphrodites are regarded by the canon and the
civil law may be gathered from the following questions and answers:—

Q.   I. Should an hermaphrodite, upon being baptized, receive the
name of a man or a woman?

A.   If there should appear to be more of the male than of the
female conformation, the person should receive the man's
name; otherwise that of a female; but should the fact be
doubtful, it lies at the discretion of the person who names the
child.

Q.   II. How often should an hermaphrodite confess?

A.   Like a man or a woman, twice a week.

Q.   III. Can an hermaphrodite contract marriage?

A.   Yes; and whether the person contracts a marriage with a man
or a woman must be determined by the predominancy of
either sex in himself, but if both sexes appear equally
developed in him the choice is left to the hermaphrodite.

Q.   IV. Are hermaphrodites comprehended in the status requiring
the consent of friends upon contracting marriage with
women?

A.   The statute does not contemplate persons having both sexes.

Q.   V. Can an hermaphrodite be a witness?

A.   No: except in cases where a woman may.

Q.   VI. Can an hermaphrodite be witness to a will?

A.   No; this will be determined by the sex which predominates,
thus, if the male sex be more developed, he may; but if the
sexes be equal, or the female predominate, he may not.

Q.   VII. Whether an hermaphrodite should be party in a law-suit as
man or woman?

A.   An oath must first be taken as to which sex predominates,
and the question will be decided accordingly; but if both
sexes are equally developed the party is incapacitated according to the decision of the Holy Church.

Q. VIII. Can an hermaphrodite enter into Holy Orders?

A.   An hermaphrodite is excluded therefrom on account of
          deformity or monstrosity; but if the male sex predominate,
          the character may be conferred, but not ordination nor a
          power of administering the sacraments.

Q. IX. Can an hermaphrodite be a judge?

A.   An hermaphrodite is considered as among the infamous to
          whom the gates of dignity ought not to be open.

Q. X. Can an hermaphrodite be an advocate?

A.   No, being infamous.

Q. XI. Can an hermaphrodite succeed in copyholds?

A.   In the affirmative, if there be more of the male than of the
          female in the conformation.

NOTE.—Others answer that though the male sex predominate, by
the appearance of the pudenda, yet, if the party seem, in other respects,
such as strength, agility, etc., to be equal to men, they may succeed in
such inheritance. Others assert that the laws granting feuds to the
descending males do not include hermaphrodites.

Coke upon Littleton mentions a law against this:

Every heir is either a male, a female, or an hermaphrodite, that is, both
male and female, and every hermaphrodite which is also called androgyne,
shall be heir, either as male or female, according to that kind of sex which
shall prevail.

Some jurisconsults are of opinion that since this monstrous exhibi-
tion of nature is not such as to abrogate the rights or destroy the
character of humanity among human beings, this involuntary misfortune implies no right to deprive those upon whom it is inflicted by
nature, of the privileges common to every citizen, and as this deficiency
is no more infectious than any other corporeal mutilation, it is not easy
to see why marriage should be prohibited to one of those unhappy
beings, merely on account of its equivocal appearance, which acts in
the character of its prevailing sex.

If such a creature, by the defect of its construction, should be barren,
this does not infer any right of dissolving the marriage which it may
have contracted, more than the same sterility proceeding from any
other cause, known or unknown, providing the person joined in
matrimony with such an individual should not, on this account, require

a divorce. It is only the licentious abuse of either of its sexes that can render such an individual amenable to the laws.

Before concluding the present Essay, some account must be given of an individual, the doubts concerning whose sex created as intense a curiosity as his talents, acquirements, and accomplishments excited universal admiration. This individual was the Chevalier d'Eon.[1]

The Chevalier was born under the paternal roof on the 5th of October, in the year 1728. His father was Louis d'Eon de Beaumont, director or administrator of the royal domains, parliamentary advocate, etc.; his mother being a French lady of Charanson.

No secrecy obscured his birth; no mystery shrouded it; the doctor, the midwife, the nurse, the relations and friends, both male and female, were all present at the solemn hour of parturition. The child was baptized two days after at the parish church of Notre Dame de Tonnère, as appears from the following document:—

EXTRACT FROM THE REGISTER OF THE PARISH CHURCH OF NOTRE DAME DE TONNÈRE

On the 7th of October 1728, was baptized Charles Geneviève André Timothéo Louis Augustus, son of the noble Louis d'Eon, administrator of the royal domain and his wife, a French lady of Charanson by lawful marriage, which son was born on the 5th of the present month. The godfather, M. Charles Regnard, parliamentary advocate, bailiff of Cusy; the

[1] See M. Hirschfeld, *Die Transvestiten*, Berlin, Alfred Pulvermacher & Co., Berlin, 1910 (the volume is a large one of 562 pages, and does not yet seem to have been translated). The subject is also discussed at considerable length, with case histories, by Havelock Ellis, *Studies in the Psychology of Sex*, Random House, New York, 1936—see Vol. III, part 2, pp. 1–110 (the more recent Random House edition, complete in two volumes on thinner paper, has been published in England by Heinemann, London). Other books on the Chevalier d'Eon are: J. B. Telfer, *The Strange Career of the Chevalier d'Eon de Beaumont*, London, 1885; E. A. Vizetelly, *The True Story of the Chevalier d'Eon*, London, 1895; O. Homberg and F. Jousselin, *Un Aventurier au XVIII Siècle*, Paris, 1904 (trans. into English as *D'Eon de Beaumont*, London, 1911); and *Queer People* by Harold Dearden, London, Hutchinson, n.d. (a volume of short studies of such people as Rousseau, Casanova, d'Eon, etc.). Havelock Ellis's one volume manual for students, *The Psychology of Sex* (which is *not* an abridgement of the *Studies*) should be seen; it was originally published by Heinemann, London, 1933, and reprinted a number of times. The New York edition was published by Houghton Mifflin, 1933. Recently paper-back editions have been published by Pan Books, London, 1959, and New York, Mentor Books, 1954.

godmother, Mademoiselle Geneviève d'Eon, wife of M. Maison, wine merchant, of Paris, who have signed.

Signed {
G. d'EON MAISON
REGNARD
BORES, Dean of Tonnère
}

At the usual age, the young chevalier was sent to an elementary school, whence, after some time, during which he acquired the rudiments of learning, he was transferred, under the care of one of his uncles, to Paris, there to prosecute his studies. Naturally fond of literature, he read with avidity the great poets, historians, and orators of antiquity.

The first products of his pen were *L'éloge funèbre de la Duchesse de Penthièvre, de la Maison d'Este* and that *du Comte d'Eon en Bray.*

But while thus occupied with literary pursuits, he evinced a strong passion for the military profession, and took lessons in the noble art of fencing, and attained a proficiency therein which was subsequently of great advantage to him.

Talents so striking soon attracted the attention of the court and the government, and, upon a difference having arisen between France and Russia, he was recommended to the King (Louis XV) to act as co-adjutor with the Chevalier Douglas for arranging amicably, if possible, the dispute between the two courts.

The complete success which crowned this, the first essay of his diplomatic abilities, soon procured him several successive appointments of the same description at several foreign courts, such as Vienna, Warsaw, London, etc., but to enter into the details of which would exceed the limits of our Essay.

The Chevalier d'Eon having gained for himself so distinguished a name as a diplomatist, was now anxious to acquire some degree of military renown. Accordingly, in the war between France and Germany, having joined his regiment, the colonelcy of which had been bestowed upon him by the king, he distinguished himself equally for courage as for military tactics at Meinstoff, Heinbeck, Osterwich and at Ultrop, at which battle he was wounded in the head and the thigh.

In 1762, the Duke de Nivernois was appointed ambassador and plenipotentiary for negotiating a treaty of peace between France and England, having the Chevalier d'Eon for secretary to the embassy.

Owing to the scandalous intrigues got up against him in Paris, the Chevalier suffered such a reverse of fortune that he lost his titles and his fortune, and thus isolated, not to say proscribed, he passed fourteen years in London.

The leisure thus afforded him, he devoted entirely to study. Throughout the winter he remained shut up in his library, working there fifteen hours out of the four-and-twenty, and receiving visitors, except on Sundays, between the hours of ten in the morning and two in the afternoon. He then took a frugal repast, the only one during the four-and-twenty hours; this finished, he again entered his library. He retired to rest very late, and rose frequently during the night to note down the thoughts that occurred to him.

In 1775, the Chevalier doffed his male attire, and donned that of the opposite sex, a change for which he himself never assigned any cause.

A French novelist, however, has endeavoured to account for it by the jealousy of George III, who, he states, but without adducing any proof of his assertion, had his suspicions of too great an intimacy existing between the Queen and the Chevalier, and upon the latter declaring it was impossible, as his real sex was the female one, immediately and peremptorily insisted upon his assuming the dress belonging to his sex.

During the Chevalier's residence in London, many reports were bruited about which gave cause for doubting the real nature of his sex, and hence two parties were formed, the one maintaining that the Chevalier was really what he appeared to be by his dress, that is, a man, while the other declared him to be of the opposite one.

It would almost appear incredible, but it is actually a fact, that the amount of bets made abroad was not less than £80,000 sterling and in England £200,000. Had the Chevalier chosen he might have cleared an immense sum (by becoming himself, secretly, a better) of not less than 25,000 louis d'or by consenting to verify his sex; but far from seizing on so favourable an opportunity of enriching himself, he was shocked at the indecency of the proposal made to him, openly insisted upon the bets being declared null and void, protested against the verdict delivered in their favour on a first trial, and before his leaving London had declared through the newspapers that as the fate of the betters could not be determined otherwise than by that which they (the betters) had no control over, it could not be expected that he would degrade himself by throwing any light upon the subject of the wager, inasmuch, as by so doing, would be to fail in self-respect, and be unworthy of the dignity of the official character with which he had been invested by his sovereign.

Such was the cause of the lawsuit, which, after lasting a considerable time, was at length terminated to the Chevalier's satisfaction by a definite judgment pronounced on the 31st of January 1778, by Lord Mansfield, Lord Chief Justice of the King's Bench, the said judgment declaring as null and void all the bets which a former judgment had declared to be legal.

The Chevalier, during his stay in London, met, as might have been expected, with many curious adventures, of which the following was one: —

In one of his nocturnal rambles, as he was passing through a dark and lonely street, his ears were assailed by cries uttered by a female voice of '*Au secours! au secours!*'

Without a moment's hesitation, he hastened to the spot whence the sound proceeded, and there found stretched upon the ground a female, while two ruffians were beating her most unmercifully. Immediately, and before the assailants could turn round, he had felled to the ground, with a stout cudgel, the one nearest to him, and the other, taking to his heels, made his escape.

The Chevalier next proceeded to assist the lady to rise; she was suffering most dreadfully, so much so, that she was almost incapable of thanking her deliverer, who, offering her his arm, which she accepted, escorted her home. *Chemin faisant*, the lady enquired to whom she was indebted for her deliverance, and was very surprised upon learning that it was the Chevalier d'Eon, but the latter's astonishment was still much greater when he found that it was the Duchesse du Barri, whom he had saved from being murdered. Four days after, the Duchesse, most imprudently, set off for Paris, where, upon her arrival, she was denounced to the revolutionary tribunal and perished on the scaffold.

The Chevalier d'Eon did not long survive the Duchesse du Barri, as he died in London on the 21st of May, 1810. Measures were immediately taken to remove the mystery which had so long been attached to the sex of the deceased. The inspection of the corpse was made by the celebrated Mr Copland, an eminent surgeon of that day. The official report he made upon the occasion was as follows:

I certify, by these presents, that I have examined and dissected the body of the late Chevalier d'Eon, in the presence of the following gentlemen, viz:—

Mr Adair, Mr Wilson, and the Rev. Father Elyse and that I have found the male organs of generation perfectly sound in every respect.

Several persons of distinction, who had been acquainted with the deceased, were also present, among whom was Sir Sidney Smith, R.N.

INDEX

actors: infibulation of, 72; castration of, 223
Affion, 46
agnus castus, 67, 68
alcohol, 107n
Amazons, 24
ambergris, 37–9, 46
anal intercourse, 102n
analeptic diet, 30–3
Androgynes, 229–30, 241–2
animals: incest in, 164, 165n; epilepsy in, 171; castrated, 193, 196, 213, 216, 217, 218, 219n, 221; hermaphrodite, 233, 237
ants, 28
Arabs: and phallic worship, 89; and circumcision, 178, 188. *See also* Egyptians
Armenians, 145
asceticism, 63–4
athletes, 113
azezome, 30

bachelors, 153; as enemies of society, 149–50, 155–6, 157–8
Bagoas, 193
barefootedness, 64
bark, 45
barons, and marriage rights, 156–7
baths, cold, 64
bed, Graham's celestial, 58–60
Belgium, 97–8
bhang, 45–6
bigamy, 173
birds, incest among, 165n
Bohemia, 164–5
books, choice of, 64–5
borax, 44
breeches, 111–12

Caffres, 183
camphor, 67–8
cantharides, 40–2, 67–8
carbo, 179
castration, 66, 69, 140; a felony, 193n. *See also* eunuchism
castrato, 192; singing, 223–4, 225
celestial bed, Graham's, 58–60
celibacy: athletes and, 139; disorders of, 146–7, 151; and longevity, 146, 150; fall of empires due to, 155–6, 157–8; vices of, 158–62
charms and counter-charms, 118–23
chastity, 29, 37; and hygiene, 64; and infibulation, 73–5; padlocks for, 75–7; advantages of, 138–9, 141; in Jesuits, 141; examples among women, 142–3; disadvantages of, 146–7; differs from continence, 151
Chervri plant, 42–3
Chinese, 46
chocolate, 35–6
Christian Church: and aphrodisiacs, 50–1; and Priapus, 93; and phallic worship, 95–9; and Judicial Congress, 125–6; and Virgin Mary, 147–8; and marriage, 152; and circumcision, 178, 186–7; and castration, 206–7, 220, 222–5; and hermaphrodites, 243
Cinoedi, college of, 160–2
Circassians, 75
circumcision, 70; in antiquity, 174–8; reasons for, 175, 178–82; of females, 178, 184–9; operation of, 182–4, 187–8
cleanliness, circumcision and, 176, 178, 180–1, 189
climate, effect on love, 17, 162–3, 166, 181